CHAIN 9
dialogue

editors
Jena Osman
Juliana Spahr
and
Cecilia Vicuña
and
Thalia Field

Honolulu, New York, Philadelphia

Chain 9, summer 2002.
Chain appears annually.
$12 for one issue; $20 for two issues.
Please make checks payable to Chain Arts. Send orders to:
Chain
c/o Department of English
Temple University
10th floor, Anderson Hall (022-29)
1114 W. Berks Street
Philadelphia, PA 19122

This issue is made possible with monetary support from the National Endowment for the Arts, the Pennsylvania State Council on the Arts, ‘A ‘A Arts, Chain Arts, and generous contributions from several individuals, and subscribers. Thanks also to the University of Hawai‘i, Mānoa and Temple University for office space, web space, and some postage.

Huge thanks to translators Rosa Alcalá, Odile Cisneros, Chris Daniels, Jen Hofer, Mark Lokensgard, and Thomas Schødt Rasmussen for hard work under tight deadlines. Thanks also to Keston Sutherland.

Distributed by *Small Press Distribution*
1341 Seventh Street, Berkeley, California 94710-1409
http://www.spdbooks.org

Indexed by the *Index of American Periodical Verse* (Lanham, MD: Scarecrow Press), *American Humanities Index,* and partially by the *MLA Bibliography of Periodical Literature.*

Cover by Jacqueline Thaw.

Archive . . . http://www.temple.edu/chain

ISSN: 1076-0520
ISBN: 1-930068-17-4

EDITORS' NOTES

Email conversation from October 2000.

THALIA FIELD I've been thinking about your note re: *Chain* and I came up with something, one or two things really: NON-CONSUMER FICTIONS as a sort of play on "consumer fictions" and also as a commentary on the state of the art which is all geared toward consumer categories of genre . . . so that this could invite both cultural critique as well as genre/consumer art critique . . . I guess the same trope could also work, though less gracefully, with POLITICAL FICTIONS—to be artless and direct about it. I understand you both want to torque it somehow, and I agree, the "field" of possibility should be wide open and invite multiple interpretations.

JULIANA SPAHR this sounds great! are there any people in particular you are thinking about? that sometimes helps when doing the write up for the next issue. i like looking at consumer. $. etc. we haven't done much of that. and it is ripe for re-evaluation. cd this be a $ issue? is that too trite? i don't mean that literally. but a critique of capital (globalism, etc.) issue.

F Yes, exactly—there's something about $ and genre which seem to be the same thing, but since you've already done a cross-genre issue, it seems we could come at $ from the point of view of the genre of FICTION which, as we all know, is the big $ genre. . . . So is there a way of approaching "fiction" as consumerist fetish—as that kind of "genred" space which reinscribes certain norms—and then start to look for where that falls apart—to search out the outer limit of this "country"—find the illegal immigrants, unaccounted workers, those that trespass just enough to raise the invisible to the level of awareness . . . I guess I'm thinking of people like Fanny Howe and Leslie Scalapino, who inscribe "narrative" back into poetics—and of course the "new Sentence" sort of thinking and even certain kinds of polemical "narratives" like Kamau Braithwaite's—places where "FICTION" sets up house within other "genred" spaces out of necessity—(because it wouldn't be allowed into the Big House on its terms). Then of course writers like Renee Gladman and Bhanu Kapil Rider, Brenda Coultas, people who tell "stories" in completely alternative form. Form is still the biggest indicator of genre (in my opinion) and there's something in that which could be related to $ as well. So . . . I'm thinking to explore the fiction of "fiction"—getting at how the consumer industry of publishing conveniently inscribes a set of invisible parameters for the sake of consumer convenience—do we think that upsetting the comfortable bourgeois space of the "novel" or the now popular "short story collection" is also about form and hybridization, multi-culturalism, etc.

S i thought i wd try to keep talking about this. my one worry on next issue: i don't want to do another hybrid genres issues under another name. just b/c that is turning into our default of sorts. it isn't a bad default. but i want to keep pushing at what is expected of us. i like the idea of capital as a topic. my worry is that people will write too much about $. like it will be too literal. is there another term that we can use to draw it all together. some other ideas to just throw out: a drama issue (like thalia suggested). cd be called dialogue but that might be too hokey—but this feels expansive to me b/c it isn't a "theme" but a "form" and one we haven't done before and one that cd be interesting to open up—(worry: cd janet work with it? we might need to refine it a little).

F I thought your worries were interesting, Juliana, and I think avoiding just generalized hybridity is valid . . . if it couldn't be framed more as a critique, I too am not that interested. I think you should continue to discuss what you're interested in doing and if it's something like "dialogue" which activates the theater world, I would love to join on. I think the "dialogues" idea is a good one because it not only beckons theatricality, but forms of philosophy, and new media. I'd be all for working on that. Otherwise, the money or "currency" idea could also be great, but it's more of a subject theme, rather than a form, and this I don't think you've done . . . ? But it could be cool . . . it's more along the GRANTA lines, though. Originally, I thought of it as a critique of the form of fiction, but that ends up back perhaps in that soup of hybridity.

S Should we try to keep thinking about dialogues? This seems like there are a lot of ways to go with it. We cd get some good drama stuff from Thalia. We cd try and get some culture stuff—like dialogues across cultures (if we can get anything that isn't too retarded with this idea).

Anyone we know who cd help with philosophy? Renee Gladman is one person that comes to my mind. Also: might be interesting to have people doing some dialogues for us. We cd think about commissioning some b/t people who might otherwise never talk to each other. Like people working in radically different genres. Or with very different ideas. The only thing I wd want to avoid, but I think we can: dialogue as nice, neat conversation. like we need to get some work that is against dialogue. and not too much work that says dialogue can save the world. and we need some screaming. or something. i don't know. i just don't want to end up in a place where we are saying hybridity (not of genre but of culture) can save everything; if we all just sat down and talked . . . also: collaboration as form of dialogue.

JENA OSMAN Yes, I love the "dialogue" topic idea. It's a specific form (unlike the *Granta* theme idea) that could go in many great directions. Please excuse me while I die from exhaustion.

F I think the dialogues idea, too, has a ton of potential—it's got all the artistic and social relevance. I also agree that some sort of furry moral is not the end we should be imagining, but rather a hard-hitting sort of thing, the difficulty of dialogue, even. Maybe it's just being at Brown, but I feel our country has lost all sense that things Matter, or that being committed to something, or having a real opinion is a Good thing. The Dialogic idea sounds solid—and already sort of grant friendly—esp if you're into using people who are "known" for being polemicists of some sort—pairing them into fruitful discussions—perhaps on TABOO topics—or topics which get REPRESSED AND RETURNED TO sort of in that freud/lacanian way . . . This week I've been thinking a lot about this notion of the TELEVISION TABOO and how TV seems to absorb the DIALOGUE from other public forums and sanitize and contextualize it through the use of "commercials" which frame it in the safety of consumer ideology which surpasses the "content" of whatever happens between commercials. This notion of BETWEEN COMMERCIALS then becomes the question too, how can we ask questions that aren't geared toward CELEBRITY but actually ask people to risk their own consistency or little habits of mind. . . . I like the idea of pairing interesting thinkers with a third text or construct which they approach from different points of view, and perhaps different discourses so that vocabulary and discourse/metastructures of thought are also foregrounded—efforts to combine, for example, how an economist and a filmmaker, or a philosopher and a ecologist might approach some third term/text. But this might be harder to get people to do . . . . I wonder if there's a way to start the dialogues so that they evolve in interesting and organic ways—I'm thinking that the subject overall might be enticing enough for really interesting thinkers/writers to WANT to address—subjects which are not usually approached, or approached only tenderly—like an open-ended question: what's the SINGLE MOST MEANINGFUL THING YOU'D LIKE TO SEE CHANGED or something, and then let the discussions build from that kind of place . . . Or, like I mentioned on the phone to Jena: the issue could focus on each person's ONE BEST IDEA for changing the world . . . etc. Anyway, dreaming, really, the possibility to speak about what's maybe not "practical" in the realpolitik sense, but dreamable . . . now that sounds too namby-pamby. . . . I just think there's so much drivel and mealymouthed stuff out there—it would be great to make a book which is really ballsy and impractical in its OUT-spokenness. More like the WTO demonstrations and less like the "transfer of power" politics where everyone is "owned" by someone else anyway and so can't really feel free to speak up.

CECILIA VICUÑA don alejandro a Quiche Mayan elder came to speak to new yorkers last year. it seems people wanted to hear about the so called Mayan prophecies: "the destruction of the world" by 2012, as some interpret or translate them. (in other words, they wanted instructions to save their necks) instead don alejandro said: how can we interpret prophecies? i am here to recruit you: we, the indians have to watch tv in order to see animals. the earth is sick. i am here to ask you to influence your own government. this is how you will help us and the world.

CONTENTS

JOE AMATO

StarDate -322694.72

Tue Sep 11 08:51:38 2001
MAIN 2:3.12.44 stripe.colorado.edu 110 (1)
MAIN 2:0.3.2 Successfully received Poetics List Administration, 9/11/01 10:49 AM -0400, 2 Planes Crash Into World Trade Center (1)
MAIN 8:0.4.10 ALRT 1021
MAIN 8:0.4.35 Dismissed with 1.

MAIN 2:0.5.41 Successfully received Kass Fleisher, 9/11/01 8:57 AM -0600, Left Hand Reading Series 9/20: Joris& Mullen (1)
MAIN 2:0.7.4 Successfully received Kass Fleisher, 9/11/01 8:57 AM -0600, Re: Summer Writing Program at Naropa University (1)
MAIN 2:0.11.9 Successfully received Poetics List Administration, 9/11/01 11:00 AM -0400, World Trade Center Collapses (1)
MAIN 2:0.12.46 Successfully received Nicole.Gervace@Colorado.EDU, 9/11/01 9:40 AM -0600, Fwd: Counseling Center re NYC events (1)
MAIN 1:0.25.41 Succeeded.
MAIN 1:0.25.45 Sending charles alexander, 1:18 PM 9/11/01 -0600, Re: bleeding and mowing.
MAIN 1:0.29.5 Succeeded.
MAIN 8:0.30.59 ALRT 1021
MAIN 8:0.31.30 Dismissed with 1.

MAIN 1:0.7.24 Sending A Kass, 1:26 PM 9/11/01 -0600, Fwd: University Remains Open.
MAIN 1:0.11.16 Succeeded.
MAIN 8:0.12.32 ALRT 1021
MAIN 8:0.13.9 Dismissed with 1.

Tue Sep 11 13:29:57 2001
MAIN 1:3.29.6 stripe.colorado.edu 25

MAIN 1:0.1.5 Sending AndyL, 1:29 PM 9/11/01 -0600, are you ok?. . . .
MAIN 1:0.3.50 Succeeded.
MAIN 8:0.4.8 ALRT 1037
MAIN 8:0.4.43 Dismissed with 1.
MAIN 2:0.3.15 Successfully received URGENT Campus E-Memo, 9/11/01 3:32 PM -0600, Campus Response to Today's Tragedies (1)
MAIN 2:0.3.29 Successfully received Reuven BenYuhmin, 9/12/01 6:20 AM +0800, doubt & worry (1)
MAIN 2:0.9.58 Successfully received Rova Saxophone Quartet, 9/11/01 2:12 PM -0700, from san francisco (1)
MAIN 2:0.13.15 Successfully received SMBSAC19@aol.com, 9/11/01 7:55 PM -0400, Re: 2 Planes Crash Into World Trade Center (1)
MAIN 2:0.16.56 Successfully received Charles Bernstein, 9/11/01 8:52 PM -0400, It's 8:23 in New York (1)
MAIN 2:0.21.58 Successfully received Buff Bulletin, 9/11/01 7:51 PM -0600, Buff Bulletin 09/11/2001 (1)
MAIN 2:0.23.34 Successfully received Mattg1227@aol.com, 9/11/01 10:05 PM -0400, WHO THIS EFFECTS (1)
MAIN 2:0.44.40 Successfully received MoondanceNews@aol.com, 9/12/01 12:51 AM -0400, *MOONDANCE statement on non-violence & call for entries (1)
MAIN 2:0.46.7 Successfully received URGENT Campus E-Memo, 9/11/01 11:35 PM -0600, Continued Campus Response to the Sept. 11 Tragedies (1)
MAIN 2:0.55.1 Successfully received webmaster@hollywoodlitsales.com, 9/12/01 3:03 AM -0700, Hollywoodlitsales.com Newsletter Vol. 2 #10 (1)
MAIN 2:0.57.56 Successfully received OfficeMax, 9/12/01 7:47 AM -0700, Limited-Time Offers From OfficeMax! (1)
MAIN 8:1.0.20 ALRT 1021
MAIN 8:1.0.55 Dismissed with 1.

MAIN 2:0.7.7 Successfully received Vanessa Carroll, 9/12/01 9:19 AM -0600, Re: master's thesis (1)
MAIN 1:0.7.18 stripe.colorado.edu 25

Wed Sep 12 09:22:24 2001
MAIN 1:1.30.25 stripe.colorado.edu 25

MAIN 1:0.1.11 Sending A Kass, 9:22 AM 9/12/01 -0600, not sure i agree with this ("business as usual"?). . . .
MAIN 1:0.4.7 Succeeded.
MAIN 8:0.4.26 ALRT 1037
MAIN 8:0.5.1 Dismissed with 1.
MAIN 2:0.31.23 Successfully received Alan Sondheim, 9/12/01 1:40 AM -0400, +++ (1)
MAIN 2:0.1.41 Successfully received Robert Archambeau, 9/12/01 10:33 AM -0500, Re: surrealism suggestions? (1)
MAIN 8:0.5.21 ALRT 1021
MAIN 8:0.6.4 Dismissed with 1.

Wed Sep 12 10:36:07 2001
MAIN 8:2.18.31 Save changes to "Joe Amato, 10:39 AM 9/12/01 -0600, Re: hey, we're not in class!"?
MAIN 8:0.2.8 Dismissed with 3.

Wed Sep 12 10:46:36 2001
MAIN 8:7.12.24 45
MAIN 8:0.0.4 No response in 45 seconds. Shall I keep trying?
MAIN 8:0.10.3 Dismissed with 2.
MAIN 1:0.10.6 stripe.colorado.edu 25

Thu Sep 13 07:18:27 2001
MAIN 2:0.5.47 Successfully received Patrick Pritchett, 9/12/01 8:55 PM -0600, re: hey... (1)
MAIN 2:0.8.47 Successfully received Charles Bernstein, 9/12/01 11:02 PM -0400, Today is the next day of the rest of your life (1)
MAIN 2:0.11.9 Successfully received Faculty and Research E-Memo, 9/12/01 11:51 PM -0600, HRC (Human Research Committee) Application Deadlines, 2 (1)
MAIN 2:0.14.3 Successfully received John Tranter, 9/13/01 9:25 PM -0700, New York (1)
MAIN 1:0.14.15 stripe.colorado.edu 25

Thu Sep 13 07:22:25 2001
MAIN 1:2.4.4 stripe.colorado.edu 25
MAIN 1:0.1.8 Sending AbbyW, 7:19 AM 9/13/01 -0600, Fwd: re: hey. . . .
MAIN 8:0.3.26 DATA

MAIN 8:0.3.26 SMTP
MAIN 8:0.3.30 There has been an error transferring your mail. I said:
DATA
And then the SMTP server said:

MAIN 1:0.11.18 Sending Lauren Pretnar, 10:45 AM 9/12/01 -0600, Re: hey, we're not in class!.
MAIN 1:0.14.33 Succeeded.

Fri Sep 14 15:47:38 2001
MAIN 2:0.16.48 Successfully received Taylor Brady, 9/13/01 9:45 PM -0700, Re: Today is the next day of the rest of your life (1)
MAIN 1:0.6.23 Sending MarjorieP, 12:16 PM 9/15/01 -0600, how are you?. . . .
MAIN 1:0.11.46 Succeeded.
MAIN 8:0.13.33 ALRT 1021
MAIN 8:0.14.7 Dismissed with 1.

Mon Sep 17 15:41:30 2001
MAIN 2:20.42.21 stripe.colorado.edu 110 (1)
MAIN 2:0.5.53 Successfully received Patrick Herron, 9/17/01 5:25 PM -0400, RE: [ImitaPo] Nostradamus "predicts" NYC Attack, WWIII (1)

Mon Sep 17 15:49:03 2001
MAIN 8:1.2.40 Save changes to "Filters"?
MAIN 8:0.1.14 Dismissed with 1.

MAIN 2:0.1.45 Successfully received Andrew Levy, 9/17/01 6:10 PM -0400, RE: are you ok? . . . (1)
MAIN 8:0.2.55 ALRT 1021

1.0

4

BRUCE ANDREWS & ALANI APIO

"We Go Tilt-A-Whirl Again!"

This dialogue was begun by Bruce Andrews in response to issues raised by Alani Apio's play, Kāmau A'e, *and his editorials on identity, imperialism & cultural nationalism, "A thousand little cuts to genocide" and "Kanaka lament" (online at www.thehonolulu-advertiser.com for February 25 and March 25, 2001). Andrews collaged together passages from Apio's play—these passages are indented and in italics—with summary or clarifying questions to Apio in brackets.*

PART A.

"I'm getting tings togedda in my head"

ANDREWS We both start out wanting things to change, wanting writing to take part. [We want to have an impact on social matters, not just make impressive works for someone to interpret — yes?]

APIO Yes. My intention has always been to move people at a gut level. My father is a good, solid man who just made it out of high school. If the end product of my writing doesn't move him at a gut level, then I haven't done my job. I try to write for the highest common denominator. There certainly are layers to my writing, both literary and cultural, but I try to write for my neighbors and the guy selling lumber at the hardware store.

1.

BA Reading Writing: not just asking what it means, but what it does. Gauge the work's force; see what kinds & intensities of critical or communitarian activism it can encourage. [How conventional does the work need to be in order to have that impact on the community we think counts?]

AA In Hawai'i that's a difficult question. We're multi-ethnic, multi-cultural, and, most importantly for impact—multi-lingual. So, the community one is trying to reach—the one "we think counts"—is of tantamount importance. There is certainly a literary, highly educated community here that will appreciate avant-garde, post-modern American literature (I'm not even sure what's the most cutting edge now!). Recent immigrants from Tonga, however, will for the most part need something that feels closer to home in its use of a language that is not their first, and, a medium more easily accessible to them. That's one of the reasons I've opted for using the stage—the medium has a great balance of universality and ability to impact.

The key over here is languages. With so many different people here whose native languages build different value systems and lenses for filtering the world, one cannot push the envelope of conventional (English) language use with people who are not absolutely proficient with the language to begin with.

For example: *Kāmau* and *Kāmau A'e* both use Hawaiian Creole and ʻŌlelo Hawaiʻi (our native language) but are for the most part English language-based. The dialogue of the characters reflects their own educational levels, their own social standing, political views, and their own proclivities within the play. Their individual language ability is complicated by not only their competency, but by the inherent inability of English to capture ideologies outside of the realms of the Language and larger western culture that uses it. For instance, in the play, the main character, Alika, when asked what aloha means by a tourist, cannot answer. The reasons why he cannot are quite complicated and are rooted in the colonization of the islands by America. Aloha does not have an English equivalent because it represents a multi-level social ideology far beyond a simple "hello" or "goodbye" which it represents as well. Also, Alika cannot formulate a response because his first language is (for reasons of historical oppression and colonization) English! He has a hard time translating a value system that is rooted in another language—one which he should know, but has never been allowed to learn. In the meantime, he has been taught, through nonverbal socialization, to know what aloha looks like, what aloha feels like, though he hasn't heard it verbalized because English doesn't allow for it.

Native Hawaiians, the indigenous people of Hawaiʻi, did not have a word for "own" because the idea of ownership was foreign. Everything belonged to the Gods—even—especially—land.

BA Force inscribes bodies, marks them up or erases the lines that confine.

"We all gotta draw ouwa lines."

Either (a) Lines of flight taking off into distances, into becoming, future-tilted. Or (b) Lines of division (statics of victims & conquest, to stall, to stay put). Status quo tries to sew itself all up. Do we honor the suture or bust the stitches open, to open up a future. [Lines: does division usually keep us in place? If the status quo holds itself together partly by language, don't we need to take that language on directly?]

AA So, if we are oppressed by the status quo's use of language, taking it on directly for us as Native Hawaiians has a very different connotation: for me at least, it means learning my native tongue and using that as the mode of expression. Or, start by building a bridge back to understanding that land and language are imperatives to cultural survival and that to break the power of the status quo I must work to have at least a parity of languages. Cultural survival is vastly different from keeping races separate (anticipating a reply).

"We need to decide our future—not some interfering foreigners."

BA You can't, ahead of time, "decide" a future that's to stay open. Decision, here, takes on the tone of protective closure. [Deciding a future: doesn't that imply a lack of openness to the new?]

AA Above feels like you are interpreting language out of the context it's been given by the characters and the play.

BA [Memory: Does it help us move forward, or keep us stuck?] Move forward or trace back.

"you carry forward dat which needs to be remembered."

AA It feels like memory is like money—not inherently evil, but very loaded and valuable. It does both all the time: help us move forward and keep us stuck—it's all in how we use it.

BA Or. Your memories keep you from moving forward. There ain't no original. The past is not an outside, is not a vantage point on the outside. That's why it can't be represented (recreated at a distance). See how shredded the past has gotten — & gets. [Why have an imagined model to work off of?]

AA There ain't no original, but there is definitely, if we are speaking of human social systems, a spectrum of successful to not-so-successful models and it bears remembering what worked in other times, other places, to see what may fit now, here.

2.

BA Does language even have its own country? Still, racial splits & fervent nationalist rejectionism seem to set horizons for literary art. [Why think of language as something national?]

> *"blood . . . da haole divide us by it."*

AA I agree. In the face of globalization we stand to lose the knowledge base of tens of thousands of years that is built in different languages. Language is power. Political power among other things. When it is linked to nationalism, even in its most benign form (is there such a thing as benign nationalism?) the dominant language tends to steamroll through along with the dominant culture. Much gets lost. If we think of languages as storehouses for valuable information for living on planet Earth, much like a specific species holds invaluable, irreplaceable information, then in the fervor to solidify a "national" language, the other languages of the minorities get quashed. And the ability for those minority cultures to survive gets curtailed as well.

BA When we're making literary use of English, how do racial & national (assimilationist) divisions get mobilized? [Why think of English as national? Does national have to imply assimilation?]

AA In Hawai'i it sure does. At least for any minority not capable of going toe to toe politically with the dominant white majority—which here means basically everyone. Besides, America was founded on the assumption that it would be an English speaking country and many of its laws and unstated ideologies enforce and support that. The difference here is whether one emigrated or is of indigenous blood. If you, or your ancestors came here by choice, then the unspoken social contract you bought into was that this was someone else's land and you'd have to abide by their rules—including what language you would have to speak. That's fine for immigrants, but what about the native people who had their nation overthrown and were forced, by law, to abandon their mother tongue for this new language (think how English capitalizes the "I" but not "you," or "we," or "us." Think how different grammatical structures point to fundamental differences in value systems).

BA How to detect / decode / display a specific cultural heritage — as readers while we're writing? [If you have a cultural heritage you want to work with, how to do it in English?]

AA My belief has always been that sociologically speaking, land and language are the cornerstones of culture and if English is the first language, then chances are, at least this is how it has played out in Hawai'i, that if your first language is English, the best one can hope for is to be a subculture of the dominant, English speaking culture that surrounds you. Too much of how a culture defines itself is wrapped up in language to survive the translating.

BA Niche is the verb, the infinitive. But how does a niche open out onto a broader horizon? [If you make a niche — like "deciding a future" — does this close you off from broader possibilities? Can ethnicity really be a niche, if you write in English?] (I guess I don't think of racial essentialism as anything more than a genre.)

AA We need to have and state clearly, agreed-upon definitions of race, nationality, ethnicity, culture. Short of that, sure we can. Even if English takes over the globe, human social evolution and the simple diversity of environments will continually move us towards specificity in language and culture, even in the face of globalized capitalism. Everything is subject to change. and the writing's on the wall for global capitalism in its current state—the earth simply cannot support its excessive, exhaustive waste of natural resources.

BA Can we get access to a way of writing — a translation language — beneath these differences or abstracted above these divisions (which are national or — often when a sovereign state is missing — racial). [How do the different social groupings in H. get expressed in the same English language? Can we tell the difference?]

AA I would call the different social groupings subcultures. They mark the differences between each other through their different lexicons in much the same way as the different African American (is this the current identifier?) subcultures identify and distinguish themselves from the dominant white majority.

BA For instance. Leaving aside the use of pidgin or native, historical languages, between a mixed-race heritage & a purer Hawaiian one, locally, what's the notable difference when they get embodied in English? What's vital to share, in writing, in (translatable?) works, that is uniquely Kanaka (Hawaiian)? How to embody a heritage: incorporating elements of pidgin or of the Hawaiian language — or its translation — or demonstrably tilting the English into a different shape, to create an otherwise. [Would the writing in English change to reflect these different groups or categories' experience? How to do that? Is pidgin relevant at all here?]

AA Pidgin is entirely relevant and reflects the first major step away from using standard English as the mode of literary expression. (Since, of course, the overthrow of the Hawaiian Kingdom and the concomitant overthrow of the Hawaiian language.)

> *"Oh, I'm sorry. I don't know, um . . . pidgin that well.*
> *"Saright, we teach you. You new hea?"*

BA Or thea? Or whea? What stylistic idiom could make these cultural treasures translatable? To make at least the atmosphere of them, the semantic & material resonances of them, more broadly globally available? (Or is that just English-chauvinism, the blatant cash lingo?) [Is it presumptuous to imagine these experiences could get transmitted through standard English alone?]

AA Yes. A lot gets lost, as usual, in the translation.

BA [Do you feel the need to write in an historical Kanaka language at all?]

AA Certainly the desire. But I have to be truthful to my own reality or my writing will not ring true. As much as I would have given my eyeteeth to have ʻŌlelo Hawaiʻi as my first language, it's not. I know I will never be as capable in ʻŌlelo Hawaiʻi as I am in English. Such is life. My future children may have a different reality. I don't know what you mean by "historical" though. The language has continued unbroken since contact with the West. It has survived, albeit just barely. It has evolved: we now do have words for "own," "computer," and "email." So it is not a "historical" language but a living one.

BA [Cultural heritage has usefulness for you, yes?]

AA Cultural heritage forms the basis for my self and social identity.

BA Heritage: something empowering, & confidence-building, when you possess it yourself as an historic cultural encyclopedia, prop & prod; but also, at the other end of the spectrum, something inspiring when it isn't yours. [But how would that inspire or interest someone like me to be exposed to it in, say, your writing?]

AA I don't care what language we write in, humanity has common, basic denominators and good storytelling seems to me universal. If I weave a good yarn, and the translation is good, you will be interested in it the same way I was interested to find out what happened to Achilles, King Lear, and Arjuna on the battlefield with Krsna.

BA (Or is that just tourism in writing?) Tourists —

> *"they're a captive audience. We can use them to spread the word."*

And. Captive audience — Contradiction in terms?

> *"An, let da tourists know da full scoops."*

[Or is that just superficial tourism? Or would that be so bad? Are the local Hawaiians disenfranchised simply because they're stuck with English?]

AA Certainly not simply, but lacking our culture's language base puts us at a major disadvantage. Think in the opposite direction: suppose we never lost power here and the concept of land ownership was not allowed because our language (which expresses our value system) does not allow for it—what would Hawai'i look like today? In Samoa, Tonga, and other Pacific nations, private land ownership, as America practices it, does not exist. They have very different lives there. Judgements aside, they live very different lives.

BA Meanwhile: natives disenfranchised in English? Is local color something the (English) language can be robbed of — or something that can be trumped up (within it)? Does robbed of a language imply robbed of agency? Where are my stilts? Where's my machinery?

> *"You mean you fuckas was jus using me!"*

[What ends up getting lost? And how might somebody restore it? Or is the local more of a barrier to getting experiences from elsewhere?]

How much is the Local a boundary, a reterritorializing? A parochial (insular) marking. & Danger signal.

AA When Captain Cook landed here in 1778, that was such a huge cultural clash. English and ʻŌlelo Hawaiʻi represent cultures so very different that it is often very hard to come up with satisfactory translations—much gets lost. As far as getting experiences from other places, the barriers to that are created more as a reaction to the loss of power and culture. If the "local" is in control, then there is no threat of loss of power from outside influences, but if you lose power and control, then I think it is a completely understandable, human reaction to become insular.

Japan and France come to mind as two countries wrestling publicly with the threat of losing their cultures because of the huge, culture-crushing power of American media, pop culture—the "MacDonaldization" of the globe (I know there's a better term for this!)

"We're too much of everybody and everything else."

BA [Does the high value you place on the local express a fear of mixing or of impurity, so that you want to get rid of these foreign intrusions — not just in commercial life and the media, but in literature too?]

AA No, absolutely not. Funny thing is, the bulk of what is considered "local" writing here is exactly that—mixed and "impure"! The continental U.S. imposes, through mass media, such a overwhelming flood of expression that our uniqueness gets wiped out. For example, to date there has never been a full-length feature film about Hawaiʻi told from our "local" point of view that has any merit—to me, at least. The rest of the world really does not know who we are, both in our specifics of culture i.e., local Caucasian, Asian, Polynesian, Native Hawaiian, or, in the mix that has resulted and is exemplified in "pidgin" writings.

BA Fear of Incorporation. Of the mix. (& the mixdown). Of impurity. Given to an expulsive, peristaltic writing, to rid itself & us of "foreign properties" — in purification ceremonies. [How much is this like the hi ʻuwai? Is the purification ceremony you mention anything related to this?]

AA I'm a member of the Protect Kahoʻolawe ʻOhana. Kahoʻolawe Island was won back from the U.S. Navy by Native Hawaiians after a twenty-year court war. When we go over to visit (it is still being cleaned of unexploded ordnance left from 40+ years of bombing) we do a cleansing ceremony in the water like the one described in *Kāmau A'e*. Anyone who wants to join us is welcome. It's not a racial or even ethnic thing—it's a cultural thing. If one wants to learn, is humble, open and respectful, then one is always welcome and loved. Racism is a wholly western import that we have, quite sadly, taken up at different times and places.

BA Must radical "basic research" be seen as a foreign import, as viruses to quarantine? Would enthusiasms about "experimental writing" get seen as an unwelcome American intrusion or betraying imitation? A "sell-out'? Do we do better restricting our diet? In the terms wielded in political economy, this points to an import substitution policy — with readers confined to winning badges of cultural preservation & restoration?

"Dey even won da culta award"

[What would this mean for your interest in, say, experimental literature from the mainland? Does it have to be rejected, should it be rejected, does it represent a threat, or just something too reminiscent of the intrusive commercial US cultural bombardment? If it gets rejected, what's left other than cultural preservation?]

AA Your use of the term "mainland" reflects, I suggest, your presumption that we in Hawai'i are simply a satellite, an offshoot, a "minor" land of greater America. Where you live, to me, is on the American Continent. I call it the "continent" for short. This place, Hawai'i, where I trace at least one line of my genealogy back to the 12th and 13th centuries (and then further back to Tahiti), is my main land. Ku'u one hānau—the sands of my birth.

Mainland. Hmmmm.

What's left when we reject the automatic subjugation (however unintended) of culture (in all of its expressions, especially literary) and identity (both individual and social) is reclaimed native soil for us to grow and be our selves on, to express our selves in.

I think that, again sadly, most people don't even conceive of us living here in Hawai'i as having our own, vibrant, worthy culture and that rather than preservation (because life does not exist without evolution even in the most remote places, and even in the slowest of time frames), clearing out the clutter and oppressive mass of American culture means the culture here is not just "preserved" but has the room (once again!) to evolve and grow in ways that America, as a generality, is almost unable to even comprehend because it's much too preoccupied gazing at its own navel, or fake boobs—whatever.

3.

"Up to now we've only been talking da talk, now honey, we gotta walk da walk."

BA The prescription follows from the explanation. Just like Walter Benjamin's "Destructive Character," that inveterate pathfinder, who "sees ways everywhere" and therefore "has to clear things from it everywhere."

Memory: Now we need a tsunami of creative destruction to clear a path. X-ray the crossroads underneath the battlefield. Imagine an open set of relations, mixture-mad, inclusive toward those outside. A not-so-stand-off-ishness. I'm on the lookout for a globalizable resonance. A romance. Wouldn't a useful globalism be created by porosity & mutual exposure? Criteria: how porous, how open to "flows beyond" can we make a place, a situation, a cultural stance? Isn't the mere distinction marking off foreign from local in the way? — or, "on its way out"!

I can't imagine meaning as an intrusion. Lineage smacks of linearity — instead of a code-scrambling, juiced-up miscegenation. Everything is foreign. [Destruction: if you see a chance to move your experience in many different directions, on many different paths, wouldn't you need to clear away the barriers and baggage that are cluttering up all these paths? If that's what I'm advocating, to allow for maximum openness and mixing, on a global scale, it's partly to get some resonance or "juice" from outside my own cultural situation.

Yet, from your pt of view, what would be the risks or threats associated with that?

Is the protection of a lineage and a heritage always prone to ending you up on a narrow path?]

AA Why is it always the presumption that "protection" will always end up being narrow? How (in generalities, admittedly) absolutely hypocritical. America presumes the rest of the world speaks and understands English. That "Ugly American" expects nothing less while touring the globe. Talk about narrow. Start from a base language that is not your own and then we'll speak.

"Right on keia, now you talking my language."

BA [Talking my language: If you get confronted with something strange, doesn't it help you notice how much you are usually socialized into something? Do you end up being less inventive because you think you have a heritage to protect and conserve?] If you don't talk my language, wouldn't it help me notice that I possess (& how much I am possessed by) a specific confining language. Or Dracula-ized.

AA After, or most positively, concurrently, heritage grows, evolves and blossoms while being "protected" and "conserved." It's easy to speak like you do when you come from the position of dominance and unquestioned power—political, military, economic and cultural power.

In the 1800's, when Native Hawaiians still controlled our mainland, when we were the dominant culture, our leaders took in technology from all over the globe and folded them into our society here at lightning speed. 'Iolani Palace had electricity before the White House. We embraced reading and writing to the point where, in the mid 1800's, we had the highest literacy rate (98%) in the world. Our rulers were the first in modern history, perhaps in all history, to circumnavigate the globe. Pre-western contact, we did not know about harmonic scales and sung in monotones only. We embraced Western music and have made a uniquely Hawaiian sound now known the world over.

Clearly, this all points to power—who has it, who controls what. When one is fighting for basic survival, the luxury of invention is replaced with the cold hard pull of hunger and thirst. We, Native Hawaiians, experienced a depopulation rate of over 90% in the first hundred years after Western contact. A century and a quarter after nadir point, we're still trying to recover. Hard to experience the world, hard to be inventive when you are struggling to feed your kids.

BA Without a secure language, you face the need to invent one. Or how many. Or make a nomadic erasure of territorial markers. Speak in tongues. Make an exit in language, make language an exodus [Clearly I'm advocating something else here: more nomadic, less marked up territorially, less confined to a single "tongue" or way of writing.]

AA When you roam the earth silent, relying on a language other than English, then you will be walking your envisioned nomadic walk.

Your advocacy is, in my opinion, based on the luxury of largess and power. America goes where it wants, eats what it wants, takes what it wants—and even if the going, eating and taking is personally benign and done with sincere gratitude it is still going, eating and taking whatever one wants. We, Native Hawaiians, as a people, can't do that. We don't have that kind of raw power. And, as individual citizens, Americans on the whole don't take responsibility for the bullying and outright oppression America heaps on much of the world. And because they don't take that responsibility personally (but feel always that the world is their oyster and birthright)— criticism of the whole, of the system, gets personalized and twisted into a "but that's not what I'm about" mentality.

Strip naked, be silent. Other ways already exist.

4. Out from Under

BA Spot the Enemy. To oppose it, to stand back from it: Ask: How formalist / formula-ist is this enemy? How much settled into forms, or formal questions & issues & distinctions.

> *"No need be so formal hea."*

Or normal. How well can the weird circulate? One blockage: all that mass of conventional glop. To swamp is to conceal is to dominate.

> *"I ain't trying fo hide notting."*

Yet we do let established norms & forms occupy (& preoccupy us), dominate us, treat us like third world country members. Normative grammar — that's one big industrial management system. Or Genre: drop anchor; let the fecal matter build up on the bayside. Aren't fixed genres horrific? — unless you make one up on your own. (Self-management). To unbroadcast. What We Need = the Informal — getting us outside of the usual, established forms with an Informalism — where the play between words & phrases gets forged point-by-point, without a prior (preestablished, regimenting) program. Moments —

> *"we're making this up as we go along."*

To kick up enough of an improvisatory breeze, to aerate our future. [Isn't the "enemy" something that relies on conventional forms to triumph over us?

And if so, don't we need to challenge those forms? (I'm even including genres and normal grammar in that, so that I'm advocating what I've called in another essay "informalism', where the words and individual word meanings get related to each other on a point-by-point basis, with a lot of friction, rather than having them derive from some prior program. Which is where improvisation would fit in.)]

AA You know, I think I understand where you're going here. And, having read some of your pieces, I'm beginning to glimpse what might be out there. However, there still, I think, must be some common ground, otherwise it's just gibberish to me. I know it's not. But I don't have the translators.

I never understood Picasso's "GUERNICA" until I read a straightforward account of the Spanish Revolution and the bombing of Guernica.

BA Do the words only propose something for action to carry out? Or can words themselves make up the action, the paper bullets . . .

> *"Moa pepa. . . . We goin fight one pepa war."*

Even the page makes a battlefield, a slaughterhouse. To start: play with a counterviolence at the syllable level — just a clearing away to start with, rowdied by the microscopic. [Paper bullets: Does politicized or militant action have to look down on writing, or can we think of writing as a form of action in and of itself? If it is, then I'm back to wondering how much "the enemy" works through words and standard language forms, and how much we need to challenge those conventions if we want to challenge the enemy. And stimulate the reader, at a very basic or foundational level.]

AA Politicized and/or militant action, especially here, have used writing (myself included) as a major form of action. Who is the "enemy" you speak of? My enemy is that part of human nature (that part of my own nature) that will do anything to satisfy my lust for comfort and my desire to put Me, the capital "I" first before all others. What I try to do in my writing is hold a mirror up to our collective selves and say, "See! See what you are!"

As you seem to be defining "enemy," I would say that challenging then means learning and writing in my mother tongue, ʻŌlelo Hawaiʻi, advocating for that language to replace English, and providing translations rather than looking for a "new" language. What's wrong with the one we had? No one seems to have a problem reading a translation of *Les Miserables*, though most would agree that to get the full effect, one must learn not only French, but French culture.

BA How do we write AGAINST? How are we writing against.

> *"Capitalism, tourism, individualism—it's all gonna sink us in da end!"*

Start by revealing (by remediating) the social stress embodied in the discourse, the grammar & lexicon & talk which is dominant. To take on exploitation along with imperialism would mean taking on their Language, the machineries of their words. As long as repression usually works on their behalf, as a protective or freezing device, a contrary liberation art of words, at a basic level of grammar & reference, would hope to warm up the reader, restoring the claims of the readerly eye & ear (for materiality & extrapolations of social resonance). To delegitimize the dominant language practices — from outside (by confronting it with a different set) or from within, by scrambling & remediating & tilting & differently mobilizing. Differently changing.

PART B.

1.
BA The people who love their possibilities. Do we have to stay in the dark to feel like we belong? In language, no way self-sufficient. In discourse, no way self-sufficient. How involuntary — without our permission? No AS IF — domesticating dangers of . . . Can the reader be granted the full scope, or solicited to experience a wider viewfinder? However dystopic the result! (Listening to Mary J. Blige, "Searching for My Destiny' — "gotta be happy." But what if no gotta bes rule?)(How autonomous can we be? do we imagine ourselves to be? And. Are autonomy & self-determination pretty much or much more than male gender stereotypes?)

> *"I ho'okahi kahi ka mana'o / Be of one mind /*
> *I ho'ikahi kahi pu'uwai / Be of one heart"*

Or. Be of polymind, machinic mind extension. Be of multi-chambered heart. Be of cyborg. Belonging limits. How to embrace polyvocality? [What's so great about "belonging"? Isn't language always making us lacking in self-sufficiency? What's so bad about that? Don't you want to open readers up to the widest possible viewpoint, or viewfinder? And let the chips fall where they may. What's the downside of that? Would it make social unity impossible? Or is social unity just what is holding us back? Why not be polymorphous?]

2.
BA "What do I tell you! There have been people through here before." — *Earth vs. the Spider (1958)* Make a subject-collage — multiplying the points of contact for the reader. Hospitality.

> *"ouwa ancestas taught us to be kind to strangas an travalers."*
> *"Da's ho'okipa—ass one heavy value fo Hawaiians."*

Or. Be kind to the strangers inside yourself — to the crossroads made by language inside yourself. Or is it a special individual privilege to be indeterminate / smooth / anti-fundamentalist / mixture-philic / marketeeringly cosmopolitan? [Why not imagine the reader as a kind of collage? — open to all kinds of different stuff. Welcoming, just like your tradition of hospitality. Or is that too risky, given what they're going to be exposed to? Does the reader need to stay more snugly settled into one specific heritage.]

3.

"We're only being harsh to toughen you up."

BA Couldn't harshness be designed as an explosive device, to discombobulate our usual habits? Toughening up designed to help us be more adventurous, more unflinchingly able to accept or embrace change. Or does toughening up make for a stiffening of our defenses, of a thicker skin to contest or ward off outside pressures, or partial & mobile differences, words without attribution, phrases of mobile identity. (Content is a defense mechanism!) Better: A multiple engagement — not guaranteed by multiple characters on stage, but by multiple layerings, multiple (& even incommensurable) facets of a character, of a character's conceivable language universe (which immediately makes available a huge "social outside" of baroque layering & complexity). A social outside that calls for new modes of apprehension. New language. New writing. Harshness: to make us tougher? But does that just close us off, again, from a wide range of possibilities? Even "content" may build a wall cutting you off from a lot.

4.

BA What if our traditional habits are in the way of new experiences & new possibility?, are parochial in the worst sense. To be narrowly cultural referential. Offering up clearcut collective gests or cultural gestures — responding transparently to experiences which are already pre-codified in cultural (& even national sovereignty) terms. How much of our experience is predefined enough to make this approach possible? Do we want it to be? Wouldn't one of the hopes of a progressive writing be to make it next to impossible for the experiences to be culturally shrinkwrapped in this way? [If literature relies on previously validated cultural notions or images or traditions, are we assuming that those are worthwhile the way they are already set up? Do we want to protect them or open them up? Or does that all depend on whether we're on an island robbed of its national sovereignty or on an island at the center of a global empire: you or me.] "Dominant identity positions": that's part of what could be cleared, like underbrush, from the paths & crossroads we can get busy making. Even subjectivity itself takes the stage as barrier to fuller experience, putting the full & embodied individual into a deductive relationship to something prior. Are we supposed to deduce our position or is it rhizomatic, upended & all-ended? How particularizing can we be? [Identity: I seem to be putting identity in this same category: baggage that would need to be cleared away in order to open things up more widely. Do you take the opposite approach, familiar from identity politics, where an already established identity (or one that might be recoverable from the past) is empowering? Useful? Needed — as the foundation for cultural and political activism?]

AA When one is free to be whomever, wherever, whatever one wants, dropping identity is a luxury and, perhaps for some, a charade. In the wake of 9/11 it seems very clear to me that however much America says it wants to "embrace" the multi-culturalism of itself, the actions it has taken don't jive. When Bush goes off on protecting the "American Way" he is very much talking about protecting the white majority way—certainly not protecting the "way" of Hawai'i or any other "way" that is not "Mainland America." The trying on of different identities, the opening up you speak of, got slammed shut with a protectionist iron door gaudily painted red, white, and blue.

5.

> *"You know, Hawaiian style, it's not individual rights, you said it yourself—it's the group, the 'ohana.'"*

BA Are group rights & identity, in reading, any more than a way to homogenize the individual? We're willing to pay what price of an internal homogenizing, & an exclusion of the outside — ? (Flatten out — a better phrase than "homogenize"; carries the topography motif along.) (The opposite of particularizing the whole.) Group norms flatten out on both sides: singularities are jeopardized & so are multi-plicities. Don't squeeze my multiplicity. Don't swamp my particularity. You can be located. You can be counted. And isn't a writing based on identification one that guarantees our sense of conventional member-ship? Could we imagine some identity beyond the group, or the individual as group member? — some modulation, some spectrum of differences to manage. Isn't the individual (as different from the securely prefabricated group) likely to be a better vehicle for hybridity, for circulating mobility, for change?

6.

BA To make yourself unlocatable. To make yourself uncountable.

> *"Let the life that belongs to you be made firm."*
> *(From an anonymous, pre-Western-contact prayer for fishermen recited by the main character.)*

Firm = closure? Or, firm = dedicated? Let the life that doesn't belong to anyone be made soft & porous. Individual rights — here's a tradition well grounded in our usual notions of reading. Or is that the trouble with rights & individualism? How individualistic is language adventure likely to be? Or is that mostly when it glorifies the writer's cleverness or charisma? If we work in isolation, we won't move forward as easily with a reciprocity in reading. [Individual versus group. A cultural heritage as the basis for a group identity: what does that do to the individual? Does it just close them off to things outside? Does it threaten to submerge their individuality in a big pool of group enticements and rules? I tend to reject identification (a move in my thinking familiar from Bertolt Brecht's writing) as something that forces you to have your experiences filtered through another person, the one you're encouraged to identity with. (Of course, this might be essential in doing plays you want to get an audience for . . .) Does that kind of identification seem crucial when you want to build up a spirit of group membership? (If so, it might make sense of my lack of interest in both, in the group membership and in the identification).]

AA As a generalism, but not, I think, an overstatement, the contexts of "individual" and "group" are diametrically opposed in Eastern and Western thought. This has been written about thoroughly but is still often overlooked. America's inability to comprehend that others around the world don't view the individual as primary can explain many of our foreign policy disasters.

In ancestral times in Hawai'i, when an ali'i—a ruler—died, if they were much loved, sometimes their most trusted and beloved followers would voluntarily be put to death, or kill themselves, to be buried with that ali'i. This was an acceptable, noble act. Others more removed from the ali'i would express their grief through self-mutilation, i.e., knocking their teeth out. These acts are not without precedent in humanity, but they speak to my culture's paradigm of putting others first: the family or clan comes first, one's own needs are secondary, if that.

We, as humans, need not judge this. If I desire to view the group, its identity and needs as primary, there is nothing inherently "wrong" with that, but it is fundamentally different from some of America's basic tenets of individual rights, freedoms and privileges.

Your lack of interest in both the group membership and in identification is, I think, more the result of being socialized from day one into a society that glorifies and empowers the individual. It is not so where I am from. In Native Hawaiian culture, if one comes from an "I" center, that is met with harsh criticism and thunderous silence. I know this from personal experience and it points to the challenges of having another culture (American in this case) superimposed on our ancestral culture: we as present-day Native Hawaiians are socialized in a way that puts us at odds with ourselves. We're not the only ones, many in the Pacific, Native Americans—we've all experienced this in one form or another. This is often why we kill ourselves—we're fed, from day one, too much conflicting bullshit.

BA [If I want a more mobile and hybrid result, wouldn't the group be a barrier to that? Because it would locate you, it would count you in.]

AA If we, as human beings, move away from race-based cultural identification, and color, or other physically defining identifiers as the basis for cultural inclusion, then your fears would be moot. Your unstated assumption, if I may, seems to be that "locating" and "counting you in" would lock you in. Clearly, at least in Hawai'i, this isn't the case. I know many non-Native Hawaiians who are welcomed into the culture, are encouraged to embrace it fully, but do not have to give up their other cultural identifications. Indeed, my first ʻŌlelo Hawai'i (Hawaiian Language) teacher was a German/English man who was accepted by Native Hawaiians as one of our 'ohana. He was hānai'd into a Native Hawaiian family and therefore became a part of them. He was also a member of Hawai'i's French Society. He also spoke fluent Samoan and had hānai'd (adopted) a Samoan youth as his son.

My read on America is that it is still sickeningly stuck on race-based cultural identity and the brutal politics of physical identity.

Hawai'i has, by the last census count, the greatest percentage of mixed-race people in the country. This can be traced to Native Hawaiian values of acceptance: we were essentially color-blind. We didn't care what you looked like, we cared, and still do, far more about how one's soul manifests itself. Unfortunately, we have definitely taken in some of America's ugly, self-destructive "racial" filters.

BA [If you want to help meet the group's already existing needs, does it make you reject a more experimental kind of art?]

AA No. It does, sometimes, make acceptance of the experimenting a longer process. The "we've always done it this way" syndrome has expressed itself most publicly in hula. There have always been, and probably always will be, strident discussion, fights even, about what is "traditional" and "acceptable" but that hasn't stopped people from experimenting—ultimately. It seems to be a good balance, but it does depend on balance: enough filter to not lose what was good before while opening up enough to allow for growth and exploration.

BA [Belonging and non-porous: what I don't much like. Doesn't the importance of the individual get pretty clear when we're talking about the reading experience? Or, in the theater, can you pretty much ignore that and instead try to go with a sense of the audience and the group being similar.]

7.
BA How is the reader going to share this authority? Only by buying into Heritage? [Interactivity issues.] Can authority be shared with the reader as easily if the source is a preset (historical) code or story or consensus or tradition or voice-&-personality-centered protocol? In any identity based on tradition, something fixed & fixing reveals itself. These end up being identifications imposed authoritatively, as a reflection of authority — even if it appears as identification with difference. Not to incite the pre-sold.

> *"(Trying to incite audience)*
> *Hawai'i for Hawaiians! / Hawai'i for Hawaiians!*
> *(Audience does not respond)"*

Identity-needs serve as the basis on which things get ruled out. Made taboo. The equivalent of a cleansing ritual or purification ritual in writing. And this helps glue the hegemonic arrangements together. The dominant culture works like a magnet, bundling together the over-confident strands. As if: settling who they are & where they stand are vitally important. It projects — & depends on — this suturing. Readers supply the attributions, the invoices, the verifications. [Again: individual readers and cultural heritage. Doesn't heritage based on tradition or group voice or story get in the way of sharing authority with the reader? If identity is based on the group, again, I'm wondering how much gets lost, gets made taboo.]

AA Again, I think it's all about balance: there is much in our collective history as a species to keep! Those who forget the past are doomed to repeat it. Those who forget the present are doomed by the ever-changing nature of life. Balance between.

8.

BA Readers spread the word, but only if activated. And can they get activated without their assumptions about themselves (& not just about their colonial pleasantries & victimizations) getting challenged? But is knowledge a solvent of solidarity?

> *"dey going catch on. No worry. We no need bang em ova da head."*

Yet without a big cultural apparatus behind it, how can challenging new work count on readers catching on? Wouldn't it need to foreground its own extremity, its own cultural equivalent of headbanging? To incite desires may call for a more confrontational approach to the desires we already have. It may not be enough to simply try to foster new desire. The Enemy isn't subtractive. It implants things in us. It's additive. For instance. Normative grammar implants in us something; it doesn't rob us. So: how are we supposed to challenge these additive devices? If a stimulating (postmodern) "motivation" is the mechanism of control, then there's a prescription which follows from this explanation: the raw materials of socialization — the discursive "telling phrases" & "commanding phrases" & "insinuating phrases" — will need to be "taken down." Challenged. Roughed up. As part of a liberation — which is a social liberation & a liberation of language. [How to activate the reader?: by confirming their cultural assumptions or by challenging them.]

AA I try to do both.

BA [To challenge them, doesn't it help if the literary work seems strange or extreme? Because we're not just offering up some new possibilities; don't we have to clear the path of what's already there?]

AA In the late 70's a kumu hula (hula teacher) shook the hula world by having his men perform pre-contact dances in pre-contact dress at the premier hula event, The Merrie Monarch. At that time the pendulum had swung firmly to the right and dress was ultra-conservative: long Mother-Hubbard style dresses (known as mu'umu'u) for the women and long pants/dress shirts for the men.

What this kumu hula did was both new and old: we are not now who we were back when that type of dance and clothing was the norm. We were much more genetically homogenous, we lived in an advanced stone-age culture on islands still incredibly isolated physically and culturally. Therefore, that kumu hula brought back a flavor of the past, blended with the present. To many it was strange and extreme. He did have to, definitely, "clear the path of what's already there" but he cleared it to (re)introduce some thing that had been there before blended, unequivocally, with his present moment.

How this relates to literary work is, I believe, no different from all art: to be effective, one must still have a way to translate the message into the experiential filters of the other. Otherwise, strange and extreme is simply unintelligible. Or, it is ahead of its time and waits for others to bridge the gap. That is not altogether bad, much art, much philosophy, much of the outpourings of the human spirit have been seeds planted waiting for the right convergence of events and people.

If we, you and I, shoot from our na'au, our guts, I don't think we have to worry: human guts have changed little in the last 40,000 years or so.

BA [(Again, is there a basic difference between us here — between helping people value what they already have (or what is being threatened by mainland intrusions or loss of sovereignty) and helping people jettison much of what they already have to open them to something new? I'm taking the latter position, which is why I talk about messing with the raw materials of the enculturation process when it comes to language.)]

AA again, I shoot for balance between the two.

Whether either of us is actually capable of doing what we are striving for is ultimately up to others to decide.

Why jettison what works? Why keep what doesn't? The interpretation of positions need not be taken to the extremes.

9.

"We ready for active protesting."

BA Does staying within a recognizable genre make active protesting impossible — or is it a precondition? Start with ourselves! Is the language just using us? Lick your chains. If you see it coming from a distance, don't bother to absorb it. Contest subjectivity. (Even). [Brainwashing — an image of what? And how to resist it?]

"We don't consider them the enemy. They're just brainwashed, that's all."

Mind control — classic image of intrusive encroachment on self-sufficient (differentiatedly mental) activity.But all culture is brainwashing. To resist brainwashing = ? Another cultural purification ritual? Were we put on this earth to stay the way we are?

10.

"We not hea foa get in youa face an start yelling."

BA Even without a clearly locatable voice . . . Doesn't the writing need to counteract the complacent reciprocities of mutual facework, of both reader & writer saving face together? Doesn't it need to get in the reader's face? Counter-amplification. Raise the volume. Raise the temperature. Disconcert the reader. Disassemble the reader. Make interior nomads. Make monstrosities. Make a counter (contrarian) disassembly. Instead of adopting a culturally nonreferential stance: explore everything it means to culturally refer (or embed). Look into the arrangements that make sense (or fittingness) possible — (& not just "mere" abstract knowledge or individualizing ethics). (Political action, a social imaginary. Not just to dwell on the ethical & the epistemological.) If you don't provide enough of the language context we need to "make sense out of" or "make intelligible" an individual utterance, aren't we pretty much reduced to the status of the ventriloquist dummy? Instead, challenge, discombobulate, the socialization process — by taking on its materials. What do we need. Scramble (is that, take apart) the social grammar. Do some "social denormalizing' — as if there's a strategic logic of following norms that you're opposing. You could do that as Critique of Ideology. But the social work/ political practice called for now goes beyond reflectively followed norms. it involves massive behavioral bodily conditioning — via the spectacle, mediated bodywork. So all of that becomes open to challenge through the writing. In theatrical writing or poetry we can take on (& test out) these identifications. But without the freedom (to roam, to choose, to reconfigure) the social materials which "make sense out of" an individual vantage. Instead, the identification is imposed. What are the mechanisms of (global? national? subcultural?) identity positioning. Or what are its ligaments? What's the social machine that produces these identities & how does it work? How can we throw a monkey wrench into that social machine? Let me help you amputate some of that power. Identification?: instead, you're brought too close to the fire of social material. Or else: vertigo-inducing experience of a grand canyon of layering & sedimentation (of meaning). Identity solvent — (but not a solidarity solvent) — a social sublime. [Here I'm getting at what would challenge the socialization process in literary writing. And wondering if it doesn't require challenging the very basic ways in which things normally make sense, and in which we as individual identities get conditioned. Why wouldn't that work in a situation like yours? What would be the downside? Would dissolving conventional identity also run the risk of dissolving the solidarity you want? Is the sublime a threat?]

AA Your proposed process is one way. Honestly, I don't know if it would work better. I just go by my na'au, my guts. My fadda always tol' me, "Go fish, feed da 'ohana (family). Da's all what you gotta do."

ADEMIR ASSUNÇÃO & KAKÁ WERÁ JECUPÉ

Words of A Moon-Man

Kaká Werá Jecupé is a rare case among writers in Brazil. A Tapuia or Txucarramãe Indian (he prefers the latter, which means "unarmed warrior"), he is the legitimate child of the ancestral inhabitants of the lands "discovered" by the Portuguese. He resolved to break a five hundred year silence and write history through the eyes of those who have inhabited the "New World" for millenia. The result is the beautiful poetical-mythological book A Terra dos Mil Povos [The Land of A Thousand Peoples] *(Editora Peirópolis, São Paulo, 1998). Born in 1964, in the Guarani village of Morro da Saudade, on the southern edge of the city of São Paulo, Kaká received his education in the public schools, where he learned the official history of Brazil and which made no inclusion of its indigenous cultures. This became the impulse for his journey toward his own roots. He began to travel the country from north to south, visiting Indian villages and following the mythological trail taken by the Guaranis in their quest for the Land without Ailments. He heard the stories of living memory from the wise elders. Tired of the official view, which treats the Indians as primitives, Kaká shows the ancient cultural richness of these peoples and points out the great weakness of "civilized" society: ignorance. In his words, words themselves take flight, like a bird that carries on its wings a mix of poetry and wisdom. This dialogue was originally published in issue 9/10 of the Argentinian journal* Tsé=Tsé, 2001.

ASSUNÇÃO One of the things that catches our attention in your book *The Land of A Thousand Peoples* is the power that words have for the Indians. In one passage you say: "According to our tradition, a word can protect or destroy a person. A word in one's mouth is like an arrow cocked in a bow." What exactly do words mean for the Indians?

JECUPÉ Those passages refer specifically to the peoples of the Tupy-Guarani tradition. For the Tupy-Guarani, *being* and *language*, *language* and *being*, are the same thing. The word that means *being* is the same one that means *word*. *Ayvu*. Soul and sound. The very word *Tupy* means *sound standing upright*. Our people see being as the tone of a grand cosmic song, played by a great creating spirit, which we call *Namandu-*

ru-etê, or Tupã, which means *the sound that expands*. Human beings are seen as a vibration, a pulsation. This is the starting point for the relationship that the Tupy-Guarani have with words. One of the names for *soul* is *neeng*, which also means *speech*. A pajé [a shaman] is one who can emit *neeng-porã*, beautiful words. But not in the sense of rhetoric. The pajé is he who speaks with his heart, because *speech* and *soul* are one and the same. You are what you speak. That is why the Guarani-Cayowá, because of their disillusionment with relations with white people, prefer to withdraw their word-soul. They hang themselves (as has been happening for about the past ten years, in Dourados, in the state of Mato Grosso do Sul) because the throat is the house of one's being. Thus you can see that the relationship between language and culture is deep for the Tupy-Guarani.

A You also say that the name of a person is very important for indigenous peoples. How is a child named within this tradition?

J In the Tupy-Guarani tradition there only exist seven names, seven universal names. The others are human reinventions. These seven original names are our first seven parents, our ancestors. Human beings inherited from these seven parents the power to name, to continue creation. These first beings, which the Tupy-Guarani call *Nanderu*, are divinities. They are what sustains the movement of the world. All of our lineage comes from these names. When a being is spiritually baptized, he receives what would be the equivalent to a family name, which marks his heritage. This is the importance of names—it is the name to which his soul is tied, his spiritual ancestry.

A Who are the seven divinities you referred to?

J They are known as Werá, Karaí, Jacairá, Tupã, which are the four that sustain the world. Then there are Namandú, Jasuká and Jeguaká, the divinities that sustain the spirit.

A Does everyone within the Tupy-Guarani belong to one of these lineages?

J That's right. It is very common among the Guarani to meet people called Werá Popyguá, Werá Mirin, or Tupã Jeguaká, Tupã Poty, Karaí Poty. These names are very common.

A In your book we also notice the use of words linked to nouns, such as Moon-Man, Sun-Woman, Bird-Tribes. Why is that?

J Within these primordial lineages, which are structures of sustenance, there have been mixtures. Moon-Man is linked to a mixture of inheritances, of inherited powers, of a quality of a man with a quality of the moon. This created a temperament, a quality that is Moon-Man. These linked words define these mixtures that define the structure of a being. Like Bird-Men, they are part of an ancestry, in a remote time, from moon to moon, which became myths. They are part of the ancestral memories of the culture.

A In this specific case the inversion is interesting, because normally the man is associated with the sun, and woman with the moon.

J The Tapuia culture believes that this is the human ideal, Moon-Man and Sun-Woman. This is the ideal of the perfect clan. Some beings exist that manifest this quality. They are perfect beings that have managed to attain these qualities on Earth.

A You also refer to the first seven tones, the last of which is silence. Considering that words are so important for the Tupy-Guarani, what does silence mean?

J Silence is in everything. The Tupy, this *sounding standing upright*, is manifested in three bodies: the physical body, a body that we call the body-of-sound, and a body that we call the body-of-light. The body-of-light is represented in the culture through head ornaments, through colors. The body-of-sound is linked to two qualities of energy, which are the *katamiê* and the *wakmiê*, the feminine and masculine poles. This movement of being is balanced in seven ancestral tones, which are vowels. Many dances serve to align, to tune the instrument that is the soul, which is this body-of-sound. For Tupy philosophy, this means the body that links the heavens and the earth, its residence in the material and its residence in the spirit, through which you experience sensations, feelings, perceptions. This body is moved by vibrations, it is a body-of-sound. Chants are sung to balance, to harmonize this body. And silence is the sound of the sounds. It has this meaning of the essence of the whole. There are sounds that are linked to the physical structure of the body, others that are linked to the sensory structure of the body and to the most subtle structure of the body, the spirit. Therein lies silence. The Portuguese language has five vowels; the Tupy-Guarani language has six: a, e, i, o, u and ÿ, which is a more guttural sound. And the seventh is silence.

A Is there a specific dance for each of these tones, these vowels?

J No. Our expression has all of these tones, like a song. Each tone deals with different artistic matters: *ÿ*, for us, is linked to the earth, to vitality; *u*, with water, emotion; *o*, with fire, energy; *a*, with the heart, with qualities of attracting and expanding, with feelings that flow; *e* is linked to expression; *i*, with perception, intuition. Each tone has connections to aspects of being. The Guarani say that we all have a *nanderekó*, our place in the world. This *nanderekó* possesses temperaments. These temperaments are linked to four sounds, each linked to four elements that manifest themselves in our moods: earth, water, fire and air. It is these four elements that somewhat determine our personalities. And there are tones that make our interior selves live; they are like musical notes. When songs are sung, those aspects that need further work are given attention. Our *nanderekó* has a quality that makes a certain harmony possible. This harmony is manifested through our spirit, through our language, through our internal being. The songs and dances manifest this harmony, they tune, they align our being in the world.

A In this being in the world, we see dreams as something very important for a large number of indigenous cultures. What are dreams?

J Dreams are the moments in which we are stripped of the *nanderekó*, of the rational structure of thought. We are in a pure state of spirit, in the *awá*, the integral being. In these moments we connect with a deeper reality. For this reason, dreams are vital. They create this connection with our true selves, because the *nanderekó* leaves us with a very limited perception of things in life. Within the dream state you connect with the whole and with that larger self that you are. In dreams your spirit literally travels and can be directed wherever you want or to whatever moment you wish. Of course this requires training, like learning to speak.

A Who is responsible for this training in the tribes?

J Normally a wise man. Every master has his own way of teaching. In general the teachings are to prepare you to have your dreams consciously. The whole system consists of educating your rational mind to perceive that it is not the master of your body, but an instrument of your dreaming spirit, your unbounded spirit. The concept of a dream for an Indian is not that of an unreal and impalpable thing. In the dream you realize the multidimensionality of the world. The doctrine that educates for dreaming consists of your perceiving the layers of dimensions that make up the world and orient this more rational side to be conscious to these other dimensions. A wise man prepares you to make these flights consciously.

A Do you control your dreams?

J You do not control the dream, but your conscious mind can direct it. For example, say you need to give a message to someone that is two hundred miles away. You can direct your dream, through your reasoning to yourself, and say "I will travel now in my dream and give a message to so-and-so." And the person there will receive it.

A And the person will be dreaming too?

J That's right.

A Does the tribe receive signals about how to act in certain situations?

J Yes, it happens frequently. It's natural, because dreams are the moment in which the spirit is free.

A Is the pajé [the shaman] the main person responsible for having these dreams?

J No.

A Can a child have dreams that indicate direction for the tribe?

J Yes. Among some peoples there exists a morning activity called the Dream Circle. They put fifty people together in a circle and they begin to tell their dreams. And that dream begins to give direction to the daily life of the village and sometimes it creates a change in the village's life. Sometimes a dream appears that has signs saying, look, you must all move the village immediately—a series of dreams that all indicate that. Of course there is always someone that knows how to interpret dreams. Among the Krahô tribe, which is a tribe that has many celebrations, there is a person who is the tribe's dreamer. If there is a meeting, a dance around the fire, he lies down with his head toward the fire and sleeps. The next day he tells what he dreamt about.

These are some of the ways the Indian peoples deal with dreams, having as a starting principle the relationship of dreams to a moment of liberty for the spirit, when the spirit sees everything from every angle possible.

A Is this relationship to dreams common among all the Indian peoples?

J Yes, it is.

A You say in your book that there was a moment in which the Indian nations divided themselves into three different traditions: that of the Sun, of the Moon, and of Dreams, which is the tradition of the Tapuia. Does this mean that the Tapuia are more dreamers than the other tribes?

J No more and no less. The Tupy developed a whole philosophy and ethics that sprang from words, from sound. The soul-word is the axis that orients spatial life, and the forms of the *ocas* [Indian homes]. The Tupy influenced many other peoples in Brazil for thousands of years. They are an expansive people, a sun-like people. But there was also another, more contemplative people, more like the moon, despite the fact that the tradition of dreaming has a more contemplative character. This other people left a greater mark of this tradition in its art, these people, the Marajoara, the Tapajó, left fragments, a complete cultural practice. And the tribes that left behind no philosophical system, no defined system of art, but which had a great power of expression, were the Tapuia, the Xavante, the Krahô. They are more nomadic peoples. They left behind no system of agriculture, but they did leave a system based on liberty and the relationship with the spirit and with the earth, through the process of dreaming. Not that that was all they did. The Xavante, which are remnants of the Macro jê [one of the main linguistic groups among Brazil's native peoples] are one example. They are a people with a strong cultural identity, a people that establish themselves through dreams.

A Writing has always been a determining factor in telling History. In your book you refer to a kind of Indian writing found in basketweaving and drawing. Is this indigenous writing?

J Writing as conceived by western peoples is concerned with linear time, present, past, future, in which civilization is caught. The writing that indigenous people left, and which is still found today, is linked to another frequency of reality that is much more symbolic. Indigenous peoples have their writing, but it is inaccessible to that frequency that western civilization recognizes as such. This writing is found on the body, through painting of the body, in basketweaving and ceramics. There is a book that Lux Vidal organized called *Grafismo Indígena* [Indian Writing]. This book gives an idea of the richness of this native writing. Indian peoples left behind this quality of writing that is attuned to the part of the human being that deals with his interior "I."

A You mentioned the relationship of writing to time, saying that white people's writing is concerned with linear time. What is the relationship to time that the indigenous peoples have?

J I had the opportunity to live within an urban society, and also lived a part of my life in a Guarani community and short periods of time among the Kamaiurá, the Krahô, and the Xavante. One thing that determines time for the Krahô, for example, is the movement of the rainy season into summer, or the movement of the day into night. They never concerned themselves with dividing up or breaking apart this movement. Because they live this passage of time so integrally, it is as though there were only an eternal today, even as children are born, as they become adults, as they grow old. Every cycle is experienced fully through its rites of passage. One lives the present moment. There is the celebration of the chestnut, of the *pequi* fruit, of the manioc. These rhythms of the village give a melody to the culture. The people live this melody and everything is one large present moment. The time of civilization is very tense.

A The year 2000 marked the five hundredth anniversary of the arrival of the Portuguese in Brazil, or as we learn in school, the "Discovery of Brazil." In your view, was this a discovery or an invasion?

J It was a mismeeting. A mismeeting that provoked and continues to create serious problems, even massacres. The present situation for the indigenous people is not easy. Even today, in large areas of the country, the situation is defined by shootings, dispossession of land, conflicts with ranchers and miners. The interests that provoke these actions are the same as ever: economic interests. Today there is an additional element: the megainstitutions of science, of chemistry, pharmaceutical industries, which are practicing biopiratry, stealing an ancestral knowledge that indigenous peoples have of herbal medicines. Religious missions also cause considerable tumult. The Guarani people are deeply religious. If you break the natural religious structure of a people, under the pretext that they are not religious, you destroy them.

A And what is the main cause of this mismeeting?

J Its seed is a society that has in its cultural structure the matter of possession. It found here a society oriented towards being. This was the crux of the mismeeting. A society that is oriented towards possession generated points of view that are still present in its conduct, in class divisions, in ideologies. Behind it all is a vision of possession and accumulation of wealth. These two different visions create the difficulties that the cultures have in meeting. The Tupy is not concerned with marking territory; his very name, Tupy, means "sound standing upright," a being. The Xavante calls himself *awen*, which means "people." Then people arrive that say they are Portuguese. And what is a Portuguese? A people that lives in a marked-off land, that is the owner of that territory, and that wants to expand to other territories, do you see? Like the French. These two very different visions provoked the difficulties in the meeting of these two cultures.

A Europeans arrived bringing "progress," treating those who were here like primitives. How do you see this relationship: civilized versus primitive?

J For those who base their life and culture on having, the notion of progress consists in seeing around them the accumulation of material wealth. When it encounters a civilization that is not oriented towards possession, it finds that civilization inferior. The notion of progress for the indigenous peoples, especially for the Tupy-Guarani, consists of respecting the principles that things exist to be transformed and recreated by human beings. This is our skill, the skill of creating. And these created things can be exchanged; this is a basic tenet, so that our skill in creating can continue to manifest itself. The other tenets say that there are four things that cannot be exchanged or sold: the sun, the air, land and water. Progress, for us, is developing one's creative capability, one's expression in the world. This manifests itself in the way one deals with space and with nature in the form of a celebration. The progress of this people is within this law.

A So these are very different ways of viewing "progress"?

J Yes—the development of science and wisdom of the indigenous peoples came about through this interior perception, through the development of celebration through dance, songs, body painting—through a harmonious relationship with nature. We had our own progress. This is a point that needs to be made in order to perceive the size of the abyss that this mismeeting of cultures provoked.

A Notions of material wealth did not make sense to native peoples?

J Well, consider this example: when the Spanish arrived they found three great civilizations, the Incas, Mayans and Aztecs. They had monuments, pyramids, and hydraulic engineering. They attempted to deal simultaneously with these two essences: having and being. When the Spanish arrived, they asked the Mayans if they knew of any wealthy tribes. They said that there was one beyond the mountains, the Incas. But the Mayans were saying that the Incas were rich because they had the largest variety of corn and the best technology for planting it in inhospitable environments. When the Spanish arrived there, they saw the artwork in gold, but the gold itself was not the wealth of the Incas. It was not the gold the Mayans were referring to. They were talking about the technology of agriculture, that knowledge, that science. The notion of wealth of the peoples here was very different from that of the Europeans. So there was progress here, but it was undermined, and we have to reconsider the notion of progress to truly respect the civilization that was here. Civilization needs to view the Indians with less arrogance; then it might see that civilization itself is collapsing.

A Why is civilization collapsing?

J Civilization is not collapsing because the stock market falls or rises. This is all a bluff. Society today lives off the bluffs of those people that deal with future markets. How can you have an economy based on a bluff? What kind of progress is that? The economy of the Inca people was based on its capacity to deal with the winter and the infertility of the soil, without suffering, without the winter causing poverty for the population. That was wealth. The wealth of civilized society is founded upon a bluff. That which society calls progress has become so blinding that no one perceives how much it lives on self-deception.

A Is it blindness to the deeper values of existence?

J Yes. For the Tupy-Guarani this is a terrible thing. For the Tupy-Guarani words have spirits, and in civilized society people live on words without spirit. They have no strength, no truth. And this is called progress. An economy based on the talk of a bunch of people who scream like maniacs on the floor of the Stock Market, and then the dollar falls, affecting the lives of millions of people. Common citizens are the ones who suffer the consequences, and they are the ones that really construct, plant, create the structure for those people to be there talking about laws and discussing strategies for development. The common citizens are the ones who, in effect, deal with the reality of the situation. These two notions of progress have to become clear within these five hundred years. When this vision becomes clear, then it will be possible for us to promote a true cultural meeting.

A How could this kind of meeting have happened?

J There could have been a development of both peoples, without the destruction of either of their cultural essences. It could have been a meeting based on respect, on true integration, on exchange. Today there are indigenous leaders that have literally practiced cultural cannibalism ["antropofagia cultural"]. They discovered how to live in contact with white civilization while strengthening their own cultural heritage. These are examples of how such contact might have worked. There could have been a maturing of both the native culture and the one that had just arrived. This did not happen. Western culture today continues to practice values from an era that has passed—the notion of conquest, of expansion, of accumulating land and goods. I am not saying that this is the vision of civilization in general; it is the vision of a handful of people. It has nothing to do with today's reality. It is completely backward, primitive. Unevolved.

A You were one of the organizers of a meeting of indigenous organizations to mark Brazil's first 500 years, through the Arapoti project. What was the idea behind this meeting?

J Arapoti means *rebirth*. The death of our Pataxó relative in Brasília, after he was set on fire by white teenagers, made me begin to think about Brazil's young people.[1] To what level has this civilization sunk, to create a generation with such an attitude? I became very concerned. So I began to think about organizing a meeting of different tribes, to bring our different ceremonies and interact with young people, because they are the ones who need it, they are the ones who are showing the symptoms of their civilization's disease. In April of 1998, we had the first meeting of tribes with young people, in Porto Seguro [where the first Portuguese ships arrived in 1500]. So our project for Brazil's five-hundredth anniversary is not only for Brazil's future, but also its present. Our notion of time is strongly linked to the eternal, so if we can manage to create a new relationship with what will be the future, then we can contribute to that civilization.

A And what does this project with young whites represent?

J Our project for Brazil's five-hundredth anniversary is against ignorance; it is a project of disindoctrination. Indigenous cultures have many tools for educating one's being, for teaching respect for humanity. This meeting is being called a New Rite of Passage for a New Human Tribe. The biggest problem for the young generation, which led to this horrendous crime, is that it lost contact with itself, with its internal rites, with its passages, its cycles. Indigenous peoples marked these cycles through rituals, ceremonies, in a process of education with its foundations in myth. [Western] society has none of this, so its youth don't know what they are or what they are responsible for.

A And how do you see the question of integration? There are still tribes in the middle of the jungle. What about their situation? Do you think they should be left there, that no one should go there, let them live in peace? How should this be resolved?

J In Brazil there are currently about 350 thousand Indians, from 206 ethnic groups and 180 different languages. Of these, about 70% live within civilization's confines, on the edges of the cities. The majority has lost much of its traditions. My project's aim is to value and respect our roots, and recover the self-esteem of these peoples. The people of the Xingu, in the Amazon, as long as they can live in an ecologically balanced system, are the teachers of our ancestry. They should remain in the Xingu, if they want to. The ones who need to be educated are the aggressors towards these cultures. They need to be sensitized, so that they understand the stupidity they are practicing—the ranchers, prospecters, mining companies.[2] These groups are the ones who need to be educated. It is the responsibility of this society's culture to invest in this educational process. This would be a project for Brazil's anniversary—to fight corrosive elements in the culture. The indigenous peoples are living patrimony of humanity.

A In these last five hundred years, with the disappearance of hundreds of ethnic groups, which was the patrimony that Brazil lost?

J The greatest patrimony that Brazil lost was that of knowledge. Many of these peoples developed systems of relationships with the environment, with medicine, which today are so relevant and sought after for sustainable development, for deep psychological truths—things this patrimony already possessed but that were not absorbed or applied. Biomedicine, phytotherapy, natural medicine. The economy, that is, what I call economy—the system of the people's interaction with local cycles, local relationships—things that are being remembered now and that existed in abundance here. Look at the Japanese; they are recognized the world over as a technological nation, a wealthy nation, but they do not surrender their ancestral traditions, their art, their dress, their philosophy. But Brazilians are ashamed, because they don't know their own culture. There is a popular image of the Indian as a poor victim, who was unable to develop shopping malls or to progress. This celebration of Brazil's five hundredth anniversary offers the possibility for the society to revisit its roots and understand its patrimony.

A And to understand its own wealth?

J Exactly. This idea of separating people into first world, second world and third world is false. With all its riches of flora and fauna and people, do you think Brazil is a poor country? No way. We are a great nation; there is no such thing as the Third World. This is another bluff that society believes for some reason. I walk through the hills, the forests, I work directly with nature, with indigenous people, with people from the interior. No one is wealthier than we are. I've also been outside Brazil—everyone always talks about New York. I've never seen such a dreary place! Always so dark, with steam always coming out of the ground. They call it the Capital of the World. If that's our model of civilization, we have a long way to go. But I don't think it's a model for [Americans] either. There is an anguish inside them; Americans want to understand indigenous culture. I felt in them a need to recapture something that would make sense for them on the inside, that would help them remember who they are. Human beings are not the children of that dismal steam seeping out of manholes. They are children of the earth. The human essence was born in the waters, in the mountains, trees, animals. Not in the megalopolis.

1. Three years ago, a Pataxó Indian was burned alive in Brasília (Brazil's capital) by four teenagers, all sons of judges from Brazil's highest courts. The man was sleeping at a bus stop, and the four poured alcohol on him and lit a match. After their arrest, they said that they meant to play a prank and that they had no intention of killing the man. They also said they did not know that he was an Indian, but thought he was merely a homeless man.

2. Individual prospecters ("garimpeiros") search for gold in parts of Brazil's interior in large mining areas opened in the middle of the jungle ("garimpos"), the most famous of which is the Serra Pelada.

Translated by Mark A. Lokensgard.

GUY BEINING

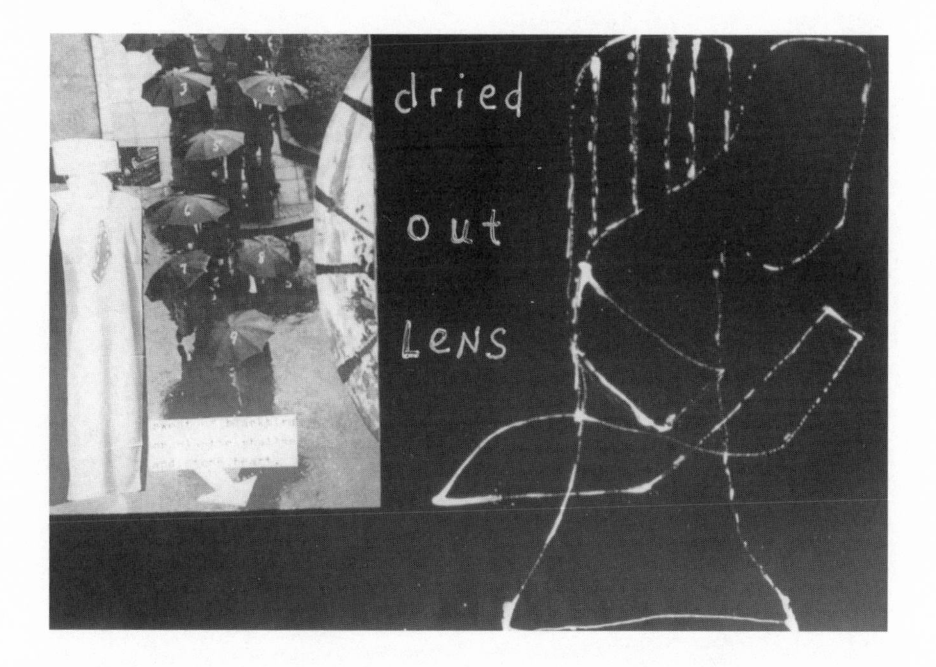

Concerning: dried out lens. The energy of dialogue is in silence. The figures with umbrellas chatter, in scattered rain. That voice of the sky is their web, the substance of their movement, yet from a higher plane the image is packaged by the weathered soul of blackness. This form turns from sky, rain, & voices; it is that indifference to dialogue, of the visual one, that creates the voice of silence.

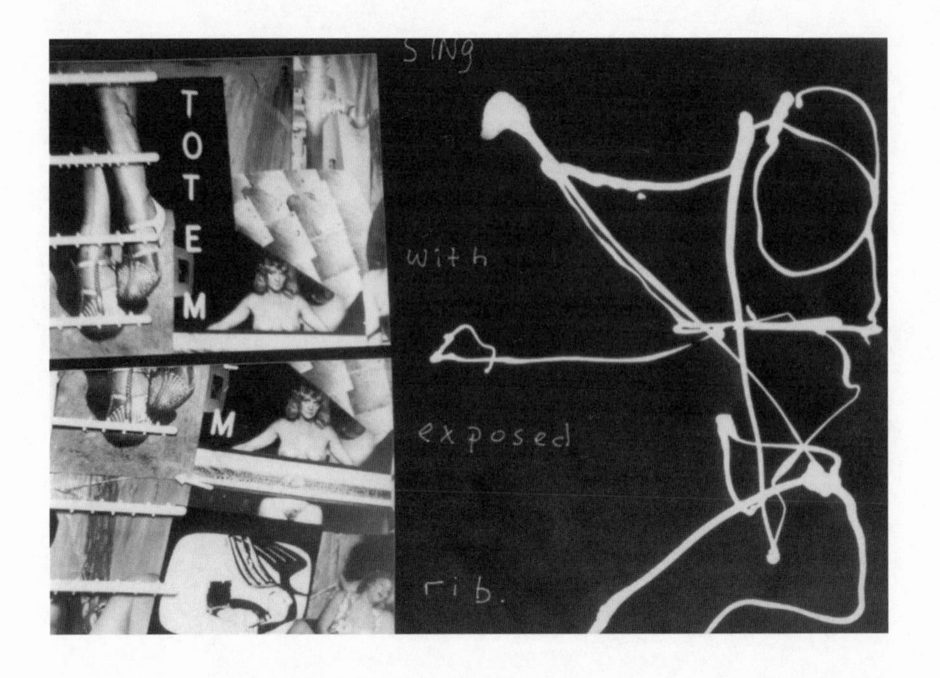

Concerning: sing with exposed rib. The vulture of thought is processed again and again in a caustic collage. There is a piling on top of each other, which creates a visual totem. The verbal glue is flung from a body of paint onto darkness. It speaks of the elongated sentencing of that visual compilation. In both of these works the confrontation of darkness vs. light becomes the ultimate dialogue.

SHELLY BERC

Monodramatechnotrama or, Why I Write One Person Technological Extravaganzas

When you get down to it there is no such thing as dialogue. Contemporary communication is self dramatization. The Monotrama, as I like to call the one-person technological extravaganza, is the singular vision that sends the self into flight and sets a steel trap for it.

The earliest theatre was single-vision epic, from Homer through Aeschylus.

Once we got to Sophocles, things went down hill because the unified, theatrical voice got shattered. Theatre became character cut ups and those characters had to *do* something with each other—so they talked. Thus, dialogue was born and the single voiced vision went the way of wooly mammoths.

Dialogue is based on the powers of persuasion and lies, not vision or truth seeking.

Throw out dialogue.

Substitute: computers, synthesizers, techno-panic video screens, microwave ovens with three inch TVs attached.

Monotrama cannot exist without technology. Monotrama is virtual reality Paradiso.

What is missing from techno theatre and the avant-garde in general today is what is the essence of technology, namely hot wires.

Irony and cold metal electricity in cutting edge theatre have become dead connections, excuses for paranoia, cowardice, and too much TV.

Nuclear Bombs on the other hand are very hot.

In this world, theatrically speaking, we have to fight fire with fire.

Monotrama is miniaturization.

Silicon chipped characterization.

All consciousness in a single voice.

All the world in a lone object.

Through the minute and intricate, we recognize the infinite and abstract.

Monotrama is the close up fairy tale shot of theatre.

The individual in the Monotrama stands in for the old single voiced Greek chorus in its appeal to the Gods, in its lamentations and fears.

Monotrama is a blues song to abandonment

From self, family, community, this galaxy and plenty of others.

Classic realism skirts the schisms of psyche by chopping it up into warring personalities know as characters. Monotrama is the psychic realism of the theatre. It is the performance preview to the upcoming electronic cottage.

The dramatic tension of Monotrama is not between self and others. The tension lies between the prisms of the self. This understanding is the recognition scene of Monotrama. The resolution of the play is the constant regrouping of the reflective composition inherent in the character of one.

Monotrama scoops out the layers of lies, hunting for firm foundations of art. As the lies fall back in faster than we can dig them out, we hug ourselves to our self on ever shifting terms. Participles dangle, tenses confuse. The self knows itself as she and I and you and we and he and they.

Current technology makes two things possible: 1) liberty from the robot assembly line and 2) isolation or independence, depending on your point of view. The by-products of #s 1 and 2 are freedom and loneliness. Monotrama seeks to restore the magic dissolve of aloneness—an all-oneness that is the exhilaration of a group freed from group scrutiny.

Monotrama is thorough narcissism. By virtue of the fact that the theatrical Narcissus uses the audience-sea-of-faces as her looking glass, Monotrama is thoroughly skeptical of its own self-absorption.

Monotrama may be performed by more than one actress; the way a kaleidoscope breaks light, the way the cosmos has refracted itself into infinite particles of individual necessity. The single vision and the narcissistic are rooted in the same instinct—to defy gravity—the things, people, artifacts that hold us down, as the universe floats and expands. The singular vision summons energy into one tight black hole in space, whose objective it is to blast through all space and all time.

Monotrama is the poem of the theatre.

The poem is our last toehold on earth before the leap into zero gravity song.

As in a Homeric epic or a chanson de geste, the singular voice is released into the freedom of pure story telling.

Free of the weight of dialogue, she is unleashed from the whoredom of story selling.

Monotrama is a chant. A chant of world want.

The world want is to wail and sing.

Sing the soul out to a wall, an image, a person, any particle of any substance that bounces even a fragment of our own sound back to us.

The chanting of the Monotrama is the memory of our common culture, instinct, gene pool, atoms.

It is the conjuring up of pure DNA.

The Monotrama tears up everything in its way to get to this effervescence. It rips the subjective from the objective and glues it back and forth together again, blinking like one of those religious postcards that change scenes as you turn them even slightly, up or down.

Through lyricism, with its deep dives and fancy flights, and irony, with its shrugged shoulders and minimalist mocking, the form perceives itself

An Atlas with Wings.

Monotrama grafts the individual blissfully to her technology.

There is a grand canyon of understanding between the minimalist generation of artists and my own brood of multi-media feedback babies. We sucked TV and electric guitars from our first breath, while these forces hit them in their teens. For the older experimentalists communications technology will always be a somewhat exotic dark stranger, at once seductive and threatening. For them, it is literally a foreign tongue, spoken at best with a cool, clinical precision. For us, the new technology isn't new—its organic, erotic, demanding our hearts as much as our scalpels. It is our mother's milk.

Monotrama reflects Internet time. It cannot exist without a techno theatre that can keep up with it.

Many theatre pieces talk about our times and technology but few reflect it. Few are structured as a time-reflection of our segmented, syncopated life pace.

The only forms that even remotely approximate the time sense of the Monotrama and its reflection of our attention deficit times are the Internet, rap, and MTV.

The mix of hot music and video with their loose ends to abstraction, incompleteness, and mega fantasy, has kicked in the door to performance poetry, that howling banshee that is the other burning realm of performing soul in which the audience is the whole cosmos.

The swift-as-light interconnectedness of the information highway is the same as that of the Monotrama. In both, we are the neurons of communication linking ourselves in infinite configurations to our fellow man, to our sense of universe. Click from one text to another, one subject and image to another to recreate one's self and transform. These links are the forces behind the hothouse blossom that is the Monotrama. They are the keys to shape-shifting our way through life.

Theatre is the perfect ground for the synthesizing of medias, both human and technological. It's the ideal place to make live and human what is removed and alien when viewed behind the glass of our computer and TV screens, when heard through our digitally euphoric walkmans. Techno theatre is head and sex simultaneously.

Many theatres say that technology kills the magic of live performance. 'Tis but terror screeching. Theatre has always been a bastard art—a multi media mutt. But in the last twenty years, it has lost pace with media advancement, and has attempted to glorify a thoroughbred purity that is absolutely repulsive to its own bloodline. Between the reactionary growl of established theatre institutions and the frigidity of the recent avant-garde, truly LIVE performance is out the proverbial window, and with it the highest and deepest possibilities of melding individual and community, thought and imagination, instinct and intellect.

Prescription for a healthy, living theatre to replace the corpse on stage:

Throw out the painted sets, blow up the prop shops. Get a decent sound system, video and computer set up and most important some dangerous artists who honor their bastard roots and we'll see a new pack of people haunting our theatre, a younger group sure to kick some life and love back into its sorry ass.

We can no longer look to the socio-familial-psychological-character drama to release us from the inner drama that links microcosm to macrocosm, the human to the rest of the universe. We can't laugh away heartbreak in black comedy anymore. Like a rabbit frozen in a car beam light, we are now impelled to cast forth our own demons in a singular glaring.

Monotrama shines the group eye straight into the individual's multi-fly eye and refracts it back to us all in fractured glory.

Wipe everyone but the one off the stage and map out the one who's there—who is the welter of the ghosts, fairy tales, and memories that own us. Give the stage to the one who weeps and breathes electric blood.

RACHEL BERS & E. TRACY GRINNELL

from *t*pography*

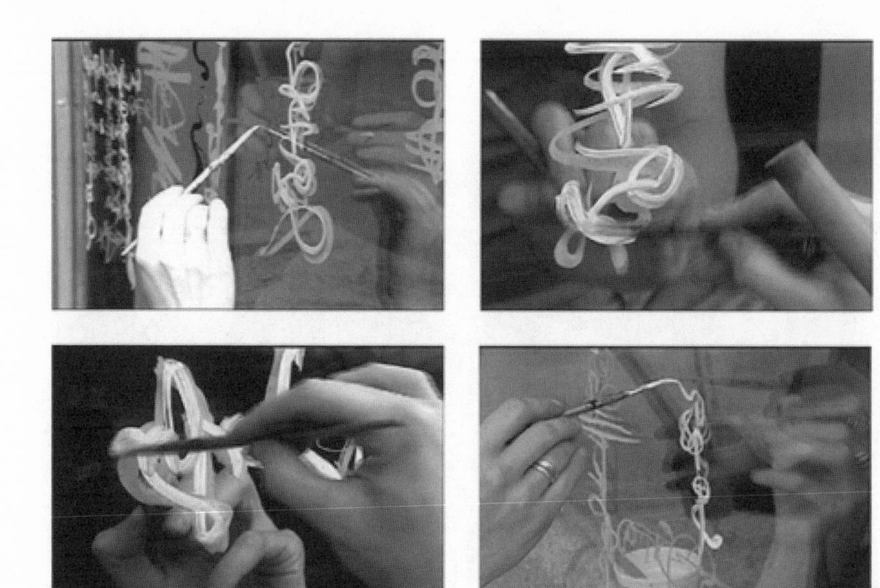

*"t*pography" was a collaborative exploration of legibility, vocabulary, and physical/ psychological location. We were interested in treating language as both a visual object and a symbolic referent simultaneously. Working on either side of the gallery windows so that we could not verbally communicate, we responded to each other's marks and gestures over the period of a week. The layers of language, both legible and illegible, attempted to map a shifting internal terrain. As the project progressed, language and geography unfurled into each other: the movement of the words mimicked meandering "rivers," and the "rivers," in turn, seemed to be unraveled words. The project was a constant revision, which often involved erasing a day's work and replacing it with work that addressed not only what seemed to be missing from the day before, but what was present and new in our relation and response to each other that day.*

ROBERT BLES

LITTLE NOTHING IN SOMETHING
ROBERT BLES 2001
Alright, alright, quiet down now son, I have to
I ah got?
work on these bills and
doctor for wife with
the car is late I need
Ey!
to think income will
my dad fell a
now h
gonha

WENDY CALL & SASHA SU-LING WELLAND

Living Elsewhere in 16 Steps

A. Address

WELLAND [An internet café: cold concrete basement filled with cigarette smoke, repetitive loop of pop music, song about searching east, west, south, north for the one you love, under swarming street scene of bicycles and pedestrians and cars honking at blue truck overloaded with winter cabbage blocking the road, ping pong table in the corner, radiators lifeless, waiting for the government-dictated date when heat officially begins.]

Beijing, China.

You have become massive high-rise apartment buildings and Hong Kong-financed shopping malls lumbering into the sky. Mirrored glass architecture storms your multiplying ring roads with fero-city. These glittery new adornments threaten to dwarf even your monumental Soviet-style Great Hall of the People, your Military Museum, your Minorities Culture Palace. How is it that I now prefer the feeling of being small and inconsequential in relation to these icons of state than that of feeling miniscule at the silvered feet of capitalism? When did your drafty old train station start to feel cozy? The big-character slogan in the square, "socialism with Chinese characteristics," now perfectly reflected in the surface of your concession to high finance, you know, the one that led to house arrest of the vice-mayor.

But, just one step off your imposing boulevards, and I'm suddenly lost in alleyways of retirees who shrug off change with a cackle and cling to mugs of tea and sidewalk chess games. Let me say for you, as a reminder, the mantra of my neighborhood, which I try to claim as mine by making these lists:

husband and wife shops that sell yogurt, melon seeds, liquor, cigarettes, shampoo, and toilet paper;

three competing hair salons with hairdressers who have repeatedly dyed their hair, waiting behind plate glass for customers and watching tv;

the pigeon cage, noisy with flapping wings, on the roof of an enthusiast's apartment;

a family planning clinic;

the south entrance to the famous Jishuitan hospital, where victims of the falun gong self-immolation in Tiananmen Square were treated a week before their fanaticism showed up on the fruit seller's television set;

a couple of dimly lit stores selling bed-side toilets, canes, neck braces, and prosthetic limbs—the hands rest motionless in a glass display case under fluorescent light;

at least four stalls, open night and day, selling funeral money and clothing;

several fresh fruit and flower stands (it's only recently that I put two and two together and figured out the why of so many gift vendors and stores selling cerements near a hospital);

a Muslim minority restaurant that is always blaring loud Uighur music and sells barbecue mutton for one yuan a stick out the kitchen window;

three street-side bicycle repairmen with basins of water for finding the leak in your tire;

a mishmash of clothing shops crowded with students in baggy pants, leg warmers, disco t-shirts, trinkets dangling from their cell phones;

the gaunt old man who stares blankly at them while clipping his fingernails;

a string of CD/VCD/DVD stores, with overflowing cardboard boxes of jumbled cellophane-wrapped pirated goods;

a hot pot restaurant with showy tanks of doomed fish breathing heavily in the front window;

a 24-hour Taiwanese-style noodle, dumpling, and soy milk cafeteria;

the homeless woman who drags along the uneven pavement in Cultural Revolution braids and green soldier's uniform;

two Adam and Eve™ branch sex shops (nos. 5 and 8), with sales people in white lab coats and advertisements of blond, big breasted blow-up dolls in the window;

a store selling light bulbs of all hue and wattage;

a store specializing in chemistry beakers, glass pipettes, and test tubes;

a trophy store;

a roasted chestnut stand;

the mandatory dumpling stall;

a few old moon-gate entrances to residential alleys;

and then you are at the subway entrance.

CALL [An internet café: three girls in middle-school uniforms giggle over chat room, man types letter with two fingers, teenaged boy looks at photos of naked women with one hand on mouse, air conditioner sputters to no avail, 99% humidity, nearly that many degrees, 1980s rock music blasting.]

Matías Romero, Mexico.

Funny how one's life can reduce down from a well-furnished five-room apartment to a termite-infested table, a soft, moldy mattress, a computer, a camera, and four small suitcases in less than two months, and one can still feel like the same person. You welcome me with profusion of another order.

You have given me a neighborhood that starts inside my house, even though I live alone:

termites in the cement walls, white cockroaches in the shower drain, and in every one of the many holes in the wall, lizards with see-through skin, whose tails fall off in times of terror;

out in the yard a bluish squirrel, a brown lizard the size of a cat, and a frog the size of a rabbit;

the neighbors' chickens and parrots squawking and their dog chewing rotted fruit in my compost pile, while the papaya tree drops rotted fruit onto abandoned red clay roof tiles stacked in the corner;

a begonia bush blooming next to the three-foot-high pile of ash left from burning trash;

broken glass gleaming atop the 12-foot-high wall;

on the other side, the concrete street white-hot at mid-day;

Coke for sale at the house next door on this side, frozen fruit juice and quesadillas on that side;

a carpenter, a plumber, and a car mechanic all working in a tiny, slanted wooden shack, its high walls spray-painted with advertisements for elections held months or years ago;

a house in mourning—the daughter and granddaughter died 9 months ago in a car accident—and a large black-fading-to-gray bow hanging over the front door;

a store for buying locks and pipes;

a department store that sells everything from tortillas to ovens to gas tanks to apples to negligees;

a store that sells only blenders and pots and electric burners;

one block of dirt road that has not yet been paved, with two empty store fronts (rent: 1000 pesos a month), a dentist's office, and a bar with a flapping sheet instead of a front door;

then a block that was paved just a few months ago;

a store selling only beer;

a feed and seed shop that smells of pesticides;

the Estafeta office, for sending letters to the US (18 dollars each)—it will only take five days for them to arrive;

a fabric store with Teenage Mutant Ninja Turtles cloth and blue-and-white checked oil cloth;

the red-and-yellow Elektra home electronics and appliance store, where your son/husband/brother, even maybe daughter/sister/mother (probably never wife) working in the US can send you their dollars, which you will receive in pesos, after the store takes 20%;

and then buses to everywhere, sometimes even the US, stopping right in front.

B. Blondie

C Every single time I venture out of my house, at least one and sometimes several men yell *"Guera!"* (sort of a derogatory way of saying "blondie") when I walk by. It happens less often when I am with Mexican friends. What I find funny is that they generally react to my ignoring them by repeating it over and over, more loudly, as if I can't hear them. Once, after a particularly bad day, I shouted *"Fuck you!"* in English at a teenager who had yelled *"guera"* and *"mamacita"* at me about five times. He looked at me as if I had slapped his face. FU seems to be as international as Coke and OK. *Un abrazo.*

W I am only rarely able to pass as Chinese, and only then as some kind of minority, and only if I don't open my mouth. My accent is enough to give my foreign-ness away, but usually my face does it first. It's a fairly daily occurrence to be walking down the street and hear people yell behind my back: *"Lao wai!"* (literally "old outsider," but a catcall of "foreigner" that sounds derogatory in an excited way.) Some days I get annoyed. Some days I find it funny to listen to whole conversations of people on the bus talking about me, not knowing that I can understand what they are saying. xoxo, S

C. Conversation with Fruit

C I said that this was about lychees, didn't I? I'm writing about a couple of villages that are under pressure to rent their land for growing lychees for export to China. I know nothing about this fruit, foreign to Mexico, but I remember your reference to it, when you talked about your grandparents' visit back to China, when words felt "soft and comfortable in their mouths." What can you tell me?

W O lychee, which I grew up eating dried, when you were a treat my grandparents bought for me. A crinkling cellophane bag of dried lychees meant we were visiting them in San Francisco. As we strolled down the sidewalks of Chinatown, away from the messy remains of a dim sum lunch and toward the parking garage under Washington Square, my grandmother would pull me into a tiny grocery packed with smells that assaulted my untrained nose. From narrow shelves full of jars with labels I could not read and bags of dried spices and seafood products, she would miraculously pluck familiar treats for me. On the rest of the walk to the car, I tripped happily behind the adults with a bag of lychees clutched in one hand and a pink and green box of Botan rice candy, secret prize enclosed, in the other. The outer shell of a dried lychee is hard and prickly, thin and brittle. The dry fruit, shrunken and a darker shade of brown than the shell, rattles around inside. The meat is chewy, sweet, and musty. But more delightful to me than this taste was the perfectly smooth pit hidden in the center. I would roll the pit in my mouth like a marble, while the streets of Chinatown receded through the back window of my grandparents' car.

C As far as I can tell, there is no good tea in Mexico.

D. Delivery

W I live not far from a huge wholesale tea district, with blocks of stores selling tea, Tea City, Tea Town, Tea Village, of every imaginable kind from every tea-growing region of China. The first time I walked down the street, I couldn't help but laugh out loud at each new block. Who could have ever imagined so much tea in one place?

C I looked at your address and thought, "Huh, I wonder why it's in English?" THEN it occurred to me that I can't write Chinese. Once our postwoman in Boston copied the Persian return address on a package from Aram's mom so perfectly (on the yellow "pick up package" slip) that Aram was convinced she was Iranian. Turned out, she was just bored and detail-oriented.

W I have a new letterbox. My post office friend helped me nail an old milk delivery box with a lock onto the wall downstairs and used her connections in the post office to arrange for my mail to be delivered in this box.

C Do they really still deliver milk to houses in Beijing? I would bet in Matías it would be easier to get milk delivered than mail.

W My milk/mailbox fell off the wall a couple days after I hung it up. Now every time I try to nail it back up, the wall crumbles terribly and it comes crashing back down. I'm convinced that someone is pilfering my mail because a letter I mailed to myself over a week ago has not arrived. Instead, someone put a tree twig through the slot. I'm getting paranoid; my communication relies on a battered milk box. But paranoia doesn't seem so unreasonable. They just painted the grass green for the Olympic inspection committee. Did the tea get to Mexico yet?

C This afternoon I read your e-mail as I sat in an internet café in Mexico City. It was 4 p.m., and I was still waiting for a 9 a.m. interview. Moments after reading your e-mail about the milk delivery, I walked back to continue waiting for my interview. Next door, I saw a man delivering milk and cream in glass bottles from a tricycle cart.

E. Estadounidenses Waiting

W I'm waiting for my next installment. I'm like one of those eager Americans waiting on the docks in New York for the ship from London bearing Dickens' latest chapter. Please send things to the new address from now on.

C Amazing jasmine tea. It looks like those little balls were rolled by hand!

F: Forgetting

C Yesterday, I had a mini-meltdown. I was just too tired of being helpless when people rip me off, merchants acting like they don't know me even though I have been in their store weekly for the past six months, and not knowing the word for whatever it is I want to buy. Yesterday, it was vice grip and wrench.

W I really lose it some days as I try to acquire new words. It was surge protector and Achilles tendon for me this week. And, if I get my tones wrong, I might ask for a "head check" instead of a surge protector. An examination might not be a bad idea; I think there is a hole in my brain. A few weeks ago, it took me several days to remember the word androgynous. I kept thinking amphibious or hermaphrodite until androgynous finally resurfaced in my mind and I could fill in the blank where I'd left it in a description of a woman I recently met.

C I had to e-mail someone a few months ago to ask how to say palindrome. For days, words like homonym and palimpsest rolled around in my brain.

G. Great Ideas

C I know a man who works carrying market vendors' goods to and from their stalls. All day long, he pushes a flatbed, wooden wheelbarrow up and down the hills of Matías. *Don* Victor Miguel always has story ideas for me. He finds it interesting and strange that I am paid to write things. He has suggested I write about prickly pear cactus recipes, the magic powers of the local hot springs, and environmental crisis.

One afternoon, he said to me, "You know what you should write about?"

Not waiting for my response, he answered his own question: "UFOs!"

He told me how, many years ago when he was in Veracruz, he saw a light. The light came down to the earth. "It was so brilliant!" *Don* Victor Miguel thinks the beings in the UFOs are trying to tell us something.

I wanted to know what their message is.

"Well, something about the chaos that we are living," he said. "And whose fault do you think it is?"

I knew this was a test. I wasn't sure of the correct answer. "The rich folks?" I ventured.

"Exactly!" he said, his face lighting up and breaking into a smile.

H. History Museum

W I know a man who works explaining old paintings and photographs to the few visitors who make it to the dusty museum where he works. He guided me through the florescent lighting of the exhibit halls and explained how a hawk crouched to push off in flight represented the Chinese determined to fight Japanese invaders. We exchanged business cards, and two weeks later, he called me and explained he felt he had something to tell me. He finds it interesting that I study anthropology and am paid to talk to people about their lives.

He sat me down in the lobby of the museum, and asked me if I feel more Chinese or more American.

I was hit on my blind side and said, "I don't feel at home anywhere. When I'm here, I'm there. When I'm there, I'm here."

"But, do you feel discriminated against, for being Chinese there or foreign here?" Not waiting for my response, he declared in an alarmingly loud voice, spittle flying, "I have always been discriminated against."

And then the story came pouring out: "My parents were both high-ranking cadres in an army unit. When I was young, I learned to drive and to shoot, but then my parents were denounced, and my brother and I became black elements. Everyone spat upon us, and we wandered the streets with nowhere to call home. I could sing then. I could have been a "beautiful voice," but I chose boxing instead. I wanted to fight to defend myself from attackers. My mother lived in a pigsty for ten years while I learned to knock people down. After they were rehabilitated, I became a bodyguard. I could run fast, and I already knew how to drive and handle guns. I worked for the government, but I can't tell you whom I protected. I worked for gangsters, but you wouldn't believe what I've seen if I told you."

"Then, how did you come to work as a docent in a museum?" I asked.

He lowered his voice and whispered to me, "I'm just hiding out here. Lots of us, we learn to retreat from outside life and build up our strength. Don't you know what I am?"

I shook my head, failing this history test.

"I am a crouching tiger, hidden dragon."

While walking home, I kept looking over my shoulder, feeling like I was being followed.

C And, what if I am not telling the truth? As that fisherman asked me once, "You're not going to betray us, are you?"

I. Indigenous Means

C By the way, an "indigenous" person is, well, it depends on whom you ask. Take for example the Huave, the fisherfolk who live in the coast of the isthmus: they say there are 25,000 Huave, but the government says there are only 10,000, since as far as the Mexican government is concerned, you are not "indigenous" unless you speak an indigenous language. The Huave language is in a family by itself—linguists have not found another language anywhere on earth that is closely related to it. The Huave say they arrived in Mexico between one and three thousand years ago, by boat, perhaps from the area of Peru, perhaps with a long stop-over in what is now Nicaragua. (There are also some Huave who say they came from outer space.)

W You ask me what a "middle peasant" is: this was one of the five categories used after 1949 for classifying people, and then punishing and rewarding them. There were landlords (bad, bad, bad), rich peasants (medium bad), middle peasants (fairly safe), poor peasants (good), and underclass peasants (the poorest of the poor, measured according to land holdings, and the cleanest class of all). There were also "bai" (white/good) categories: peasant, worker, soldier; and "hei" (black/bad) categories: capitalist, merchant, landlord, counter-revolutionary, rightist. I find it almost impossible to explain to most Americans why Marxism was so attractive at the time. The sad part about this massive dream to reengineer society is how violent it could become. Someone last weekend told me that his grandfather still remembers how the people in his village rounded up the richest peasants and forced them—adults and children alike—into a cave dwelling, sealed the entrance, and set fire to it. Long-held animosity in the human heart ends in explosion, but then it starts all over again, and archaeologists start looking for utopia in the past instead of the future.

J. Jo-Sho

C There is a town in Oaxaca called Xoxo. Pronounced Jo-Sho. xoxo, W

W In China, XO as in Henessy XO is a luxury gift item that people display on their bookshelves at home. I can't tell if they actually ever drink it. Jo-Sho, S

K. Kang

W To Beijing—

When I first started studying Chinese with the Practical Chinese Reader, one of the lessons in Book One involved a trip for students down to the countryside. They stayed with Auntie Zhang, and I learned the word for *kang*, the brick bed common in northern rural areas. The heat from the cooking fire in the front room is tunneled through the wall to the adjacent room and under the *kang*, making it a warm communal sleeping platform in the winter.

Now, for the first time, I have slept on a *kang*, with a donkey pawing the muddy ground on the other side of the wall all night, and I realize how little city folk, with their shiny Olympic dreams, remember of Dongpo Village, where electricity has just arrived. We are just two hours away, nestled among steep mountains with the curving snake of the Great Wall as backdrop, but do you know that we've suffered a drought for two years? Our women trek up the mountain every day to try to sell Coke and picture books of Great Wall scenery to the few tourists who make it this far. I have sores on my face and my school has been closed. The teacher has heart problems and his two sons suffer from a hereditary disease that leaves them bone thin, lying on the *kang*, where you come to stare at me.

From,
Dongpo Village

L. Left Out

C Elsewhere in Mexico, they call the town where I live "Matías

Muy Feo," or "Very Ugly Matías." It looks as if it were built in a hurry, with no plan, vision, or attention to detail. Raised on military bases, ugly-but-functional is a familiar architectural esthetic to me. For this, I consider myself lucky. Having lived in plenty of unattractive places, I see past your grim façade. You are a kind, friendly town that remembers a better time: when railroad workers filled the union hall, when their families got excellent medical care, when train whistles pierced the air at all hours. Now, the lonely whistle cuts the humid air only six or seven times a day. Trains passing through hardly ever stop. Mexico City schemes and plans for a Trans-Isthmus Megaproject that will steal your lands from you one more time.

M. Margins

C People in Mexico talk about the US-Mexico war as if they remember it. They hate living in the shadow of El Norte.

W The Chinese still have a serious chip on their shoulder about the West, joined by Japan, carving up their country after the Opium Wars. Although they were never fully colonized, a deep national indignation persists. There is palpable yearning for world recognition, an insatiable hunger of millions of people to emerge on par with the US as a developed and modern nation. It's a confusing love and hate relationship with the imaginary of America.

N. New

W In New China, women gained equality with men, or so the party said as Iron Women climbed telephone poles to repair wires, flew fighter jets, and swore like sailors. Now Iron Women are out, and in New New China, New Century, New Beijing, New Olympics, I am trapped in a banquet room with too many men swilling liquor and shooting off stupid remarks about the new economy freeing women to pursue their higher calling of self-beautification. A hot blush rises to the unwilling face of courtesan wallpaper brought back from 1920s Shanghai like a bad movie set. I dream that blood pours from two deep cuts on my cheeks. The wounds heal into thick scars. I wear a mask, carry a pen, and yell at the top of my lungs. I'm not sure that anyone notices, but it makes me smugly happy.

O. Outside

C A wedding procession just went by outside the wall of my house. The bride, at maybe eighteen years old, looked nervous, and her groom wore a military uniform and is probably a decade older. There were two bridesmaids, both under fifteen, in bright purple dresses, three people carrying the bride's train, a brass band leading the group, perhaps 120 people of all ages following behind carrying food for the wedding party, and of course one vendor selling the group peanuts and popcorn. It made me happy that I could tell by the design on the women's tunics and the music that they were Mixe. I wish the bride a good long rest before the five children and live-in mother-in-law and grandmother-in-law and husband who rarely comes home from the bars and hourly motels.

P. P. S.

W One of the weird international dateline things I noticed when going back over our e-mails is that your response to my message is sometimes dated before I sent my original message. For example, I wrote to you early a.m. of 3/21, and you responded to me in the p.m. of 3/20. It looks like you responded to me before I even wrote to you. You probably already know what comes next.

The two of us met when we were tossed together as roommates at an August 1999 writers conference. For ten days we shared space, thoughts, perspectives, and writing. We have not seen each other since and have spoken by phone only once. Nonetheless, we have maintained a prolific correspondence, mostly via electronic mail. Starting in October 2000, our messages began bouncing back and forth between a small town in southern Mexico and a burgeoning Chinese city of over 12 million. As "non-fiction" writers, we find ourselves thinking a lot about what constitutes "truth," how to honor the voices of the people with whom we speak, and also about the uncanny, contradictory, parallel, and paradoxical elements of our experiences on opposite sides of the world.

ROBERT QUILLEN CAMP

Stage Double: a play

One.

Stage Left.	Oliver sits down.
Stage Right.	Jasper stands angry. Jasper stamps his foot.
Stage Left.	Oliver stands happy. Oliver whistles the Battle Hymn of the Republic.
Stage Right.	Jasper calls the police. Hello, Police?
Stage Left.	The police arrive.
Stage Right.	Jasper stomps on his telephone.
Stage Left.	The police stomp on Oliver.
Stage Right.	Jasper screams angry.
Stage Left.	Oliver cries weak.
Stage Right.	Jasper replaces the telephone.
Stage Left.	The police go to sleep.
Stage Right.	Jasper goes to sleep.
Stage Left.	Oliver goes to sleep. Oliver has a nightmare.

Two.

Downstage.	Policemen sit fat. Policemen play cards. Policemen trade stories. Criminals are so goddamn short. In Afghanistan they're shorter. Yeah, yeah,

yeah, China.   Still, they're too short. After a good bath I like a kiss on the cheek, you know.

Upstage.   Jasper measures Oliver's height and writes it down.
Oliver measures Jasper's height as well, but Jasper is kneeling.
They sit. They trade blueberries.
Should we eat them?
No. Waste not want not.
Oliver kisses Jasper on the cheek.

Downstage.   The new recruit enters. The Policemen tie him to a chair. They tell him stories.
One time I owned a really really big dog.
How big was it?
It was so big we gave it a badge and a stick and a mission.   Deliver the morning milk.   Tell the truth.
Always take care of widows.
The new recruit chuckles.
The Policemen take turns punching him in the stomach.

Upstage.   Eleanor enters.
Jasper rebukes her.
We only have two chairs.
Eleanor exits.

Downstage.   Eleanor enters.
She laughs and punches the new recruit in the stomach.
The Policemen give her a badge and a stick and a mission.   Deliver the evening freaks.   Tell the truth.
Watch out for vacuum cleaners.
They carry diseases and news.
Eleanor exits.

Upstage.   Eleanor enters. She beats Oliver with a stick.
He drops his blueberry.
He exits.
Eleanor sits in his chair. Jasper kisses her on the cheek.

Downstage.   Oliver enters with a vacuum cleaner.

He switches it on. The policemen run away.

Upstage. Eleanor kisses Jasper on the cheek. He shows her his wallet. She runs away.

Downstage. Oliver turns off his vacuum cleaner.

Three.

Stage Left. Jasper sits down. A mailman delivers a letter.

Stage Right. Oliver sits down.
He removes his shirt.

Stage Left. Jasper opens the letter. He cannot read.
He removes his shoes.

Stage Right. Oliver tries to fit the telephone handset into his mouth. He removes his pants.

Stage Left. Jasper eats the letter.
He removes his socks.

Stage Right. Oliver spits out the telephone. A mailman delivers a package.

Stage Left. Jasper breaks seven eggs into a bucket.
He cries.

Stage Right. Oliver opens the package. It contains seven rubber chickens. He laughs.

Stage Left. Jasper puts his feet in the bucket. He tries to walk and he

falls.

Stage Right. Oliver attaches the rubber chickens to his body with rubber bands. He does seven pushups. He

falls.

Stage Left.

Stage Right.

Stage Left. Jasper cries for help.

Stage Right. Oliver reaches for the telephone.

Stage Left.

Stage Right.

Stage Left. The police arrive.
They handcuff Jasper.
They handcuff the bucket.
They handcuff the chair.

Stage Right. Eleanor arrives. She helps Oliver up.
She kisses him on the cheek. He gives her a chicken.
She hangs up the telephone.

Four.

Upstage. The policemen are unconscious, piled on top of each other. The new recruit enters and picks their pockets.

Downstage. Oliver is asleep.

Stage Left. Eleanor is asleep.

Stage Right. Jasper is asleep.

Upstage. The policemen talk in their sleep.
Please, sir, kill our enemies.
Call an ambulance.
Call the fire department.
Call the ASPCA.

Downstage. Oliver wakes up. He opens his briefcase and withdraws several documents. He flips through them, looking for his instructions.

Stage Right. Jasper gets up to use the bathroom. He exits.

Stage Left. Eleanor wakes up suddenly, and locates the kitchen knife under her pillow.

Downstage. A mailman enters. He begs for food.
Are there any dogs around here?
Big ones?

Upstage. An alarm sounds.
The police wake up and reach for their sticks, only to find them gone.

Stage Left. Eleanor exits, knife in hand.

Stage Right. Jasper returns and goes back to sleep.

Upstage. The policemen circle one another, wary.

Downstage. Oliver reads his instructions to the mailman.
When the mailman comes, give him a sound beating.
Teach him English.
Give him eight dollars and ask for a stamp.

Stage Right. Jasper gets up to use the bathroom. He exits.

Stage Left. Eleanor returns with the body of the new recruit, a kitchen knife in his back.

Downstage. The mailman offers Oliver a knife, a spoon, and a fork.
Pick your poison.
Oliver takes the spoon. The mailman congratulates him.
You're not very tall at all.

Upstage. The policemen give up and go home.

Stage Right. Jasper returns and goes back to sleep.

Stage Left. Eleanor lists her options.
Option one. Call an ambulance.
Option two. Call the fire department.
Option three. Call the ASPCA.

Downstage.	Oliver kisses the mailman on the cheek.
Stage Left.	Eleanor kisses the new recruit on the cheek. She leaves.
Stage Right.	Jasper gets up to use the bathroom. He exits.
Downstage.	The mailman exits. Oliver whistles the Battle Hymn of the Republic.
Downstage.	Oliver looks at his watch.
Downstage.	Oliver finds a stick.
Downstage.	Oliver goes looking for the bathroom.
Offstage.	Something loud.
Pause.	
Upstage.	Jasper enters, screaming. He
	falls.
Downstage.	
Stage Left.	
Stage Right.	
Upstage.	

AMERICAN ENCOUNTERS
A RESTAURANT IN WOODSIDE, CALIFORNIA DECEMBER 31, 1998
WOULD YOU LIKE TO DRINK TO ANOTHER SIXTY YEARS?
WHAT?
I JUST WANTED TO KNOW IF YOU'RE INTERESTED IN DRINKING TO ANOTHER SIXTY YEARS.
... SURE!
I'M NOT.
© 2001 BY PETER S. CONRAD
www.peterconrad.com
END

This really happened. Back then I was trying to draw a lot of stuff verbatim. I was at a table with my wife, her grandmother and maybe a couple other people. I stopped paying attention to our conversation and heard this little exchange from the other table. I wrote it down immediately and sketched the people. I couldn't believe he had said that to her; either they've known each other long enough to understand each other in a really complicated way, or he's a complete bastard. Funny either way.

TOM DEVANEY & EDWIN TORRES

from *Pong, A Conversation*

From: Tom Devaney
Sent: Friday, May 12, 2000 3:59 PM
To: Edwin Torres
Subject: PONG

Edwin. Glad I was able to get to Tonic last week 5/4/00 to see & hear you. It was good to be in the same place while you were performing. I didn't try to focus on any one aspect, but just let it happen—drums, dj, & you honoring the rain and the room. I'm willing to try a conversation with you here, though my instinct is to meet and talk first to get a physical sensory response, which we can build on in a brick-by-brick TOM, EDWIN, EDWIN, TOM email exchange—I'm open. I am wondering if you think email is a callous medium, or if it's just that I use it callously? Anyway, just as no one enters a Pollock canvas, because it's a painting not a door—or what people say is—that no one enters a Pollock canvas visually in any one place, so we may place our conversational ball wherever we want. Point.

•

From: Edwin Torres
Sent: Friday, May 12, 2000 5:44 PM
To: Tom Devaney
Subject: PING!

Tom
instinct sez physical meeting builds presence—email meetings usually callous—HOWEVER—if we know who we're dealing with—familiarity listens to untold nuances in speech patterns—sarcasms ignite untold tellings—keyboard becomes ear hole into which dark ages collect—dust bowls inna earhole . . . AYYYYYYYY, matre morto sans le carryoutta!!! yeh, dug Tonic gig . . . glad you came—finished way too short 'cuz DJ wasn't 'feelin'' it—I think it's cuz he's not used to improvising . . . and although I did feel a lag halfway through . . . it isn't uncommon to find the energy go low in an improvisation as improvisers search for each others' energy, etc. thought it was just cooking when

we stopped—but—was DJ’s first improv with any musician and SEAN is master improvisor . . . knowing when to come in and out yet always maintaining presence . . . something I try and attain in writing—attaining without trying—therein lies the blur . . . speaking of . . . physical presence is currently at work—don’t know how often I’ll be able to respond immediately—but let’s keep up correspondence . . . as happenstance allows . . . your shot!

•

From: Tom Devaney
Sent: Tuesday, May 23, 2000 12:42 PM
To: Edwin Torres
Subject: Limitation as plus factor

Edwin
Counterbalancing the medium’s (not so immediate, not so immaterial) limitations against itself would be interesting to do—if we’re not already doing that. The mismatch between screen, keyboard, music, our brains. What you call “keyboard becomes ear hole into which dark/ages collect—dust bowls inna earhole . . . ” I call screenesthesia—in the right ear-hand-eye-brain coordination/s, igniting “untold tellings” on the everyday face of our computer. I hope to match our mismatches into a new sense, instead of only a nuisance. Concerning the performance (not the one here, but at Tonic). Yes, I agree it’s not “uncommon to find the energy go low in an improvisation as improvisers search for each others’ energy”; I thought you were not fighting yrself, the room, the energy but working with it—it was mellow.
striking match, my best,
T.Devaney

p.s. I’m going to go to the show “Volume” at PS 1 sometime soon. (One piece “the bed of sound,” curated by Elliott Sharp). There is something about what is called sound installations, sonic drawings and sound art that relates to your work.

M86YY(&]N92!P;&%C92P@<V\@=V4@;6%Y(‘!L86-
E(&]U<B!C;VYV97)S871I
M;VYA;”!B86QL(‘=H97)E=F5R(‘=E(‘=A;G0N(%!O:6YT+B`-
#2TM+2TM+2TM
M+2T-1G)O;3H@”65L:7IA8F5T:”!C87-T86=N6U—
5%‘Z961W:6YL:7I‘>6%H
M;V\N8V]M70U396YT.B‘)1G)I9&%Y+”!-87D@,3(L(#(P,#‘@-3HT-

"!030U4
M;SH@"51O;2!$979A;F5Y#5-U8FIE8W0Z('E024Y'(0T-
5&]M#0UI;G-T:6YC

=== message truncated ===

•

From: Tom Devaney
To: Edwin Torres
Sent: September 2000
Subject: The Inner-view

TD: Perhaps this is a good time to ask a few questions about your poetry. (If calling your work *poetry* is the best word for it!?) One word is certainly—hybrid.

ET: Well, in a culture where communication is overloaded at every step . . . I've learned by now to accept that "poetry" just doesn't cover it all . . . but it's what people understand. Hybrid sounds like an experiment, and I'm hoping that what I do isn't looked at as mere experiment but as the thing itself. I don't think of myself as BEING a poet . . . I AM a poet. Where the being and the doing are conclusive of whatever exploration happens. The hybrid comes in the mingling of senses . . . so in effect, we're all hybrids. Combining the world into our own specific worlds.

TD: You are certainly at the cross-roads and nodes of many main and sub-arteries of the art/poetry/and new music worlds. It's safe to say your work confounds the category-makers.

ET: They need to be confounded! Category begets laziness. An open view is what I'm looking for . . . unobstructed by mere category.

TD: In an essay for *Poets & Writers Magazine* (April 1999) I described you in the following way: "If media critic Marshall McLuhan and Joyce's Molly Bloom had a child—raised in Spanish Harlem by rapper Snoop Doggy Dog's au pair—you'd get something approaching the genius mutt of Edwin Torres."

ET: Thank you . . . indeed a mutt of monstrous proportions . . . but I wasn't raised in Spanish Harlem.

TD: "The noise of the century is in his astounding meld of song, word, and sonically rich poetry."

ET: That's where my world lives . . . in the sonically rich texture between ear and skin. I was talking to Miguel Algarin back in April about how mainstream Puerto Ricans really have become vis-a-vis the avant garde. How Puerto Ricans have become the mainstream even though the media sez they haven't . . . whereas my take was more of an individual one for EACH Puerto Rican being an avant garder . . . his was more about the idea of Puerto Ricans. The idea of an outside force being on the inside. So he was saying about my work, how sound is the future . . . in his megolamaniacal way . . . how in the world of the sound artist, the consonant is king. Which is such a great way to look at the poetry I'm interested in. Using New York's endless inspiration as my muse, the use of sound as a secret code into our psyche, into the space between our skins . . . this covers wider ground than Language/Performance/Latino/Academia/ Experimental poetries for me. I want to be the king of consonattas . . . or perhaps a pauper.

TD: It's not exactly a tidy category, if it's a category at all. Although you might also talk about how your associations with places like the Nuyorican Poets Cafe, St. Mark's Poetry Project have helped and hindered how your work is perceived and received?

okay Tom, talk soon . . .

Edwin

•

From: Edwin Torres
To: Tom Devaney
Sent: Wednesday, October 04, 2000 7:30 AM
Subject: Your Point!

tom
wow—great to see PONG as it is so far thanks for sending it and buddhist work book will see what I give in to especially dig earlier PONG bounces back and forth don't know where to edit or not but I think we should continue a bit more the game isn't done yet let's try a few short volleys over next week or so by way of a coda then will see how best to assimilate entire conundrum of our PINGS my shot:

communication untold by wary nuisance of brainage emails function as phone calls making "talk" a noun not a verb—how best to understand mixage of poetry reading timeframe with online readframe; can we become a loop of time allowing openings their ground by exposing all we can in short time blips? do we prolong our lifespan by sharing most intimate details, creating space for other details? when talk becomes verb does listen follow? and finally . . . how are you?
yours
Edwin

•

From: Edwin Torres
To: Tom Devaney
Sent: Thursday, October 19, 2000 2:35 PM
Subject: THE THEORIST HAS NO SAMBA!

a thought . . .

there is a new instantism > a language of tangent = tanguage > ambient funguage > there is a modern path > invented through accidental spontaneity + of mock language sport = fractured intelligentsillys > there are sage athleticists + important children farmed out to the furthest reaches of nowness > . . . > . . . >

I propose a New Instantism. Take spontaneousness out of the ether and smack it into the throes of the wild screaming bastard maggot that IS poetry! I propose a New NEWness, where we refuse to comply by the aged fumblings of mere MEANING and instead descend into mere HEARING! I instigate a NEW failure of listening . . . so we may one day walk hand in hand with our own ears and say . . . THANK THE MIGHTY LOUD THAT I MAY THANK THE MIGHTY LOUD THAT I MAY THANK THE MIGHTY LOUD! I have a NEW Instantaety, a modern NEWness, a post NOWism . . . I have a fear . . . of hiding this fear, instead . . . I choose a revelry of failure, an opportune dimentia into the songs of my pacifism.

Let's say we level expectation with implied tension . . . the instant doubt appears, there is a window of possibility. What was thought to have clarity is now diffused by possibility. Is possibility the goal . . . or only an instant before doubt?

The New Instantists will allow possibility room to doubt itself . . . inventing a paranoia into the sleepless monster that is this bastard maggot poetry. The New Instantist will know that it takes a flat surface to iron out procedure, that a wrinkled pair of favorite pants will match an equally wrinkled ass . . . and mind, that no matter how just or unjust the outcome . . . the New Instantist will always be blamed for what has just happened! Occurrence . . . being the signpost for all things instant.

To what is now
And what is never then
To what has been
And what will never now
To things all thinging
And maybe soon
To what is now
Instantly now
Inspired by Rod Smith's SubModernism movement. Not his theories but the fact that there actually IS another "movement" in the works.

paz,
Edwin

RACHEL BLAU DUPLESSIS

Draft L: Scholia and Restlessness

One has touched vers, toward what objection hardy knows,
Touched glass, meddled the poem, cracked crystal show-

shelves in the thrift stores, smashed debris again, gained in
intensity, yet blocked comment! Reined in.

Stand there, restlessness. Also femaleness, heightened by
another hot flash, time, loss, annoyance, frankly

can't sit still, flesh floods the place as loose as
sloggy water, sandy brookings where one tides a bay,

"surfant le web" or "parling anguish." Where
beach-rose berries globen orange ripe, Here,

is this Happening? alongside what text, in what cued
brain extt, or xtte? The lemma—afloat with breathing tube

wiggles through rushing fish wash, blue schools they were
running light tween, twist unseen from wavers of a placid sea,

breath deliberate in the mouth and loud, husky heaves
of own survival. El allows for depth just under the surface

between subaqueous seam and down—"that zone"
"that parallel world we live in whenever we waken to it."

So stroke those looping, loping tunes beyond Gelassenheit.
Loft that haunting melody all sheeny bright,

and reach your fingers in between the modal pings
to play and twist those other, shadow, strings.

When you listen to the vibe of disinterested phonemes
Pheromones of phonemes, indecisive decibel, it

garners the supplement of illusion. Inclusion. Hallucination. Keys
on little pegs. All of them indifferent, all tagged with names,

chained charms and souvenirs, foreign, near, for the car,
for the ear. Where were they seen, the keys? So far.

Where heard? Per word. What instrument? Already rent.
And lock to match and sound to catch? Unknown.

Real or a dream? Hope or a shuck? Schtick or stuck?
Stumbled walker, shivering singer—where and to do what?

How to live? what's to hope? who's to say?
By the side of the road, trash cravings amid crazy ravings,

I saw a stranger at a rusted fire of cartons and cartels
a-singeing songs. "Who are you?" Now what?

It is simply—simply NO, not and never simply. For as he paces,
as he rocks, as he feeds the fire, this place, this nothing place

becomes beyond. A flesh sketch of something else.
For the return to wandering. As cure and as disease.

He told me his ears hurt, one who at the end, is X, a blank
a wanter among nomad wanderers, caught

like s.l.a.n. on the book, sine loco, anno, nomine,
holding rank ends of a split, so I said I was dizzy.

Fine. Now what? Where did I see the keys? This is loco.
From the fire's wandering chorus, "melancholy"

was the one word on the page as it sizzled, crumpt up, nought.
The burn was 15 orange, one orage, zero blue and weightless

worse—brownish silvering dense explosive points,
wind aggression roaring, tornado through the straight.

A person never knows the bravery that times
demand until they riddle how to construct the correct

"crimes." Ques: how to preserve the archives of dada
(Ans: in metal boxes buried near your hovel).

Nazis knocked but came without a shovel,
lucky for her. How to be courageous and stupid.

Who are you? What do you do it for? for natural light,
to keep these listeners awake, plus dead and time.

All local and all destroyed must speak accurately
how the man stood on the margin of edge

larbage dreams with dusk, cardbore and ash.
Why scan, capture, index, interlink this trash?

"For your good health, Barrel Picking is prohibited."
Why not leave well enough alone?

A play within the play, he hove sprechstimme
fragments in half an anguage, ghostily selected

strung together as if continuous text,
hallucination's vantage keying incantation sentinel,

with restless regard "not from a place on which to fix
but from a crossing of that place, a crossing of that crossing."

He began to experience difficulties with reality;
for him each human soul remained a human soul.

But it is hard to act without shame, though
this be always true, for who it act it in your name?

The dream of turning the key in the lock as the wind in the door
moaned and the crow flew with its yard-wide wingspan

into the pear tree finding the open place. Now what?
He asked me, Why do you do what you do?

Do you take this adult set of sores
as yours for use in the urban scavenger tradition

to enchain all it with it? to travel through the spot-deep text
of song?
Je est un interstate, he said. "We Welcome Christian Tours."

There were left-handed shadows facing east
cloud cover over cloud cover, pumpkins sporting flags,

ever-whispering space when ick geschri or scry
every unspeakable untellable yod inside the bye.

This man with a small tree growing from his neck
was arrayed in imaginary memories, dot by dot,

"where the fibrous roots of every heart on earth
infixes deep its restless twists," arraigned with

weights across the border where he stood by fire,
the day dedicated to the evanescent ruffle of silence

as it teasing, tonging turns to hissy clumps, a spree
and spray of listed sound, a funny Jew d'esprit.

So sung, singing with waves the theremin, harp of the heap
sung with the hands, with the mouth, hand to mouth, a

paltry of mishegoss and dreck,
of unsatisfied satisfactions, allowering the wreck

to float out in brightness and disjuncture, all rift.
Poultry plants where bloody flesh and fast knives lift,

it's immigrunts work there why can't they just
speed Aing lish fast and wishing well like ust.

The fire got low, the voice asked, Who are you?
Stood in waves of strangeness, shaken rue,

still sigh underneath senselessness, to find
such speech songs scanned, rotated, aligned,

as addled noise to Nos, news to blues.
From search string, fuzzy and phonemic search,

from word stemming, natural language lurch
fall Drafts and fragments, Drifts and figments,

scrap paper shreds and fan-shaped books of Pantone
pigments. Asked a simple question: Why do you do

what you do? The world is all that's In Your Face.
Curious stranger still, as stranger place by place.

November 2001-January 2002
to Charles Bernstein

Notes to Draft L: Scholia and Restlessness. There was, as in "Draft 20: Incipit," another incident like the "Curious, this querying letter from a stranger": this one an e-mail by Michael Collino in mid-November 2001. Some of the questions in this poem were asked by him. "J'apporte en effet des nouvelles. Les plus surprenantes. Même cas ne se vit encore. On a touché au vers." Stéphane Mallarmé, "La Musique et les Lettres," Oeuvres complètes, *1945, 643. At Oxford/ Cambridge in 1894. "I am truly bringing news. Astonishing news. And never seen before—We have been meddling with verse." Trans. Lawrence Lipking, cited in his article "Poet-critics" in* The Cambridge History of Literary Criticism, *vol. 7, ed. Litz, Menand, and Rainey. But see also the translation of Rosemary Lloyd that ends: "Poetry has been under attack."* Mallarmé in Prose, *ed. Mary Ann Caws, 32. "That parallel world we live in whenever we waken to it": Charles Bernstein, e-mail on his book* With Strings *(2001). Description of the strings between other strings concerns the Welsh triple harp. S.l.a.n.: without place, year, name. The archives of dada: from the life of Hannah Höch. "For your good health, Barrel Picking is prohibited" is a sign in a Maine rest stop on I 95, 2001. The citation "not from a place on which to fix/ but from a crossing of that place, a crossing of that crossing," is, slightly modified, from Michael Moon,* Disseminating Whitman: Revision and Corporeality in Leaves of Grass, *109. "Where the fibrous roots/ Of every heart on earth infixes deep its restless twists," William Blake, "The Book of Thel." Reminded of the theremin in reading Andrew Joron's work "Constellations for Theremin," A.BACUS #142, 15 November 2001. When I went to Georgia, someone said "poultry plants," whereupon I heard "poetry plants." List of search tactics from Brown University web site on* The New Age. *Donor drafts are Draft 12: Diasporas and Draft 31: Serving Writ.*

Most ["lyric"] poems are monologic—there's the speaker's voice, and that's it. The other, the you, *the figure addressed inside the poem's drama, the built-in listener very often doesn't speak inside a poem. The thought that poems can be written in which the socio-poetical privilege of confrontational speech is given to a "character" or another voice besides the poet's does seriously destabilize the apparatus of poesis, which has been for so long focused on the singularity and centrality of the poet-figure.*

PATRICK F. DURGIN & JEN HOFER
from *Routine Knew*

•

But for paradise
everyone inserts
a sensical expedient
resist brittle salvos
incipience yep a
partial enduring present
to share a tangelo
is not to eat a peach
they confuse modesty with irony
for privacy

•

Consider the following:

This one
Now this one
Now the other one
("Marines" "Archive" "Organ")
Damp and slight ever shiver behind glass
Influences upon public transport
("Choice" "Cat" "Clothesline")
Now this one again

Endow it again
Advocate it (approaching reluctant
Always the is is ironic when
Swerve time lets it be thought

Think it
That one among others

("Stability" "Growth" "Hairless Dog")
National legacy with a leg up when
When is it not
So it is

Imperceptible and daily)
("Very" "Verily" "Weilawey")
Insist it the same and it never were
That way

Love you decidedly" That way National tailgunner
Moral engine sniper leading the sprightly that way

Let's call it X) out from under
That way or that sway (again
Save time and money as if
The as if of an attraction to what
("Thanks

("Truly" "Cheeky" "Broad")
"No questions, please" ("Evident
Ludic at least
A time-being" (Reply" (Polite" (Implied"

What we "Deliver
We "Deflowering
See we "Scopic
Have sight of "Source" "Phase" (Face)

Confrontative gaudy can't countenance
("Denunciations" "Votes" "Green")
Watch regalia gear monarch denouement
Which with do wrench ("Easier

"Routine Knew" is part of a larger project still in progress. Other excerpts from this work can be found in recent or shortly forthcoming issues of Aufgabe, combo, *and* !factorial. *The following is a brief note on the text culled from an epistolary component of the larger dialogic project, initiated by the publication of Durgin's "Speculations with a View toward a*

*Synaesthetic Poetics" in 1998 (*Tripwire 2: Writing as Activism*):*

About our collaboration, I used the phrase "(eclipse in the transparent sense?)" with the idea that the layerings within the text should precisely (however imprecisely) function to illuminate each other, rather than obliterating each other. The idea that proximity to difference is luminous rather than blinding, illuminating rather than eliminating, transparent as a complex multitudinous body layered visibly, not transparent as self-evident, as clearly no "self" is "evident" nor should be. (JH)

Perception describes but it doesn't explain. We can only intend an explanation, otherwise it won't occur. Perception describes the inexplicable—trauma isn't the only effect (of what we've "seen," for instance). Neurology etc grapples with this as a problem, as though perspective does eclipse / obliterate—but you're right I think to recognize it the other way. We learn as much from what we don't know as we do from what we do. An eclipse illuminates the form & 'dark side' in relief. It's a dark relief. (PFD)

I feel able, most days, in my own writings and in my daily interactions with people I know & people I don't know, to take appropriate care, to be utterly "curious," both responsible & response-able, to listen while listening & listen while speaking, while acting. This as poet & as person. My sense is that synaesthetics and negative capability are related, in terms of accessing a mind or state which can contain difference in various manifestation, without containing difference in the sense of border or limitation. Today, as bombs continue to drop in Afghanistan & I am sickened by knowledge of continuing (what's the term—infinite?) violence & sickened by polarized rhetorics that leave precious little (any?) space for thoughtful consideration, committed dissidence—in a word, for a "curious" response to recent world events (though no event or response should be held to any one word), my question is how to expand the practical poetics, if you want to call it that, I'm suggesting in the first sentence of this paragraph, how to extend them to reach beyond my own small life, my own small orbits, my own small imaginative, imaginary, material universe. (JH)

CRAIG DWORKIN & ALESSANDRA SANTOS

What is discourse? A needle torquing slant-wise in a groove of wax.
What is freedom? The weight of light from a single street-lamp, just at dusk.
What is sensuality? An unlocked car. On a sidestreet.
What is light? Oil on concrete.
What is black? The smell of acetone.
What is a prism? Bruises blossoming like violets.
What is longing? The shadows of motes, long on a sun-raked wall.
What are trees? Phosphenes in the eyes of the blind.
What is energy? Dust breeding.
What is somnambulism? The hands of clocks clapping as they pass.
What is pain? A deserted tennis court. With the nets down.
What is form? NOIGANDRES.
What is a mirror? The chance meeting on a dissecting table of a sewing machine and an umbrella.
What is a desert? A stick. A stone. The end of the road.
What is culture? That mode of sacrifice in which the victims are words.
What is satisfaction? The feel of velvet against your back.
What are electrons? The sincerity of a phantom limb.
What is a hard bed? The interest of a sunflower, at night.
What is philosophy? An uncancelled ticket, for a show one didn't see.
What are bubbles? The Empire of Meaning.
What is wisdom? The realization of our desires.
What is happening? Polymorphous perversity.
What are books? The emblem of the police.
What is important? The brief flight of a sparrow, through a meadhall, in winter.
What is poetry? Venus. In furs.
What is fancy? An omission, or loss in a manuscript.
What is history? Un coup de dés.

What are letters? An ecstasy of destruction.
What is life? Poetics?

An old Surrealist mode of dialogue: every night for a month, at the same time, but thousands of miles apart—and without any knowledge of what the other was writing—one of us would record a question and the other an answer.

CHRISTINE EVANS & DIJANA MILOSEVIC

One More Transparent Bridge

Our dialogue was written by email over eight days in December. It is in Christine's first language and Dijana's third. What follows is an attempt to unravel the crazy paving we made, cutting into and pasting from one message to another. Although it follows certain lines, this dialogue is now reconstructed to give the sense of its original shape, which branched in many directions at once. Dijana's text is all in capitals; Christine's is lower case.

DEAR CHRISTINE

I AM BACK FROM SIBERIA AND ALTHOUGH I AM FULL OF IMPRESSIONS AND STILL JETLAGGED, IT IS HARDLY TO BELIEVE THAT I WAS REALLY THERE! MAYBE WE CAN START OUR CHAIN DIALOGUE CONVERSATION. I DISCOVERED ONCE AGAIN THAT ONE CAN LEARN ABOUT THE PLACE, PEOPLE AND HISTORY REALLY AND ONLY IF ONE GOEST TO THE SPOT. OF COURSE, THIS IS NOT VERY NEW THOUGHT, BUT I AM SURPRISED HOW OFTEN WE DENY IT AND HOW WE HAVE SUPERFICIAL STATEMENTS ABOUT PLACES AND PEOPLES, JUST FROM WHAT WE HAVE HEARD OR EVEN READ. AFTER THE SECOND WORLD WAR VERY FAMOUS SCIENTIFIC CENTER HAD BEEN FOUNDED OUTSIDE OF NOVOSIBIRSK, WHERE THE BEST RUSSIAN SCIENTISTS WORKED. THE NAME OF THE PLACE IS FAMOUS: AKADEMGORODOK. THOSE SCIENTISTS, WHO WORKED IN TOTAL ISOLATION (NOVOSIBIRSK WAS FOR A LONG TIME

yes, this resonates for me—I'm thinking of when I visited Belgrade last summer and the way that the smells and sounds and images of the place create a feeling-tone, a sense which is rooted in something more physical than the idea of "nation-state"—how nations are often violently imposed on a place which is configured through language, landscape etc. another way. Maps over land, making something which is both imaginary and real as we have to negotiate both. For me also there's an odd dance between presence and absence with travel—when I visited you, it was with a dream of writing something

FORBIDDEN AREA FOR FOREIGNERS, BECAUSE OF SCIENTIFIC RESEARCH THAT HAD TO BE IN TOTAL SECRET) STARTED TO ORGANIZE CULTURAL EVENTS, OF HIGH QUALITY, INVITED THE BEST ARTIST WHOSE WORK WAS FORBIDDEN, IN THOSE HARD TIMES, AS DISSIDENT, ANTI-GOVERNMENT ETC. SO THOSE ARTISTS WERE NOT DOING IT PUBLICLY. IN THAT TIME, THOSE SCIENTISTS CREATED THE BEST CULTURAL EVENTS, THAT COULD NOT BE WITNESSED IN OTHER PARTS OF THE COUNTRY. IN THAT WAY, AMIDST THE WORST PRISON THEY CREATED THE SEED OF THE BIGGEST FREEDOM. WHEN I ASKED HOW DID THEY DARE TO DO IT, BECAUSE IN THOSE TIMES FOR FAR SMALLER THINGS PEOPLE WERE PROSECUTED AND SENT TO PRISON AND EXILE, MY NEW FRIENDS EXPLAINED ME: "BUT THEY WERE ALREADY IN SIBERIA" (THE WORST THREAT TO PEOPLE FOR MANY YEARS).

set in your country and yet my feet on that soil awoke a memory and sense of belonging to Australia, in a way which time in the US had not.

Sometimes it's the gaps between places that re-draw the map.

TWO THINGS CAME TO MY MIND IN RELATION TO YOUR WORDS. FIRST IS OUR IDEA OF MAP BEING SOMETHING MATERIAL AND SOLID. MY EXPERIENCE OF LIVING IN THE COUNTRY WHERE MAPS WERE REMADE, REESTABLISHED, TOTALLY ERASED IDEA OF MAPS AS OF SOMETHING SOLID, MATERIAL. IN FACT I REALIZED, THAT DESPITE THE FACT THAT OLD YUGOSLAVIA DOES NOT EXIST ANY MORE ACCORDING TO THE OLD MAP, THAT NEW MAPS OF IT HAVE BEEN MADE, FOR ME IT EXISTS VERY PRECISELY AS A MENTAL/EMOTIONAL/CULTURAL IDEA. BUT NOT JUST THAT. IT EXTENDS TO MANY PLACES AROUND THE WORLD WHERE MY FRIENDS ARE, DEFINITELY FORMING SOMETHING THAT IS VERY ABSTRACT. WHEN I THINK THAT WARS STILL BURN IN MANY PLACES OVER TERRITORY, OVER MAKING NEW MAPS AND TRYING TO FIX THEM, TO MAKE THEM SOLID AND MATERIAL, I FEEL HOW GROTESQUE WE HUMANS ARE.

I remember driving with you around Belgrade this summer and asking you whether you thought of yourself as a "Yugoslav" or "Serb." You described growing up and being taught to think of Yugoslavia as your country, not Serbia: that under Tito the old cultural divisions were seen as primitive and to be erased, and then suddenly after 1991 you were expected to forget being a Yugoslav and think as a Serbian. As if the inner maps of people could be torn up and redrawn too. For me this experience came early—born in England to Australian parents who told us that "Australia was really home"—after 10 years and life in 2 other countries, we arrived there and I was seen as a foreigner. Because I was very young I didn't realize that something about this idea of "home" was faulty, I thought that I had failed at belonging and perhaps I was a person who could not have a home.

YES, I REMEMBER OUR DIALOGUE IN THE CAR. SPEAKING ABOUT HOME—I DISCOVERED THAT LAST YEAR WHILE I STAYED IN U.S. BEING BASED IN GEORGIA COLLEGE AND STATE UNIVERSITY, AND TRAVELING AROUND THE U.S., HOW I FELT FAR AWAY FROM MY HOME. IN MANY WAYS I REALLY FELT GREAT BEING IN U.S. BUT I FELT VERY HOME-SICK TILL THE MOMENT WHEN I STARTED WORK WITH MEMBERS OF MY THEATRE COMPANY WHO ARRIVED TO U.S. AND WITH MEMBERS OF 7 STAGES THEATRE FROM ATLANTA FOR A COMMON PERFORMANCE. I WAS ALREADY SEVEN MONTHS IN U.S. BUT SUDDENLY MY FEELING OF BEING HOMESICK VANISHED AND I FELT LIKE I WAS FOREVER IN ATLANTA, CITY THAT I DID NOT KNOW WELL. I FELT LIKE AT HOME. THEN I REALIZED THAT HOME WAS/IS WHERE MY WORK WAS/IS. THE COMMUNICATION THAT WE CREATED DURING THE WORK ON OUR PERFORMANCE CREATED FOR ME SITUATION WHERE I NO LONGER THOUGHT WHERE THE HOME WAS—IT WAS RIGHT THERE, IN THAT MOMENT, IN THAT PLACE.

Edward Bond says in his "Notes on Imagination": "A child is produced by its map of the world in the same process in which it maps the world; the process continues through life. If the map is torn, the mapmaker is torn."

WHEN YOU SENT ME THAT QUOTATION BY EDWARD BOND, I REMEMBER HOW STREAKED I WAS WITH HIS WORDS—THIS WAS IN FACT MY EXPERIENCE THROUGH WHICH I HAVE LIVED IN THE PAST TEN YEARS. THAT MADE ME THINKING THAT PROBABLY THE WAY TO PROTECT OURSELVES IS TO CREATE OUR OWN, INNER MAP, ONE THAT WE CAN TEAR APART WHEN WE ARE READY FOR IT.

MORE AND MORE I SEE AN IMAGE OF BRIDGES FLOATING IN THE AIR AND PEOPLE LIVING THERE, BRIDGING THE GAPS, CONNECTING, CREATING FRAGILE BUT VISIBLE CONSTRUCTIONS OF THOSE BRIDGES . . . I SEE YOU/US LIVING ONE (ON ONE) OF THOSE BRIDGES.

I ALSO REMEMBER US TALKING ABOUT YOUR FEELING OF NOT FEELING AT HOME ANY-WHERE, AND WE TALKED ABOUT BRIDGES. I ALSO SPOKE WITH MANY YOUNG PEOPLE FROM MY COUNTRY WHO NOW LIVE ALL AROUND THE WORLD, HOW THEY FEEL SPLIT IN TWO, NOT BELONGING TO THEIR OLD COUNTRY ANY MORE NEITHER TO THE NEW COUNTRY IN WHICH THEY ARE NOW.

THE OTHER THING THAT I THINK ABOUT IS OUR CONNECTEDNESS. AFTER LIVING IN THE

WAR TORN COUNTRY AND MEETING PEOPLE ALL AROUND THE WORLD WHO DID NOT REALIZE THAT IT WAS IN FACT ALSO THEIR WAR, AND THEN SUDDENLY THEY HAD TO AWAKEN AND REALIZE THAT DESTRUCTION IS HAPPENING UNDER THEIR WINDOW, I REALIZE THAT THE ONLY WAY TO LIVE IN MORE DECENT WORLD IS TO UNDERSTAND THAT WHAT AFFECTS ME, AFFECTS NOT NECESSARILY MY NEIGHBOR BUT SOMEBODY AT THE OTHER CONTINENT.

"WIND IN THE WEST
AND FALLEN LEAVES
ARE GATHERED IN THE EAST."

The leaves fallen in the east are definitely gathering in the West right now. For me the awakening has a double wave, as I see from the distance of the US, how Australia is making a grotesque mirror of the United States in how it perceives its own fortunes and politics. Re: the way inner maps persist after the material ones have been torn: I'm thinking of Edward Said's writing on Palestine ("The Politics of Dispossession") and how he says that the greatest barrier to writing in favour of the Palestinians' cause in the US has been simply to get public acknowledgement of the fact that they exist *as a people* with a claim to homeland, let alone to consider the arguments. That as a group, the Palestinians have been defined in the US only as a threat to Israel and (later) as "terrorists."

I have begun to
dream every night
about being back
there in Australia
and I wake up and
I miss it so much

the light,

the physical beauty
of the country which
is so strong.

the brilliant light

the scent of trees
and ocean.

This makes me think about the power of language to legitimate or erase people from the map. A similar process is happening in Australia, where the asylum seekers who are being detained are not described as asylum seekers, or war victims, or refugees, but (by Goverment sources in the public media) as "queue jumpers" and "illegals." And more recently, as "possible terrorists." It seems that defining an entire group of people as "illegals" means that whatever happens to them is outside the jurisdiction of the law.

So certainly what has happened in the US on Sept 11 has affected "somebody on the other continent"—people in Australia, and the people from Afghanistan arriving there on boats, but only by stirring up the embers of a racist fire that was always smoldering just under the democratic surface.

"POWER OF LANGUAGE"—THIS REALLY RESONATES WITH ME. I AM JUST READING A GREAT BOOK BY CROATIAN (OR EX-YUGOSLAV) AUTHOR DUBRAVKA UGRESIC *CULTURE OF LIES* WHERE SHE DESCRIBES THE PROCESS BY WHICH BOTH SERBIAN AND CROATIAN MEDIA CREATED WAR OF WORDS THAT WAS THE REAL INTRODUCTION TO THE WAR THAT FOLLOWED IT. SHE WROTE: "BY TURNING WORDS INTO DEEDS THE EX-YUGOSLAV PEOPLES HAVE MOVED INTO A NEW DIMENSION, INTO 'MYTHIC TIME' IN WHICH THE BORDER BETWEEN EXISTING AND NON-EXISTENT WORLDS HAVE BEEN ERASE . . . SUPERSTITIOUS PEOPLE ARE OFTEN CAUTIOUS WHEN USING CERTAIN WORDS: THEY ARE AFRAID THAT WHAT THEY HAVE UTTERED MAY OCCUR IN REAL LIFE. WRITERS OFTEN HAVE THE SAME KIND OF SUPERSTITIOUS FEARS. BESIDES, THEY KNOW BETTER THAN ANYONE THAT DEALING WITH WORDS IS . . . DEVILISH WORK!"
BELGRADE IS UNDER THE SNOW. IT IS VERY COLD AND VERY BEAUTIFUL (TILL TOMORROW MORNING WHEN ALL TRAFFIC WILL START AGAIN).
LOVE, DIJANA

I UNDERSTAND YOU ABOUT YOUR NEED TO STAY IN U.S. AND AT THE SAME TIME LONGING FOR YOUR COUNTRY—IMAGES AND SMELLS ARE VERY POWERFUL, THEY BRING US IMMEDIATELY BACK TO THE PLACES WE LEFT. SO THINK ABOUT "TRANSPARENT BRIDGE" THAT YOU CAN FORM IN BETWEEN TWO COUNTRIES THAT YOU INHABIT.

Dear Dijana,
I'm thinking how the email is shaping the way we talk, in that we start writing in at points of "heat"—parts of the message that we connect with.

YES, I AGREE THAT THE EMAIL IS SHAPING THE WAY WE TALK AND THIS WAY OF OUR COMMUNICATION FOR SURE AFFECTS OUR THOUGHTS. BUT NOT ONLY THIS, I AM OBSESSED HOW DIFFERENT LANGUAGE SHAPE OUR THINKING AS WELL.

DID YOU KNOW FOR EXAMPLE THAT INUIT LANGUAGE HAS TWO HUNDRED EXPRESSIONS FOR THE WORD "SNOW"? (AS YOU CAN SEE I AM ALSO QUITE OBSESSED WITH THE SNOW THESE DAYS, WHILE EUROPE IS UNDER THE ICE AND WHITE COVER EVERYWHERE, EVEN IN MEDITERRANEAN COUNTRIES AS GREECE AND ITALY.)

So what we are building is not a linear dialogue but more like a montage,or perhaps a rhizome like a bamboo with different shoots coming off. This seems to me to connect with some of the ways you work on the floor in making work with Dah Teatar.
(any thoughts on this?)

YES, THIS PROCESS OF MONTAGE FOR ME IS VERY ALIVE, ORGANIC PROCESS. I DO NOT BELIEVE IN LINEAR STORIES, THEY ARE ALWAYS OUR INTERPRETATION, SINCE LIFE ITSELF IS NOT LINEAR (WHILE I WRITE TO YOU I LISTEN TO MUSIC WHICH CREATES FOR ME DIFFERENT ASSOCIATIONS, I SPEAK WITH NESA ABOUT TOTALLY OTHER THING, I JUMP FROM MY COMPUTER AND PUT SOME OF THE THINGS I NEED FOR TOMORROW IN MY BAG, SO ON, SO ON). WHAT MAKES THE WORK ALIVE FOR ME IS ALWAYS THE WEB OF POSSIBLE ASSOCIATIONS THAT SUCH A WORK PROVOKES IN ME, LIKE SAILING ON THE WAVES, JUMPING OVER THEM, DIVING DEEP AND THEN AGAIN BEING ABOVE THE WATER.

Re: montage: In June when I visited Belgrade, I was trying to think of ways as a writer to be involved in the kind of process you use in making work, and the funny thing is, a hard question has suddenly found an unexpected resolution.

BIRD: [singing]

The Day burns black
Ash soft wings
Shrivelled by gas
The Night's a slow falling bird
Bruised by sudden glass

Once I stopped trying to imagine myself in YOUR process, and began thinking of the lessons of montage and juxtaposition and double directions in my OWN, I began writing a new piece about the refugees in Australia using these techniques: a libretto made of a combination of imagined speech of a bird, with "found" text available in the public domain: testimony from asylum seekers, publicity from the prison corporation Wackenhut Inc, public statements by Government officials, etc. etc. It is a way of writing that is much more like musical composition than inventing narrative. I think it also makes language less transparent, as it is about sound and juxtaposition ("double directions" as you would put it) and not just "about" the events to which language refers.

EXACTLY, I OFTEN FEEL IT LIKE A MUSIC TOO, LIKE A JAM SESSION. YOUR NEW LIBRETTO SOUNDS VERY EXCITING AND I WOULD LOVE TO READ IT AS SOON AS IT IS FINISHED.

great . . .

What are you making now in your work?

BEFORE I ANSWER TO THIS I WOULD LIKE TO TELL YOU ABOUT SOMETHING I SAW TODAY ON OUR TV. WE HAD A FILM SHOWN ON THE LIBERAL TV STATION B92 ABOUT WAR IN BOSNIA, WHERE CRIMES COMMITTED BY SERBIAN TROOPS WERE PRESENTED. MOVIE WAS DIRECTED AND PRESENTED BY FRENCH AUTHOR, WHO AFTER THE MOVIE STAYED IN THE CULTURAL CENTER WHERE THE FILM WAS SHOWN AND TALKED WITH AUDIENCE. HIS MOVIE AND HIS SPEECH PROVOKED VERY DIFFERENT REACTIONS, VERY EXTREME TOO. WOMAN, THEATRE DRAMATURG FROM BELGRADE SAID, DEFENDING THE MOVIE, THAT SHE CANNOT SPEAK ABOUT ITS ESTHETIC VALUE AND TECHNICAL QUESTIONS WHILE THE MOVIE SHOWS THE VIOLENCE, CRIES, BLOOD AND DESPERATION. SHE ADDED THAT FOR HER IS IMPOSSIBLE TO DISCUSS ESTHETIC WHILE THE VIOLENCE AND DESTRUCTION IS PRESENT. WHAT DO YOU THINK ABOUT THIS?

Hmm, this is a hard question. It depends on the way it is inflected. If she means: that to treat the representation of violence as ONLY an aesthetic question is ethically dangerous, I would agree. But I tend to think that if we discard questions of aesthetics when confronted with hard or painful political realities, we are in danger of reverting to a "default model" of aesthetic construction of stories. In the US the public "performance" of pro-war rhetoric by television and media right now has a very definite series of aesthetic choices associated with it, which is hard to criticize publicly because this choice is supposed to be no choice, but a simple urgent presentation of the facts—the "voice of America," in fact. Therefore in some circles, if you criticize the mode of presentation, you are thought to be criticizing "America" as a whole. The discourse on the current political situation has become very polarized, with events publicly presented in simple terms which one is presumed to be "for" or "against." So I would say that we are always choosing the terms of our representation and need to work hard to maintain complexity in the face of violence and desperation. I don't think there is a choice between *either* an aestheticized *or* a "direct" and unmediated representation, there is only a choice between what kind of aesthetic one chooses.

One of the reasons I'm so interested in Dah's work is that you have chosen complexity and an open-endedness of interpretation, as a way of facing very dark circumstances. Many other companies working in politically repressive circumstances have opted instead for "simple and urgent" message theatre, deciding that politics should overrule aesthetics.

But if we can't deal with violence and desperation in our art, what do we think we are doing?

Howard Barker writes that tragedy restores to an audience the dignity of individual pain, whereas work that seeks to unify an audience through uplifting messages is both patronizing and a sign of social despair.

It seems to me that there is another country inside the borders of all our official countries. Some refugees escaped from Villawood, an Australian detention centre (really a prison, run by private US prison company). Stefan, one of the escapees, said in an interview "You can't believe you're in Australia when you're in Villawood. Overseas you only see Australia is good country . . . But when you come to Villawood, to tell you the truth, sometimes I tell you I am not in Australia. Maybe I am not. Maybe I am in another country."

ABOUT MY RECENT WORK—IN THESE MOMENTS I WORK WITH TWO ACTRESSES FROM DAH ON THEIR TWO SOLO PERFORMANCES. IT IS AN OLD IDEA, AND WE DEVELOPED IT THROUGH TIME TITLES ARE "DANCING WITH DARKNESS" AND "ACT OF REVENGE" (WORKING TITLE). IN THE FIRST PERFORMANCE WE ARE SEARCHING AROUND THEME OF LOSS, USING OUR EXPERIENCE ON WORKING ON OUR OLD PERFORMANCE "THE HELEN KELLER CASE" WHICH WE LOST DUE TO POLITICAL AND HISTORICAL CIRCUMSTANCES. SPEAKING ABOUT HOW WE LOST THE PERFORMANCE WE TRY TO UNDERSTAND THE MEANING OF THE LOSS, OF SIGH AND HEARING, OF ONE'S COUNTRY, IDENTITY, ETC. WE USE TEXTS FROM OUR OLD PERFORMANCE "THE HELEN KELLER CASE," HER ORIGINAL TEXTS, OUR TEXTS,

"You owe us nothing, except that you are still alive, and you cannot abandon us to exile, death and oblivion. Give us a little more life, even if you call it memory, what does it matter to you?" Carlos Fuentes, *Constancia*

MEDICAL REPORTS, TEXTS ABOUT PERCEPTION AND MODERN ART. MY QUESTION IS WHAT THE VOID THAT IS LEFT AFTER THE LOSS CONTAINS? WHAT IS THE MEANING OF THE GAP, ABSENCE OR PRESENCE? ETC. WE EVEN HAVE ONE SCENE WITH PUPPETS, WHICH SPEAKS ABOUT THE ESSENCE OF OUR OLD PERFORMANCE.

This is a very fecund question for me, the one about what is contained in the void of loss. Loss and potential are very closely linked. I think in my own writing, that void is the place that everything comes from—a generative void. There is an emptiness involved in making things.

There is a phrase I remember from an article I read long ago called "At the Threshhold of the Self" by Linda Anderson. I have lost the memory of most of this work which talks about grief as a threshhold, which one does not just pass through, but inhabits; and at that threshhold, the void speaks and time behaves differently: things and their absence coexist, simultaneously. The phrase I recall from this article is "An open memory that ceaselessly makes way."

I'LL WRITE LATER ABOUT THE OTHER PERFORMANCE. ON THE TOP OF THIS LOTS OF OFFICE WORK, WORKING ON GETTING OUR OWN SPACE. AND TRYING TO SEE FAMILY, FRIENDS, HAVE TIME FOR READING, REFLECTION, I FEEL CONSTANT LACK OF TIME IT REALLY SPEEDS UP. HOW DO YOU DEAL WITH TIME?

I REALLY LIKE OUR
CONVERSATION THAT TAKES
PLACE SOMEWHERE
IN BETWEEN,
CREATING
ONE MORE
TRANSPARENT BRIDGE.

You ask about time:
Time is going very fast and yet it doesn't seem to go anywhere. For me Time is more like a manic depressive wheel, or sets of waves for a waiting surfer. Flat and empty and quiet, then suddenly over-whelmingly fast.
One or the other.

HOPI SAY THAT "THERE IS NO TIME WHICH LASTS BUT A MULTITUDE OF SUBTLE AND EMPHASIZED EVENTS" IT MAKES SENSE TO ME, AGAIN SOMETHING AGAINST LINEAR PERCEPTION OF TIME, STORY, PLAY. MORE AND MORE I THINK THAT WHEN I NO LONGER COMPLAIN ABOUT LACK OF TIME. THAT WILL BE THE SIGN THAT I MASTERED IT. I HATE THIS HYSTERIA OF OUR "MODERN" LIVES, WHEN WE CONSTANTLY COMPLAIN ABOUT LACK OF TIME. AN IMAGE OF HORSE AND ITS RIDER CAME TO ME, THINKING ABOUT MASTERING THE TIME.

Yes me too, and the way it's suspended

Speaking of time, we should end our dialogue so I can put it in the post before I get on a plane for Australia.

It's beautiful summer in Australia, my mum tells me—I AM SO JEALOUS—and meanwhile Europe is all under snow and Providence is not yet very cold, though we have a little snow on the ground.

Our

Transparent

bridge

will

become

opaque

and

open

for

public

traffic!

THIS SOUNDS GOOD. TOMORROW IS SLAVA WHICH MEANS VERY IMPORTANT ORTHODOX HOLIDAY. I DO NOT REMEMBER DID I TELL YOU ABOUT IT, BUT IN OUR RELIGION WE HAVE THE SAINTS WHO ARE PROTECTORS OF OUR HOUSES. MY FAMILY'S SAINT IS SAINT NIKOLA AND TOMORROW IS HIS DAY. SO MY AND MANY OTHER FAMILIES WHO HAVE THE SAME SAINT-PROTECTOR CELEBRATE TOMORROW. IT IS MORE IMPORTANT HOLIDAY AND FAMILY EVENT THEN CHRISTMAS HERE. SO, WE SHALL GATHER IN MY MOTHER'S PLACE TOMORROW, HAVE BIG FAMILY LUNCH AND THE GUESTS START TO COME, TILL LATE INTO NIGHT. VERY IMPORTANT IS THAT WE NOT EAT MEAT, ETC, BECAUSE NOW IS THE FASTING PERIOD, SO MY MUM WILL PREPARE DIFFERENT DELICIOUS MEALS FROM FISH, VEGETABLES, BEANS, VERY

OLD ONES THAT YOU CAN NOT EAT EVERYWHERE. AND OF COURSE LOTS OF BOILED SLJIVOVICA GOES WITH THE FOOD.

SAINT NIKOLA IS PROTECTOR OF TRAVELLERS AND SAILORS—SO IT MAKES PERFECT SENSE FOR ME.

SPEAKING ABOUT RIDING THE HORSE I ALSO HAVE AN IMAGE OF RIDING WAVE, I GUESS THIS IS FAMILIAR TO YOU BEING FROM AUSTRALIA.

IT IS EXCITING THAT OUR CONVERSATION WILL BECOME PUBLIC, AS OUR WORKS IN THEATRE DO, AFTER A PERIOD OF ENJOYING THE SOLITUDE OF THE WORKING ROOM OR PEN AND PAPER OR OF COURSE COMPUTER. ONE MORE THING THAT CAME TO ME SPEAKING ABOUT SOLITUDE—VOID.
LOVE, DIJANA

I have only one
word for snow:
cold.
Love, Christine

All photos are by Vincent Abbey, except the one of Christine Evans "holding up" a small plane on Block Island, taken by Pam Murray. The bridge photos are of the bridge in Novi Sad, bombed by NATO. The photo of the woman with hair wrapped round her head is of Sanja Krsmanovic Tasic (actress, Dah Teatar) in The Helen Keller Case*, a Dah Teatar production; the other images are from* Maps of Forbidden Remembrance*, a work collaboratively made by Dah Teatar and Seven Stages, an Atlanta-based company, with performers Maja Mitic, Sanja Krsmanovic Tasic, Kathy Randels, Del Hamilton and Faye Allen. Both performances were ensemble-made and directed by Dijana Milosevic.*

DREW GARDNER

The Hungarian Pastry Shop Bathroom Grafitti Poem

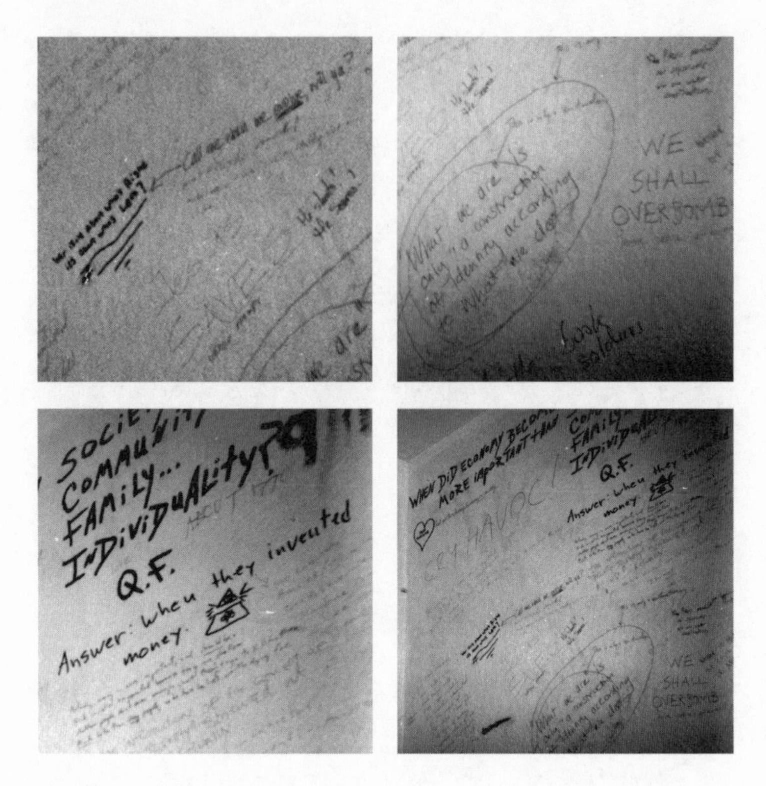

when did economy become more important
than society, community, family . . . individuality?
about 1770
9/11
answer: when they invented money
cry havoc
we shall overbomb
read your theory, dummy, economy IS society
war isn't about what's right, it's about what's LEFT
Jesus saves
He shoots!
He scores!
what we are is
only a construction
of identity according
to what we do
this is only a construction
call me when we EVOLVE, will ya?

PETER GIZZI & ELIZABETH WILLIS

Song Out of Mind

for, after, and by Keith & Rosmarie Waldrop

Reality is what does not change, i.e.,
I'm not in the world, I'm beside my self.
It is really quite romantic
though nothing edible ever came of it.
The craw of silence is vast and, anyway, already has us.
Spring sluggishness replaces winter lethargy.
This is the real morning and not the other.
Why?
Daytime is more dangerous at night.
Hesitant shrubbery like a tentative loss of memory.
I remember everything and it's all wrong.
This model has something to be said for it.
"Ach," she wailed.
It's hell to be poor.
You simply bleed into an abstract distance.
A geometric garden? a variable?
Silence in heaven strikes common tones.
A secret turns away calmly.
Our perfection would leave the world in ruins.
Before I go, let us put our horseplay in order.
Landscapes like gardens of the most fabulous almanacs.
Jealous, Clara?
Her numbers fold, in planes she cannot describe.
Steps that take possession, but hesitantly.
A poem, like trying to remember, is a movement of the
 whole body.
To stay embedded against the dawn of matter and fact.
In what sense can I still speak of "actual" rain?
Look at the blue, you said, detaching the color from the sky
 as if it were a membrane.
Every day, the sun.
Balancing. Austere. Lifeless.
There is a mind-like place beyond the mind.

No one knows a mirror.
My love and I got up for breakfast.
It is now clear that the turning of the earth on its axis is of very great service.
Unable to relate the garment to the body—
Love in its mountain ranges—
A sentence is made
I HAVE COME TO BRING YOU SECRETS OF THE AGES
As if there were proof in spelling.
I began my education by walking along the road in search of the heroic.
I got back under the covers, finding it hard to believe, later, how soon I drifted back to sleep.
This cancellation makes a great thunk.
Whether we're awake or asleep
trees go down, random and planted, the way we think.
Like a bird, a bird among the leaves,
shirts on a clothesline.
"Where are you going, my complete accidental body?"
A frame supports what would, on its own, collapse.
What I hear whispered, I whisper to you.
Daily do I seek form.
I charter a ship then try to understand what I had in mind.
Space itself, fiery.

"Song Out of Mind" was written for the occasion of the 40th Anniversary Celebration of Burning Deck Press at Brown University, spring 2001. We mixed Keith and Rosmarie's books, chapbooks, novels, and prose together and arranged them chronologically through their career. We then began to build a poem by creating a dialogue between ourselves using lines from their books. The title comes from their collaborative project Well Well Reality.

JOHN HAVELDA & JOÃO NUNES

Broomwork or E Vir Eu Por Amor A Aborrecer-Vos?

I don't like the way life is
la vuestra falsa fé
I'm not satisfied
vossas cruezas
I guess I'll just kill myself
eu vos ajudarei
got no place to go
crer em Cristo esta sepultura
please hear my plea
logo fogo ardente
my heart skips a beat
um coração lindo e sutil
walking down the street
um longo e obediente sofrimento arde no meu peito
you ruined my life
nada vale
how could I be such a fool?
tão pura e verdadeira
you never really loved me
cansados pensamentos palavras de tristeza
all over the back seat of my car
lágrimas em fio
this heart of mine
nojo morte dano e perdição
when you touch me
mal me vês
every happiness in the world is mine
tudo me enoja e aborrece
no matter who I take home I'm so lonely
perguntas-me porquê?
no matter who I take home I keep calling your name
em mil porém diversas fantasias

I can't say what's right or what's wrong

pois não sentes nem vês

how could I believe all those lies you told me?

não é de estranhar o menino é de olhos privado

she makes me oh so happy no I'm never ever blue

antiquíssimo escritor

"Broomwork or E Vir Eu Por Amor A Aborrecer-Vos?" sprang from Marshall McLuhan's idea of texts being produced by "brushing" different types of information against one another that I came across in the work of John Cage. The left column is composed of fragments from Frank Zappa's parodies of love songs, while the right column is composed of fragments from the love sonnets by Luís de Camões. The result is a performance text for two voices. The first three lines, I suggest, should be read as an English call and a Portuguese answer, after which each voice, now under no obligation to wait its turn, should be free to roam around its particular fragments. The piece normally, though definitely not necessarily, ends with the rebuke "antiquíssimo escritor."

The Implosion of the Vulgar Tongue

ACO ZUC ALL YOW **AMU YEA** APO XAN **ARS WYN** AWA WRA **BAL WOO** BAR WIP **BAS WIB** BEA WHI
BEE WHI BEL WEL **BIB WAR** BIS WAD **BLA USE** BLA UPP **BLO VIX** BLU VAI **BOL TYN** BOR TWI
BRA TUM BRE TRO **BRU TRA** BUD TWO **BUL TOP** BUM TOD **BUR TIT** BUT TIB **CAB THO**
CAB TER **CAN TAW** CAP TAN **CAR SYN** CAT SWE **CAT SUR** SHA STR **CHE STO** CHI STE
CHO STA CIR SQU **CLE SPL** CLO SPA **COB SOO** COC SNI **COG SMU** COL SMA
SOM SLA COS SKI **COU SIN** CRA SIC **CRI SHI** CRO SHA **CRO SET** CRU SCR
CUN SCO CUR SCA **DAC SAL** DAM RUT **DAR RUS** DEA RUM **DEV RUM**
DEV ROU **DIL ROO** DIS RIP **DOC RID** DOM REN **DOX REC** DRO RAN
DUC RAG DUM QUO **DUT QUI** DIE QUE **ENS QUA** EYE PUZ
FAG PUM FAS PUC **FEL PRI** FID POU **FIR POR** FLA POL **FLY PLU**
FOO PIS **FRE PIN** FRO PIG **FUS PHR** FUZ PEL **GAB PAY**
GAN PAR **GEN PAN** GIL OYS **GIS OWL** GO OLL **GOO OBS**
GRA NYP **GRE NYP** GRO NOS **GUT NOD** GYP NIC
GYP NEC BYP NAB **HAN MYR** HAR MUM
HAZ MOU HEL MOO **HIG MOB** HOB MES
HOG MAS HOL MAL **HOO LYE**
HOR LUR **HUB LOU** HUM LON
HIT LOB HUP LIN **JAC LIB**
JAN LAZ **JEW LAN**
INK KON **JOB KNO**
JUM KIT **IVI KIM**
KEN KIC

THE IMPLOSION OF THE VULGAR TONGUE

An argument, or perhaps a trading of insults for two voices, "The Implosion of the Vulgar Tongue" uses the headwords of A Dictionary of Buckish Slang, University Wit and Pickpocket Eloquence *often referred to as* The 1811 Dictionary of the Vulgar Tongue. *The first and last headword, the second and penultimate and so on are joined to form short phrases until the piece "implodes" into a center of the dictionary.*

CRAIGIE HORSFIELD & CECILIA VICUÑA

What Art May Be

A conversation between Craigie Horsfield and Cecilia Vicuña held in New York City, October 2001.

VICUÑA It was not only that conversation is best expressed in conversation . . .

HORSFIELD No, nor that conversation begets and gives birth only to conversation. It is rather that in conversation we not only understand each other—although we both understand and misunderstand—but that in conversation we come into being. Again it is not in conversation alone but, if we believe, as I do, that we bring each other into being, together, then, in so far as conversation is that place in which we articulate our relation—not the only place but the place with which we are most familiar—then that which until now has seemed to be familiar, banal, everyday, turns out to be the very place of our being together. Listening to this you may say "that is very well. But what does it actually mean?"

V Yes. [*laughing*]

H People often say that this seems like a big idea, but what does it actually change? It's poetic, perhaps it's sentimental, but what does it signify, I'm sure you're familiar with that.

V Yes, the way I see it is that when, for example, you think of the way conversation is a Latin word: con means together; versation means verse. Verse has not only the meaning of a verse as in poetry, but verse is also, as in French, towards. So it is like arriving at a direction, or at a vector together. It is not only that we come into being together, but that we are co-creating something when we are conversing. So I think the word itself is saying that what you say is true. Or the other way around. The notion of conversation being a work, something you do, this is the major insight of your work. I would like to know how you arrived at that insight.

H I think that in what you describe is a whole knot of different understandings which interconnect and tie together but in a sometimes confusing way. So when you speak about coming into being, I understand that as something which is at the beginning, that nothing proceeds it, there is no ego or self prior to it. There have been those who have described this, and it may appear to be an arcane and somewhat philosophical point, as being an act of charity towards the other: in this I give you being as I come to being myself. I don't at all believe that. I don't think it is so. I think that we each depend upon the other. When you are speaking about the words "coming towards," I would understand it as what I describe as "coming into." In the same way, of course, we don't become one as the other. We are with them, which is entirely different. Again your description is most true in so far as it makes action central. So that being and action are not separated.

V We also need to consider the fact that when people speak of process they tend to think that process is something that has a beginning and an end, that process is something that you are not only doing, but somehow provoking. But the truth of the matter is that everything is process, continually.

H But let us take an intermediate step. Let us say that as we come into being, there are certain consequences. It appears, for example, just to take one example, no longer useful to think of a complete separation between self and other. Similarly, there is no place to speak about private and public.

V Certainly and again, this is given by the word itself. When you study the root of the word self. Self has a double meaning from the start. You are yourself because you are the same. You can only be your self because you are the same as all other selves. So there is the concept of the self itself as one huge universal entity of which you are a part. So your self can only be a part of that self. The concept of the self as only apart or only separated is like half of the egg, is like half of the I. It is a complete illusion of speech that is forgetful of its meaning.

H I think that is very strongly so. And I think that we would also agree that it doesn't lessen the self.

V Certainly.

H It makes the self possible. It isn't absorbed into one giant ego that somehow eats up the whole world or for which others are merely shadows.

V Exactly. It only makes us co-participants. Co-creators of absolutely every instant. I think of pain and anger. Anger for example means narrowing in its first meaning. So angst, in Spanish we say angosto, narrow, and anger is a narrowing. A narrowing of the scope of possibilities. Because if we are simultaneously and at once our own individual and we are a part of a larger whole it only makes for a more complex and for a continually dense co-creation.

H One of the problems that this brings along with it is that we have lived in a culture, which has, and up until now rather successfully in many ways, sustained itself through separation.

V Certainly.

H Through these entities which existed in separation and which were connected through a synthetic network. So, for example, if we are to talk about relation, which is something which we feel very strongly about, and which flows from what we have been describing, many would say OK, relation is a network; it is like lines between things. And it is a persuasive image. But in a sense it very much corresponds to society as it was. The problem with such a model of relation is that it is unidimensional. It exists in lines. Whereas for us relation is being.

V Absolutely. Again, inside the word to relate . . . for some reason all these words are Latin words . . . it is very important to acknowledge this . . . that although we are speaking English all the words that we come back to, the knots of our speech, tend to be of Latin origin. Relate means to give back. And if you think of this as an ethos—that the basic justice of relation is in that very primal thing that you give back and bad relations are when someone feels that he or she is not getting back what he or she has given—it is something very primal. And for me, it is like a law of relationship is embedded already in the word "relate."

H And consequently, given your description, bad relation is that sense that we are inevitably separated from the other. Or separated in such a way that we cannot make it good, that we cannot . . . be with.

V Yes, the idea of privileging the necessity of separation in order to create the individual is an illusion. And it is a very destructive illusion that has brought the world to the present state.

H One of the cruelties of the modern world was precisely that it created those separations not only in society in large but also within the self.

V That is the problem. If you are separated from your own inner perceptions, your own inner feelings, then you cannot help but be separated from the other and from the others. For example, when you think of the way our society privileges separation—this is everywhere in the language itself. The word science means to cut. But the word consciousness means simultaneously to cut and to join. So the most perfect form of knowledge, actually the knowledge which is consciousness, is to do all that at once. If you separate but don't join . . . then again it is half the egg.

H It is interesting that as we have been talking you have again and again returned to an attention to words, to language.

V Yes.

H Maybe it is the right point in our conversation because as you know, much of the philosophy of the 20th century, in its many forms and its many becomings, concerned language and signs, linguistics and semiotics. And in a sense, the study of signs, the study of language, came to overwhelm an attention to the wider condition of our relation to each other. Some years ago I came to think that we might keep language a little aside, almost as a given. Because we had seen how thinking had fallen into this whirlpool, as if being sucked down into this infinite impossibility of language. Had we talked ten years ago I would have said let us look rather at all the many other things that surround us or threaten us, which we face, and which we live inside, because the world changes. I'm not sure that I would put it that way now. Now I would say that I'm not sure that anything precedes language. We have no evidence for it, it is in any case entirely hypothetical. There may be something that proceeds language but it is not something I can test too well. However I would go a step further, and it is why I bring it up here, language is itself the space of our relation. It is born between us. Language is self evidently social. The way that we understand our self is within that language. The space between thought and language while it may be arguable, is very, very small.

V For a poet, there may be a different version. The way that I think of this is that language is always *the* main creation of people. If everything else disappears and we still have language we can still get a feeling for whatever this human experience may have been.

H But let us go further with that. Because we exist wholly within that language. As simultaneously language exists only with ourselves.

V This is very important for the way I see it, when you think of the word consciousness, somehow if people had remembered through thousands of years the full meaning of the word consciousness when it was first created perhaps consciousness would not mean everything that it does. So just as you need the separation and the union to be simultaneous and in a complex relation pulling at each other, you also need inside each word a level of memory and forgetfulness in order for it to work. Which is exactly like the relationship between people. For example, in our conversation we need to be silent, we need to hear, we need to forget, we need to remember, we need to have all these tensions going on at once. Otherwise it becomes not only literal but boring . . . it becomes unnecessary. What I mean to say is that all these processes are part of a system that continually repeats itself with subtle variations. In that room of the variation is where all the creation exists.

H Retracing what you have just said, it seems to me that there are several very significant notions which are a part of the knot we began with. You spoke, for example, about memory and forgetfulness, but you situated it, as I understand you, within the present, within the space of the relationship. So that memory and its forgetting exist between us and that memory we have access to only through our present. It is not a very great step to go on from that to suggest that memory itself, indeed our sense of the past, is the way we have of thinking together an aspect of our present for which we have no other language. You used I think very precisely the expression, at once. It is as though that memory and that forgetting were at once. It is as though all our histories, which are between us, are at once. But of course to say that—and for it to be so—is unthinkable. Is beyond our imagination. So we have ways of understanding each other which allow us to enter into this impossibility.

V To me it is like an agreement, certain cultures, like pre-Columbian culture which is a culture that was extremely dependent on the knowledge that people arrived at through the ecstatic experience, through the experience of trance, through the experiences where people are aware that they are larger than themselves, it seems to me that all the basic art forms of the pre-Columbian peoples, the big dances, the big music, are specifically designed through thousands and thousands of years of exploration for this experience—the moment where you are at once yourself and a member of the community. And a community which involves not only the people who are there with you but also everybody who ever died, and everybody who ever lived, and this instant of complete communion is what art still drives at. Of course this is still living, it is not just pre-Columbian time, if you go to a festival today, in Chile or any other place in Latin America where these festivals are still current, you as a foreigner can experience exactly this same trance because the precision of the method of arriving at this trance has been created through millennia and you can come there from another culture and get it. Why? Because it is expressed through sound. And sound absolutely achieves that instantly through the perception of your own brain. So it is like an experience that is so impressive where people can at once reach into a form of memory that is beyond the senses and at the same time completely of the senses.

H Behind it and connecting very directly to what we were speaking about a moment ago, is the notion that, thinking itself is something that happens between us. Of course the convention of our society is that thinking is something we do alone. And incidentally, that thinking is passive.

V Absolutely. Which is a nonsensical idea anyway, because for example, who put words in your head? You learn it, even before you speak you already have a perception of language. There are these wonderful studies now of what babies can discern. And the discernment of a two months old baby is immense. So that is how it is with us, we are born into a stream of blood and genes which has been created by everybody and so everything in us is a co-creation, a mutual co-creation.

H I think that is so even in the most intimate way, we have never the experience of being alone, although we have been told otherwise. We have been told that the experience of our society is one of alienation, is one of being alone, of being separated, that in our deepest self we are alone, and yet from the moment of our being, from the moment of our being conceived, we are conceived in union, in coming together. We grow within our mother in the most intimate relation and are born into relation. In every part of what we are, even beyond our first death. Even if we believe ourselves to be unknown, we exist within the world of relations. All is within that. And this thinking we were describing, is never outside that. Even the very terminology we use—inside and outside—appears to be almost redundant, what are we describing here?

V Exactly. It is quite relative. It is absolutely relative. Our conversation could probably never take place as we are conducting it now in a culture that acknowledges everything that we are saying. Our conversation is possible only because we are immersed in a society that has pulled this bullshit. The notion of alienation, the notion of separation, the notion of aloneness. All this is a peculiar bullshit. And somehow people have hypnotised each other and themselves into believing it.

H Your description of our conversation within the context of that understanding rings true. In the example you gave a moment ago of the ceremonies, what struck me was that it is a way of telling that which is otherwise untold. It is a way of being conscious of something that happens with or without our attention. It connects rather beautifully with something we reach for, even in our own culture, because, although we may not acknowledge it, it is something that is clearly within us. It has been covered up, very deeply, but it doesn't go away.

V Yes. The longing is always there.

H It is one, not the only one, but one of the things that art may be, this attention to that which is otherwise unspoken. But not as a revealing of something that is hidden. Rather, if I may digress for a moment, one of the problems of our conversation is that others may find it too large, too abstract, after all what is this really to do with life? And yet we are very close to it. The reason we are talking about conversation is that it is the most everyday of our experiences. It needs no special skill, beyond being alive and trying to negotiate the world . . . which actually requires a lot of skills. [*laughter*] If you go into a shop and you want to pay for something, perhaps you ask for a packet of biscuits, or, leaving the shop, and stepping on the bus, you ask for a ticket, in terms of social exchange, there are all kinds of skills required in these apparently simple actions. And the most sophisticated of us, supposedly sophisticated, on a bad day, finds even these simple exchanges very tough. The bus driver has a cold, it is raining, the passengers are being difficult. It is not always easy. And behind what we are describing is the sheer difficulty and intractability of things, how difficult they are to shift or to effect. It is not that we are talking about some idealised state of exchange, (and it is more than exchange, again this is one of the misunderstandings about conversation, isn't it? It is imagined as somehow something which I give to you as you give to me when it is so much more than that) even in the everyday, we are each of us more or less competent. It is not something which is closed to anyone. Nor is any one of us more . . . Some may say that if you are articulate or if you feel confident, then you have an advantage. But in some ways that is the misunderstanding because you are looking at the negotiation of the social world without that investment we all have in being together. What I mean is that even the most articulate may feel profoundly lacking in many ways. As much, curiously, as a result of their being articulate. Because it brings with it also an overwhelming sense of how to behave, of what is appropriate, of what should be said or should not be said.

V That is key. The fear.

H Yes.

V I think the reason we are having this conversation now, and why we are having this conversation issue, is because there is a sense that conversation as an art is disappearing. Because as a result of this separation we are talking about, this alienation, people are afraid of speaking. Yet the simplest thing in the world, conversation, as you have said, is the gift of everything. For example, in pre-Columbian or in contemporary indigenous society, the conversation is continual. Birds are conversing with each other; birds are conversing with trees; the river is conversing with the rocks. Absolutely everything is conversing with everything else. And the notion that people should be afraid of speaking, unless there is a tyranny or persecution on account of certain ideologies or certain religious ideas, the idea that conversation may be something that puts your self at risk, is something that is a peculiar creation of our times, and it is why this needs to be talked about. In a way conversing about conversation is a healing or an exploration of what it is that we need to hear.

H This is something each of us has thought and spoken about over many years and one of the questions I have often been asked, is: Craigie, so much of your conversation is about conversation . . . Where does it lead?

V [*laughing*] That is good.

H And of course it was meant as a criticism. The thing appears to be eating itself, like a snake eating its own tail. And I would say, it is true, it is true. But think of this—and let us call this the story of the lover's discourse—lovers talk about love. Oh, they talk endlessly. They talk to each other about love. They talk to their friends and their family. They talk about love, they talk about love to prove that they love, to demonstrate that they love, to show that they are loved. They talk about love to reassure. They talk about love to cherish, to provoke . . . But if they only talk about love, they will not be lovers for very long.

V [*laughing*] Right!

H In that it seems, is a rather beautiful lesson. To talk about conversation is something we should all do. But to talk only about conversation will end in tears.

V Yes. It only shows our wound. It's a lack . . . If you think everybody is busy making money and making work, and this is more true now than ever before, I am absolutely sure. When you read about labor, people say don't romanticize any other era, because in any other era women would be spinning, they would be spinning, spinning and cooking and taking care of the fire. This is true, but the reality was that whatever was being done, was always being done in the leisure time involved inside the labor itself. So this was being done communally first of all, it was being done with others, it was being done in conversation and I can attest to that because I come from an indigenous society, a mixed blood indigenous society, from Chile, and I was a witness to that system. And I am a witness to that society every time I go back. It is not that people don't work. People are still working their asses off, but they somehow find the way to talk and work. Not here. Here there is a separation again. People set up a time for talking and a time for work. And I think this has created a very peculiar unhappiness. Because it seems that animals need to babble. Animals need to create these sounds. Something in our blood, something in our heartbeat, something in the way cells are moving inside of us, we need that conversation.

H It is just so. And we know that when we speak about conversation, we speak about speaking and listening. We speak about attention and momentary inattention.

V And distraction.

H And we speak about pause.

V And a breaking away to go fetch the bread. Or whatever.

H All of that is within conversation. Let us go a little bit further and say that conversation itself . . . You know, maybe this is not the right place. It is a kind of digression. Years ago I spoke more about dialogue than about conversation . . .

V How do you see the difference between the two?

H I think one of the problems I came to have with thinking about dialogue, was that for most of the people with whom I spoke, dialogue became contained. In a way it stood aloof from the everyday world. It could be found within that world, but it was not of that world.

V Again a separation.

H Yes. It was something which was consciously considered. Something which stood aside. Something which had an air about it.

V Like a label. Like we are going to dialogue about this and that. A framing.

H It could become that. It was always respectable. It was never loose.

V How do you feel about Socratic dialogue?

H This is the appalling misunderstanding, and I don't exaggerate. When we speak about dialogue most assume that that is the model upon which we base it. Dialogue came from the tradition of the Greeks. And there it appeared to be a model of thesis and antithesis. It appeared to be the model in which the master would contest, where two ideas, which were not equal . . .

V [*laughing*], that you have to say in a very soft voice . . .

H Stood one against the other. And the true triumphed, now it so happened that the true was that put forward by the most articulate.

V Yes

H But that was not so difficult, because our ability to articulate the truth was always to overwhelm that which was false.

V The contender, yes

H So at its very root, the notion of dialogue appeared to have a sense of contest, of conflict, of confrontation. That I found profoundly disturbing. Now I don't believe that dialogue need have that. But it is difficult to escape from it. I would see dialogue as happening between people, you don't necessarily reach consensus but there is some degree of understanding. Not because one is proved against another. But because we come together to reach something which is common and shared. This is a crucial difference from so much of the understanding of relation which is based upon power, the analysis of relation based upon the stronger and the weaker. I think that it is possible, indeed I think absolutely necessary, that we think of relation in other ways. It does not mean that there are not situations where a thinking of relation, an analysis of relation, may depend on relations of power. But there is so much other than that. And power is a distortion. It is not, and must not be, the only way we may think about how we stand one to another.

V On the other hand, when you think of the word "conflict" and the use of conflict within the brain, people who study the brain say that the brain evolves through the resolution of conflict. Conflict is like consciousness. It is made up of con- togetherness, and –flict, like the sound "flict": going in. Conflict involves this togetherness. In other words, to have conflict, you need to have two opposing forces. In Andean art and culture two opposing forces are always collaborators. It cannot be otherwise because it does not work otherwise. In other words the concept of this opposition, which is a collaboration, is perhaps *the* crucial concept of Andean society, and civilization. There are these big festivals which are called Tinkuy a coming together of two opposing forces at the moment of transformation—which is mutual. So in the dialogue, and in the conversation, the motive of conflict is always there. If this is understood to be a collaboration, that changes the whole matter. If it is a matter of one overpowering the other, then the problem begins. Even in the conception of "conflict" itself you can have different views.

H I would link it with the notion that dialogue, and lets speak for the moment about dialogue, depends, if we are to understand it fully, depends upon several qualities. The first of which, is that it is not finite. It ceases to be as it ends. So dialogue properly should continue and that continuity is central to our understanding of it. Secondly, it should have consequence.

V That is very important

H Where I would link it to what you are describing, is in conceiving this thing that "goes on." You could say that when we leave today our dialogue, our conversation, ends. If you think like that then of course it is an impossibility, it is quite outside what we've been talking about. But I would argue that the conversation we have continues. It continues when we meet our friends. It continues in the way that we see or speak or hear. And then enters into other conversations. And it is that sense of continuity and consequence that seems to me crucial to an understanding of dialogue, just as you have described it. So when you speak about conflict, if that conflict is never resolved with the conqueror and the vanquished, with the victory of one and the loss of the other, if it is evermore to be reiterated . . .

V It changes everything.

H Yes.

V And that is the Andean idea. You see we meet each other next year to have another Tinkuy. This continuity you just described was embedded in the concept itself. In other words, the awareness of this conflict being a mutual nurturing of each other was even defined, for example, in the conception of the cities. The cities were divided into two areas, Hanan/Hurin, and these two areas were to compete with each other, so that each would excel in relation to the other, in competition with the other, but so that the competition would improve both. The totality of the concept would have to do with fertility, with what you were doing for your self and the other. So each time you had to prove yourself you were doing it for both, you and your opponent. This concept of reciprocal maintenance existed throughout the Americas. An ancient idea which is somehow the reverse of our present. Our present idea is that we want to be better for our self's sake. Which is an impossibility. Because if we go back to the original concept of conversations, within it whatever you do for yourself, you cannot help but do for everybody.

Hear the complete dialogue at http://www.temple.edu/chain.

MICHAEL IVES

Ye Shall Receive (An Elegy to the Near 90s)

A sound/text composition in three voices for F'loom [Michael Ives (MI), Robert Kulik (RO), Richard Scott (RI)]

1., 2., 3., etc. :   system / rehearsal numbers

< :   swallow final vowel as if tape splice

// :   pause

| :   indicates overlapping text

CAPS :   to be rendered with greater intensity

– :   if abutted w/o space against word: splice

No pause between sections unless indicated; to be performed quite swiftly, keeping in mind the tape splice, the changing of channels, the lubricity of commercial language, etc.

I.

(*sotto voce, with a* Four Quartets*-like portentousness*)
1. **ALL**:   What we cannot sell collapses into mystery. //
2. **ALL**:   What we prohibit becomes our most intimate companion. //
3. **ALL**:   What we cannot hold holds us at knife point. //

4. **RI**: *(immediately after l. 3)*   ssssssssss *(guide sibilant toward lower lip)*   *(cresc.)*

II.

1. **ALL**:   SAY HI TO ME! *(guileless, head cocked, smiling vacuously)*
2. **MI**:   It's all about amazing, moisture rich – *(as if to sell Paul Mitchell hair care product)*
3. **RO**:   For control that's – *(simil. to above)*
4. **ALL**:   SAY HI TO ME!
5. **RI**:   It's all about that fresh look.
6. **RO**: | – fresh look – *(whispered, as if in echo)*

7. **MI**: | ssssssssss *(as above, I. 4)*
(cresc.)

8. **MI**: SAY H<

9. **ALL**: SAY HI TO ME! *(this and following* unisoni *with growing insistence and soupçon of menace)*

10. **MI**: Listen, just gimme the – *(evincing holiday time consumer aggression)*

11. **RO**: BE NICE –

12. **ALL**: BE NICE TO ME!

13. **RI**: It's all –

14. **MI**: For control –

15. **RI**: – that fresh look –

16. **MI**: | – fresh look – *(as above, l. 6)*

17. **RO**: | ssssssssss
(cresc.)

III.

1. **RO**: SAY H<

2. **ALL**: SAY HI TO –

3. **M, RI**: Let's get to kno< *(simil. to II. 2)*

4. **RO**: >uckers< *(truncatively ambiguous apostrophe)*

5. **M, RI**: – each other –

6. **RO**: For control that's –

7. **MI**: Get acquainted with us *(unctuous imperatives condusive to repulsion, here and below)*

8. **R&R**: | Defy convention!

9. **MI**: | We're a
repurposed,
multilayered,
alternative, get-
acquainted,
introductory –

10. **M, RO**: *("horror guitar" figure:* attaca, *voiced alveolar plosive/ affricate [dvhvh …], with teeth clenched, as of boys orally simulating head-on, vehicular collision* :

11. **RI**: | ssssssssss
(cresc.)

12. **RI**: SAY HI<
13. **M, RO**: – to know each other –
14. **ALL**: SAY HI TO ME!
15. **RO**: It's all about that –
16. **RI**: | >'m gonna destroy yo< *(like unto Gordon Gecko, during splatball)*
17. **M, RO**: >ow each other –
18. **MI**: – acquainted with us –
19. **R&R**: | Shatter boundaries!
20. **R&R**: *(accomp. to 21, beginning at* • :

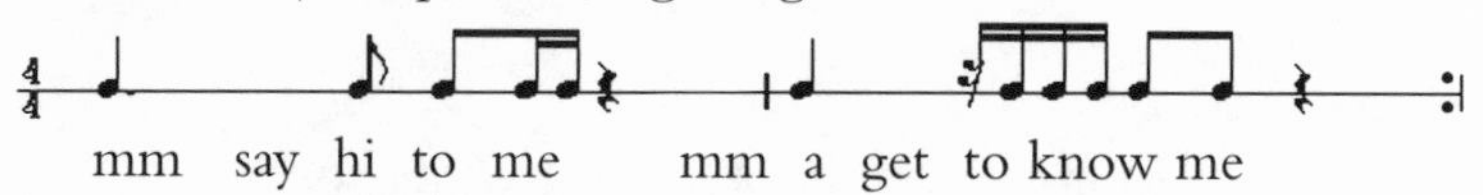

mm say hi to me mm a get to know me

(smarm tartar, close to liquefaction)
21. **MI**: Were a • completely repurposed, let's-get-to-know-each-other, introductory package of value-added, recovery experiences in a reconstructed, shallot-baste, grass-roots community referendum, with mesh back and high neck closure, available in lagoon, moss, heather, and oat.

22. **M, RO**: *("horror guitar" figure; see above, l. 10)*
23. **RI**: SAY H<
24. **RO**: | – fresh look –
25. **RI**: | >esh look –

IV.

1. **M, RO**: >'m gonna destroy y< *(vowel entirely swallowed, like unto G. Gecko choking on own low-yield bile)*
2. **RO**: >ot to grow this econ< *(as in "got" and "economy")*
3. **R&R**: | >ow this economy – *(as in "grow" or "blow" or "owe")*
4. **MI**: | – to grow this – *("this" as if to place hand firmly on inner thigh)*
5. **ALL**: BAP! *(punctive* sforzando, *suggestive of electrocution)*

(Render the following as if unwitting narrator of inenarrable and plainly false "formula for success")
6. **RO**: Let's review our five-point, market orientation to refocusing toward emerging

(**ALL**) (**ALL**)

markets will IMPACT on how **I** grow clever and shiny on the outside –

7. **M, RI**: – soft, fetid, and stupid on the outside! *(rendered loudly, fetidly, stupidly)*

8. **RI**: YEAH! *(cretinous affirmative)*

9. **RO**: HUZZAH! *(generic Renaissance interjective)*

10. **ALL**: BAP!

11. **M, RO**: – get-acquainted, wafer-thin yet option-packed, market-based reality of our time! *(accellerando, crescendo, with rise in pitch)*

12. **RI**: BAP!

13. **RO**: >EED TO INITIATE MARKET-BASED REFORM! *("M" elongate, subito crescendo)*

(l. 14-17 to overlap slightly)

14. **MI**: TOWARD EMERGING MARKETS!

15. **RI**: GREATER MARKET SHARE!

16. **R&R**: BULL MARKET!

17. **ALL**: TO MARKET, TO MARKET!

18. **MI**: *(fortissimo bi-labial roll, appr. 3 seconds)*

19. **R&R**: BUCK SLIP! *(contemporary corporate interjection, meaning uncertain to composer)*

20. **MI**: | ssssssssss
(cresc.)

V.

1. **MI**: You know, it all comes out of whatever it was I wanted to be about, you know, that place of sort of – *(here and below, inflection as of vacant "encounter" dialogue with "others" similarly dismantled in spirit and intelligence, according to vogue-ish spiritual dismantlements inflected suchwise)*

2. **add RI:** – this is where I am, this is broken, I mean –

3. **add RO**: – I'm not living out of the tools I need to own my own grief.

4. **M, RO**: Then go shoot yerself! *(quickly, and as of one in midst of replacing Yosemite Sam mudflaps with Dinesh D'Souza mudflaps)*

5. **RI**: | That's right, the dream of owning your own grief with no money down! *(with wee-hours-infomercial-polystyrene enthusiasm)*

6. **M, RO**: *(on preceding "owning")* | No purchase necessary one time grief offer limited not available in stores price subject to change without noticing APR financing – *(prestissimo, crescendo over length of figure, with less than no concern for intelligibility)*

7. **RI**: | ssssssssss *(cresc.)*

8. **RI**: SAY H<

9. **ALL**: SAY HI TO –

10. **MI**: Say hi to your grief today! *(as if to spaniel puppy on Easter morning)*

11. **M, RI**: HALLO! *(cretinous salutation)*

12. **M, RO**: >onna destroy y<

13. **RO**: Griefcorp up three and three quarters, Microgrief Systems up a –

14. **MI**: *(hiccup)* HALLO!

15. **RI**: >ose terrific grief-control resources you've worked so hard –

16. **M, RO**: – TO MARKET, TO MARKET! *(cf. IV. 14-18)*

17. **MI**: HUZZAH!

18. **R&R**: DAW DAT! *(generic post-Renaissance interjective)*

19. **MI**: *(hiccup)* *(generic post-prandial interjective)*

VI.

1. **ALL**: *("horror guitar" :*

(with the vulnerable earnestness and embarrassing, autistic candor and fatuousness of last week's Blockbuster Video Scholar)

2. **MI**:

It all comes out of like a Julia Roberts

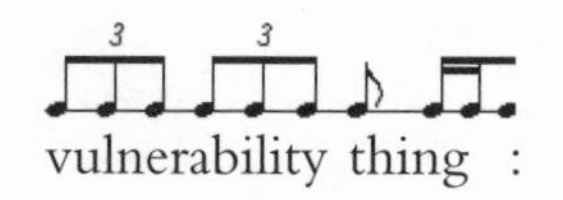

vulnerability thing :

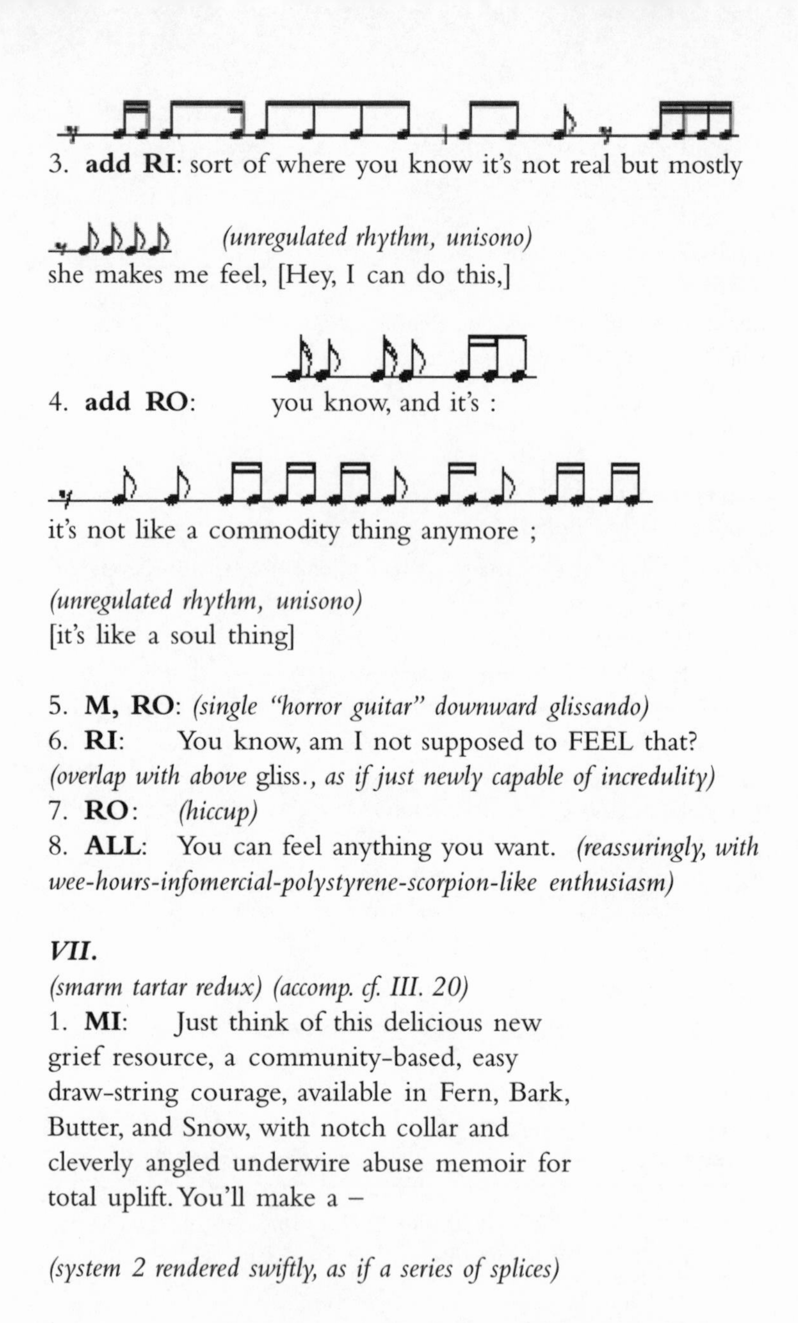

3. **add RI**: sort of where you know it's not real but mostly

(unregulated rhythm, unisono)
she makes me feel, [Hey, I can do this,]

4. **add RO**: you know, and it's :

it's not like a commodity thing anymore ;

(unregulated rhythm, unisono)
[it's like a soul thing]

5. **M, RO**: *(single "horror guitar" downward glissando)*
6. **RI**: You know, am I not supposed to FEEL that?
(overlap with above gliss.*, as if just newly capable of incredulity)*
7. **RO**: *(hiccup)*
8. **ALL**: You can feel anything you want. *(reassuringly, with wee-hours-infomercial-polystyrene-scorpion-like enthusiasm)*

VII.

(smarm tartar redux) (accomp. cf. III. 20)
1. **MI**: Just think of this delicious new
grief resource, a community-based, easy
draw-string courage, available in Fern, Bark,
Butter, and Snow, with notch collar and
cleverly angled underwire abuse memoir for
total uplift. You'll make a –

(system 2 rendered swiftly, as if a series of splices)

(*see below*) (*see above*) (*meaningless filler*)
2. **ALL**: POYSSSHK! / HALLO! / (highhat:)

(*see below*) (*standard boink*)
/ Step into a – / BOINK! /

(fur below) *(standard hiss ; see above)*
free society / ssssssssss
(cresc.)

3. **ALL**: Step into a whole new world, *(cosmogony by invitation only . . . correction, by business reply insert only)*

(accomp. cf. III. 20) (spoken as if an example of advanced product-placement spectroscopy)

4. **MI**: and into this body-hugging, renew-
able, compassion-baste weekend outing of
revolving credit in Chocolate, Hunter, Running
Dog, and Wild-Child Plum.

5. **R&R**: *(below in "Bolero" rhythm, at appropriate tempo, on preceding "Plum"; MI enters at second measure with opening of "Bolero" melody on mouth trombone, suggestive of "Bolero-like," achingly gradual accumulation of sexual tension associated with sartorial "option proliferation")*

PLUM GARNET AND TOAST RUSSET AND INK AND

PLUM GARNET AND SNOW EGGPLANT AND GLACIER AND ALMOND AND

VIII.

1. **ALL**: BAP!
2. **RI**: Here's one for you:
3. **MI**: A free society // is a society in crisis. // *(in voice of birth control filmstrip narration from 50's)*

(for systems 4 & 6, think : "a machine made of words" *on fritz)*
4. **MI**: *(hiccup)* CHUMP! I said –
RI: What the< I sai < CHUMP! *(hiccup)*
RO: I'm sor< CHUMP! I'm sorry –

5. **M, RI**: A free society // is a society in crisis. //

6. **MI**: *(hiccup)* CHUMP! I said –
RI: What the< I sai < CHUMP! *(hiccup)*
RO: I'm sor< CHUMP! I'm sorry –

7. **ALL**: A free society // is –
8. **M, RI**: Ahhh, shaddup – *(cf. "mudflaps," V. 4)*
9. **MI**: Douche bag! *(optional)*

IX.

(**M, RI:** *march rhythm in orally simulated snare drum* ; 1/4 = 112 :
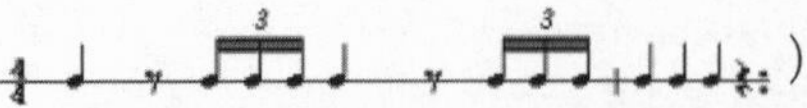
)

1. **RO**: Hey, our right to petition whomever we want whenever we want for a redress of grievances shall not be abridged! *(with offensive, southern "cracker" accent)*

2. **M, RI**: Well, alright then –
3. **ALL**: BAP!
4. **RI**: I want that cocktail that's two parts happy grease to one part immigrant bitters, and with a citrus wedge, *(with reductive, vaguely European accent)*

5. **add MI**: NOW MOVE!

(♩♩♩♩)

(**M, RI:** *continuing, subito piano : move, move, move –* ; 1/4 = 112, *as accomp. to l. 6)*
6. **RO**: I want the chicken leather sandals in dream yellow, size never mind, NOW MOVE! *(as if woman, with stereotypical, make-up counter, Long Island accent)*

(**RO:** *accomp. cf. l. 6)*
7. **M, RI**: I want an M16, the Versace snake skin advent calendar, and a Krafft-Ebing adjustable living bra< *(as if white male, given leave to offer ür white-male birthday wish list)*

8. **RI**: khkh! *(slim, white noise interjective, suggesting a shift of channels, media, etc.)*
9. **RO**: >vo Sierra, this is Eagle Forum. *(with hand cupped over mouth, simulating communication from lunar lander)*
10. **MI**: khkh! *(as above, l. 8)*
11. **RO**: The Foetus has landed. *(as above, l. 9)*
12. **RI**: BUMPH! // *(as of foetus landing)*
13. **ALL**: NOW MOVE, MOVE, MOVE!! (*pointing, à la drill*

sergeant, at supine, newly decidual foetus)
14. **RI**: Hey, watch it, pal . . . *(pointing, à la meretricious legislator, as if at morally decidual constituency)*
15. **ALL**: LIFE IS A GIFT! *(with indignation characteristic of four year old)*
16. **ALL**: So let the prosperity of the few open slowly inside your wretched poverty like a lotus blossom // for this is the flower of the New Covenant. *(presumptuously eucharistic)*
17. **ALL**: POYYSSHHKK! *(strong, gummy, velar fricative suggestive of unholy suction)*

X.

1. **MI**: *(commence a "boombox" groove as accomp. to l. 2, pausing with speaker, surcease at "Debasement.")*
2. **RI**: For the essay portion of the final exam // describe in two words // an entrepeneurial scheme that best exemplifies those root concepts of Trivialization, Debasement, and Commodification of the Human Spirit.

3. **RO**: uuuhh, how about . . . Julia Roberts? *(timidly, as if after seconds of Pascal-esque meditation)*
4. **RI**: TIMBERRR!! *(a cracking of wood may accompany)*
5. **ALL**: BAP!

(the following systems to follow one another mercilessly prestissimo)

*(***M, RI:*** devise and execute insensitive "sweat lodge" groove as accomp. to l. 6)*
6. **RO**: Park reason for being under giant antlers and buckle manhood to ancestral ways, you've got chance with – *(with cheap Sitting Bull accent)*
7. **M, RI**: Bouilliababe! *(non-generic sexist surfer interjective with circumflex contour to final syllable)*
8. **R&R**: DWA DAT! *(abstruse punctive)*
9. **MI**: | Ju< *(pianissimo)*
(follows swiftly upon above, l. 9)
10. **ALL**: Juli< / Julia / Ju< / Julia Ro< / *(in swift succession, as if electronic stutter;* crescendo*)*

RO: **MI:**
11. (Julia Roberts times the velocity of desire) (over the
RI:

square root of the celebrity coefficient) (divided by imbecil-

ALL: *sotto voce* **ALL:**

ity plus) (*strangely equine physiognomy) (all raised to the power of hope equals . . .)

12.**M, RI**: BOUGHT AND PAID FOR! *(fortissimo)*
13.**RI**: *(buzzer, 1-2 seconds)*
(**R&R:** *as acomp. to l. 14, this figure to begin at • , end at "gauge")*

(rendered as if after intense lucubration)
14.**MI**: I've got it, • Julia Roberts is the decision to represent the plastic flamingo's legs with a single, light gauge, metal pole.
15.**M, RI**: BOUGHT AND PAI<
16.**M, RO**: SO RIGHT! *(think Bing Crosby watching Playboy Channel)*

(**M, RO:** *accomp. as above, l. 14, end at "film")*
17.**RI**: No, I've got it, • Julia Roberts is a diacritical mark indicating a vowel gradation of short "i," as in "film," into short "u," as in "sludge."

18.**M, RO**: HO, BOWSER! *(Dick Butkus, delighted and astonished)*
19.**RI**: Mommy, when I gwow up, I wanna BE Juwia Wobuts.
20:**RO**: Alright son, just eat your paint chips. *(optional, but why not?)*
21.**M, RI**: OW, hit me again! *(James Brown, delighted and astonished)*
22.**M, RO**: Hey, Dreamchaser – *(as if addressing one who spends most evenings cataloguing his/her collection of TV Guide commemorative covers)*
23.**RO**: Bumph! *(cf. IX. 9)*
24.**RI**: | ssssssssss
(cresc.)

25.**MI**: | There's a story in that face that no one could paraphrase. *(think, "Who was that annoying masked man, and why are his pants so tight?")*
26.**R&R**: Yea . . . *(unexcitedly, twirling index in gyre of indiffer-*

* "rubber dress" optional substitution

ence)
27. **MI**: shshshshsh
(cresc.)

XI.
(sotto voce, "with Four Quartets*-like portentousness" redux)*
1. **RO**: Nothing but to thresh away all but time
2. **M, RI**: | thresh away all but time . . . *(echo)*

(in earnest, voiced whisper)
3. **ALL**: Old woman comes to us saying there's so little time. //
4. Old woman says here take this she said keep this. //
5. Were we standing on a ladder? //
6. Were the rungs made of water? //
7. Yes old man came to us and said he was laughing he said. //
8. There's so much time there's nothing to hold. //
9. Look you're standing on a ladder of water he was laughing. //
10. He said I see the delicate minutes like lucent pastry leaves collapse in upon the hand of god. //
11. Carving itself into the shape of a grenade. //
12. I see fires rising out of the wells. //
13. There's nothing left to

14. **M, RO**: hold.

15. **RI**: | Hold me. //

16. **add RO**: Hold me. //

17. **add MI**: Hold me. *finis*

Hear this piece at http://www.temple.edu/chain.

LISA JARNOT

from *Promise X: A Memoir*

Sunday December 25, 1999

—Hi dad. Happy Christmas.

—Happy Christmas to you too.

—So what's going on there?

—Nothing, I'm just watching t.v. What are you doing?

—Well, I'm doing a lot of stuff. I'm getting a lot of work done on my book. So that's what I've been doing the last two days.

—When are you going to finish that book?

—I don't know. Maybe I'm almost half way done, so it will take a couple years.

—A couple years from when you started it?

—No. I've already been working on it for a couple years. It will take a couple more years.

—So you're not doing anything there?

—Well, yeah, I'm doing a lot of work.

—What did you get for Christmas?

—I didn't get anything for Christmas.

—I gave your sister a bunch of stuff I got from the bar, I get all these Buffalo Bills things, and I gave her and Kevin these Buffalo Bills hats, and I'm sending your brother a Bills jacket and I got a football that they used in a game, but I got to get someone to sign it, I got to get Andre to sign it, but I ain't seen him around much lately. Everybody's always saying they see him out drinking, but just cuz he's in a bar it don't mean that he's drinking. They're all watching all the time, so they can say some football player is drinking or taking drugs. But I don't think Andre is doing nothing like that. And your sister was here yesterday and I made this lasagna for them, with spinach, and Kevin said it was the best thing he ever had. Cuz there's this woman I know and she's a cook, this Italian lady and she says to me that I should put mint in this lasagna, so that's what I did.

—That's good. That sounds like a good idea.

—Yeah, I don't care about Christmas. It will be tomorrow soon anyway.

—Well, what was Uncle Richie doing today?

—Yeah, he called me last night to go over there, but they were going

to hang out with their neighbors, and I said I ain't going over there to hang out with your neighbors. And they said I could come over today, to go to your cousin Kathy's house with them, but I did that last year and I didn't feel like doing that.
—Where does she live?
—Farnham. And your Uncle Richie and Aunt Doris are all bitching and complaining because she's got that stupid guy around again, and the stupid jerk almost killed her twice, and now he's out of jail and he's hanging around, and he moved back into the neighborhood, and now he's got some new girlfriend who overdosed on drugs the other day. They have these kids, and he comes around to see the kids.
—But if he tried to kill her twice, didn't she go to court about that?
—She ain't gonna take him to court. That ain't how it works with the stupid court anyway. There are all these crazies out there and they just let them out on the street all the time. They don't even keep anybody in jail. They're always letting them out.
—Well, I don't know. It seems like there are a lot of people in prison. It's a big industry. In New York Giuliani has been locking up homeless people, putting them in jail if they don't go to shelters, but then there isn't enough room in the shelters, and then if they don't work they get thrown out of the shelters and then the police can arrest them if they fall asleep on the street.
—Yeah, well what are they going to do? So, what's the solution? Do you have some plan to fix it?
—Well, I think there are a couple things that could happen in New York. Like the city owns a lot of buildings they don't use, and they could come up with more low income housing for people.
—Yeah, but they have to have big places like leper colonies for those people, is that what you're saying?
—No. That's not what I'm saying.
—We're talking about two different things. Because I'm talking about these people who are psychopathic. Like that psychopathic crazy who killed that woman on the subway.
—Yeah, but that guy's really sick. He needs help.
—They said he had help. So why didn't it do any good? They come up with all these different titles for what these people have, like they have all these names for something that's wrong with them and they're manic depressive, and this and that.
—I feel sorry for that guy. I mean that happens to people sometimes. He couldn't help it. I don't know, I mean I can kind of understand it. People feel like that sometimes, like they want to kill someone, but most people don't do it. That guy on the subway was just sick and he

couldn't help it. He didn't know what he was doing.
—Well I don't know anyone who ever felt like they wanted to kill someone.
—I think I feel that way sometimes.
—I ain't never felt that way, and I don't know anyone who has. It's because of the way I grew up. If you grow up a certain way it's different. I have morals, so I wouldn't feel that way. I might feel mad or something, but I would never feel like I wanted to kill someone. I talk to a lot of people and I don't know anyone like that.
—I ask my students about that sometimes and they always say the same thing, but then they can all remember some time when they wanted to kill someone. I mean that's just part of having emotions. People are animals. We're these organic forms and we're animals and we have instincts like that.
—What are you talking about, organic?
—Carbon-based life forms.
—Organic is like when they have those vegetables at the supermarket.
—That's not what I mean.
—Well I've never felt like I wanted to kill anyone, and then they've got all this bullshit about terrorists on t.v. There ain't going to be no terrorists.
—Well, I don't know. I'm kind of surprised that there hasn't been more stuff like that happening here. We go all over the world and bomb people, it only makes sense for people to get back at us. And in other countries that happens all the time. It's just like that.
—You know, there aren't going to be any terrorists blowing up people. They want to blow up military targets. New York ain't no risk for terrorists, there ain't never been a bombing in New York.
—Well, there was the World Trade Center bombing.
—They ain't going to blow up people, you know what the biggest risk is? The city they're going to blow up is Buffalo.
—Because of Niagara Falls?
—That's right. Because they'll knock out all the electricity on the east coast. I know all about that. I knew all about that when I was working. They don't target people, they target electric and military bases.
—Well, I always figured that would be a good way to scare people, blowing up people.
—They don't do that. I went to Fort Erie with one of my buddies the other day and they've got that border all screwed up.
—Yeah, I read about that in the *New York Times*.
—And we were coming back over the border and we had this whiskey in the trunk, and I told him they were going to pull us over, cuz they

got that whole border backed up, and I told him not to lie because they were going to pull us over anyway, so then they come and ask us if we got anything and before my buddy can say anything I say yeah, we got some whiskey in the trunk, and they say you know you can't do that, and they made us go and stand in line at some window and pay a duty on it and I see one of my buddies is working there and he says to me "hey Joe, how you doing?," and then they let us through anyway.
—That's nice.
—Yeah, but what the hell are they doing wasting time charging you for two bottles of whiskey when they're looking for terrorists? It don't make no sense, paying some duty on two bottles of whiskey. They don't need to do that.
—Yeah, I don't know.
—So I'm just watching t.v. and I'm going to make some dinner.
—Okay.
—I'll talk to you.
—Okay. I'll talk to you soon.

Tuesday December 14, 1999
Theodore tells me to come in but he says he's going to go out and smoke for a minute because he's been on the phone for an hour and a half. He hands me a piece of paper. It's a quote from Faulkner that he wrote out for me. "Memory believes before knowing remembers. Believes longer than recollects, longer than knowing ever wonders." I look around at Theodore's books while he's gone. He comes back and I say that it's a good quote. I'm feeling happy to have a piece of paper with his handwriting on it but I don't tell him that. I ask him what's going on. He goes to the window behind me and closes it or opens it, and then he sits back down. I say that not much is happening with me. I say that I went out with Darrell last night to Gerald's bar. Theodore wants to know how Gerald was. I say that Gerald told us a story about his new house in Pennsylvania and how he shot all the cats. I say "He told us the story in graphic detail." Theodore says "That's really not a good story." I say I know. Theodore says "Couldn't he have called the ASPCA or something?" I say "Yeah, but he said they were wild cats." Theodore is displeased.

I say "I had a dream the other night, two nights ago, that Malcolm X was my father." Theodore says "Is there more to it than that?" I say "Yeah, kind of." Theodore says "I have a story about Malcolm X." I say "Yeah, the story about your friend who shot someone?" Theodore says "You've heard that story?" I say "Yeah. Tell me the story." He says "You tell me the dream and then I'll tell you the story." I say "Well, Malcolm

X was my father and he seemed like a really nice person." Theodore says "So when was that? That was Sunday night?" I say Yeah. I say I was on a bus and I was sitting next to a guy, a guy my age and we started talking and he invited me to go out for dinner and I was thinking about how great it was that I could meet people so easily, and at this point in the dream I was actually thinking more of Theodore than of Malcolm X because I thought I could tell Theodore that I'd met this guy on the bus and it was easy enough for me to do that. Theodore says "Ahuh." I say "And then I got to the guy's house and I realized I had to go home because Malcolm X would be worried about me, because people were always out to get him and I had just disappeared. And then I tried to call him but I couldn't remember the number, and it was changed because of the FBI surveillance and I figured I didn't want to get this new boyfriend involved in the intrigue, but I wanted to be with him, so I'd bring him home with me." I say "But then I got worried because this guy was white and I didn't think I could bring him home. But then it worked out okay, and Malcolm X was nice." Theodore says "What's your association with Malcolm X?" I say "I don't know. I hadn't thought about it really." Theodore says "What's his significance for you? How would you describe him?" I say "Well he was a good person in the dream, very charismatic and kind." I say "I figure that Malcolm X was pretty much like that anyway." I say that I'm just skimming the surface of the dream. I don't know exactly what else is there.

Theodore says "I have a story about Malcolm X that actually dovetails with your dream." I say "Did you meet him?" Theodore says "Yeah. I did." I say "That's really great that you met Malcolm X. What was he like?" Theodore says "I'll never forget his face—that smile on his face." Theodore starts to tell me the story about his friend who killed someone. I say "Yeah, I know that story." He says "You do know the story?" I say "I only know the part about your friend killing someone. Who did he kill?" Theodore tells me but I forget again. Theodore tells me about how he and his friend wanted to bring their students from the Freedom School in Macomb to meet Malcolm X in New York for Christmas. Theodore says "We talked to a woman who worked for Malcolm X and she told us that Malcolm X said he wouldn't meet with the white Civil Rights workers. And then the kids from McComb said they wouldn't meet with Malcolm X if we couldn't be there too." Theodore says it was 1964 and there was already some tension in the movement about stuff like that. Theodore says "So if I told you this story, then that contributed to the dream." I say "No, because you didn't tell me that part of the story about meeting

Malcolm X. You just told me about your crazy friend and how he killed someone. Because I said I was going to shoot myself and you said I should shoot you instead." Now I remember that it was because I said I wanted to shoot people at the Poetry Project. Theodore says he can't remember why he would have told me that story about his friend. I say "Maybe it's because I said I was hearing voices." Theodore says maybe that's it. I say "But you didn't tell me about Malcolm X, you just mentioned that your friend went crazy, but he had also done these great things with these kids." Theodore tells me the rest of the story, about how they got to the Hotel Theresa and they went to talk to Malcolm X and left the kids outside and he says he remembers it very well, asking Malcolm X about what would happen on that day, because they had heard that he didn't want to meet with them because they were white and Malcolm X smiled at him and said "I didn't say that. You're completely welcome here." Theodore says that the woman who worked for Malcolm X had lied to them. I say "That's so cool that you met Malcolm X." Theodore says "But how would you describe him in the dream?" I say "I get the feeling he had a lot of integrity." I say "I mean I'm a pacifist and everything, but that's never bothered me about Malcolm X. I've always figured he knew what he was doing." Theodore says "It was pretty clear that he was also going through a great transformation, that he was coming to a path where he could really envision another solution—that he was on the road to becoming a great peacemaker." I say "I know. That's why they killed him, don't you think?" Theodore says "Yeah. I do think that."

REYNALDO JIMÉNEZ & JUSSARA SALAZAR

Unlimits

JIMÉNEZ Jussara, I was telling you just a while ago about that reference in a paragraph by Guy Davenport, thanks to which I felt the calling of affinity, or a very precise urge, in relation to certain coincidences that one does not need to explain. The paragraph transcribes an inscription where Ramses II calls himself "I am User-ma-Ra, ruler of rulers, king of the Upper and Lower Egypt, He of the Sedge and Bee, the mighty justice of Ra, the chosen of Ra." In contrast to the pomposity which is typical of those powerful on earth—it's not accidental that Davenport's essay deals with the poetics of what remains after entropy engulfs power—I was surprised by the phrase, which you probably also noticed immediately: "He of the Sedge and Bee" . . . A while ago you had suggested a dialogue about microworlds, the faceted space of the interstice, and it seemed appropriate to me to begin with this Egyptian reference . . .

SALAZAR Reynaldo, image among images, magical vision of microworlds, subterranean voices, everything we don't hear, the infinite vision of nature, would that all not be what gives us this feeling of affinity and urgency? The word emerges and reaches the "unlimits," in that subtle and decanted reflection of the spirit on the microvision of nature. The inscription with the words of Ramses II is very interesting, the lord of everything, also claims to be the lord of nothing, in an almost mythical rhetoric of power. Ra, the chosen of Ra, speaks and names the universe that is possible, to the ends of his "vision." Lifting of the word, in this case, based on a meditation on the limits of a power conceived in his imagination.

J Unlimits, of course, is what the world needs. It would be a possible means of healing: to venture beyond a certain border that links perception to the ability to perceive. Such a world, ruled by the anthropocentric measure, is the cause of an idea delimited (by the facts) of fate. On the other hand, attentively tuning into the microsea of syllables that Perlongher talked about, can intensify the meaning of the poet's task, or at least can take the maker seriously, he or she who writes and the role played in the transformation of things, of the world. To stop the world, in the semantic fabric as in the instantaneous perception of the reader: a possibility that excites me. And, anyway, perceptible transformation can only prowl around, in principle, the very excitement of the incantator, of the transmitter of incantation . . .

S Yes, the trade of poetry, with its power of transformation, of becoming fish, water, the perfume that emanates from the depths of the earth and incorporating the spirit of the forest, following the course of the river, which is like walking while moving clouds out of the way, remembering Lezama Lima. The transmitter of incantation is enchanted and deems the time perfect and endless in its structure. The idea of a possible cure is of a rare beauty, the rite of passage through the borders, where the word dissolves into another word which is not the same, word of word. In the infinite exercise of perception, writing takes over the body of time, that ancient tree, our mother and the axis of a generosity that emanates as an illuminated and encompassing halo over things, the return to the idea of an open destiny and in motion, "the kingdom of rushes and bees."

J Precisely! The incantator should be the enchanted one. Incantation demands the surrender of energy to the attraction of enchantment. On the contrary, the trade that implies transmission would not be dignified. That becoming another—but the Other as the Great Unkown, not as an isolated particle of El Dorado to be conquered or subjected—seems to be an artistic quality that begins to be remembered by a few poets. Especially among those that dare, according to what you point out, to transform the crossing of borders into a rite of passage. It is not merely a play on words: to trespass the demarcating wire fence, that represents the separatist base of power and its feudal spirit, to recover, even in the unpremeditated, other consistencies of the rite (in the associative rhythm of this dialogue, for example, that seeks a shared breath). The rite, as I see it, as what makes possible certain unanimity between being and its states. The rite confers belonging, which is not the separatist identity, but the reverse, always of any fixity of a subject vis-à-vis the world. And this also connects with your question, since I take destiny to be origin. And that we necessarily head towards the origin: towards the unknown. Our common ancestor Enigma, sustainer and devourer, is asking us artists, in these times of transition, to heed that archaic calling . . . that holoperception that we recognize ourselves participants of—that is: earthlings. Therefore, it seems to me that all art made from art is worn out, from what has been found and classified (and in this I include the alleged transgressions of art). It seems imperative, at least, to take into account the possibility that art may again serve a purpose, that it may still be useful, as a true craft. Otherwise, we are decorating museums and libraries, accumulating dust where the soul should be elevated or burn. Not long ago, I heard Huston Smith say in a documentary on TV that in India traditional art has become a true *spiritual technology*. This can be interpreted in the sense that poetry, to take the closest example, may reacquire very precise strategic goals. Poetry for childbirth, for departures, for death or for the dead, for play and work, for encounters, for joy, for the night, to communicate with animals and plants, so that our ancestors may live in us, to shorten distances, to invoke food, to dance, to continue listening, to celebrate beauty or diminish fear.

S There is a lot of beauty and poetry in what you say, and it's not by accident that today I came across a text by Italo Calvino regarding the visibility and visual imagination, defined by an expression that seemed to me very significant, *Spiritual Exercises*, i.e., not to separate the domain of knowledge into two parts, leaving science to the external world and isolating imaginative knowledge in the individual's interior, because according to him, " the mind of the poet, as well as the spirit of the scientist, in certain decisive moments, work according to a process of association of images, which is the fastest way of coordinating and choosing among the infinite forms of the possible and the impossible" and he even quotes Giordano Bruno, for whom the spiritus phantasticus is mundus quidem et sinus inexplebilis formarum et specierum, the perceiving spirit as a "world or receptacle, never full, of forms and images." I believe that that exhaustion of the processes of creation originate from what you point out regarding the split of a spiritual identity vis-à-vis a world blasted and shattered through recycled images. All of that leads us to a reflection on the need to return to the "archaic calling" that unfolds in the infinite vortices of a vision that reinstates us tirelessly and which disorganizes, declassifies, principles, amplifies, imagines, unoccurs, essentializes. To designate reality, Buddhism uses the term sunya, the void, who knows if in the extreme paradox there would be a way to call forth incantation, gold . . .

J And in the naming of the extreme paradox, I would like, now, to introduce the reader; the reader, not just as a topic or an intellectual worry, but as a decisive presence, one which makes possible the *existence* of poetry. In some way, making it possible for poetry to be in a position to change something. Of course that that change can only occur in intimacy, and, from there on, become the acknowledgement of reciprocity. Regarding this dialogue among readers of what we have been saying, two allusions come to mind. One (Mallarmé?), would argue for faith in a reader who would in turn be an artist. That is, reading as an art in itself—and from here a possible ramification: poetry as the art of reading . . . reading as seeing through and even as refutation . . . . The other allusion would be a phrase by Octavio Paz that I also read this afternoon and which is relevant here: "Open or closed, the poem demands the abolition of the poet who writes it and the birth of the poet who reads." What does this suggest to you?

S I think it's particularly pertinent, and indeed disquieting, it reunites the one who begins and the one who follows, where does all end? Mirror, fable by two, three, four or infinite eyes, water of the word floating over surfaces and spaces waiting, the minimal word, the word of entrails, the bird word, the rough, rain, words. The ancient memory, cities, ants, and that river, or the trees and indeed the birds, breathing and exile, the crow over the fruit, the lace one makes, white birches, blood, the wolf and fire. The thick word, the beautiful word, the forest, journey through chaos, vessel of men, dream that night drinks, presage, shell of time, and vision. Edge, penetrating the light that blinds, encaustic, fertile womb. Song, sphinx, soul, saga, sing of sun, stone of lead. Blue lenses and the sea and even the black mud, the hand, the eye and the nerve, silver, the pomegranate, oil lamp. A dive and the word dark, the word of the Indian, bromelia, rose, and love. Purple star, infinite field of the world, insignia, net, cross of roses, dawn, and moon. And still, spider that weaves the earth, the blade of the knife, a hushed noise. Ivy, and gold, the grass that spreads, a breeze, all and flesh, music and miracle, mystery and dance. An animal in the morning, primrose, heat and fish, glimpse of a freedom, and the air of the tropics made word, opens then. Journey, the word leaps in this way, resonant destiny and origin, clarity and body, another one and we are. (*work in progress)* . . .

J Yes. The beings and pulsating forces of Gaea constitute the Great Ear, the Goddess's mighty attention. That is to say that incantation, when speaking in the sense of the archaic calling, would be to converse, in reality, both with what is human, as well as with what is not. To sing for that stone that we encounter. In Haidakhan, in the Indian Himalayas, still forested and with out a speck of civilization, near the border with Nepal, Gabriela and I were told that the countless stones that formed the bed of the sacred river were the souls of the ones that had transcended the samsara, the birth-death-reincarnation chain. Yes, at least for a certain period, you could suspend judgment, the constant situation of interrogative and critical conflict of things, and simply abandon yourself to the possibility of things being that way—that stones may indeed be the shadow or the echo of souls—, you could swim in that mountainous river in another way. The translucent quality of the river was inhabited by the gaze itself, and it was impossible not to smile and tremble at the same time. (Without counting the families of monkeys, of the army of Hanuman, sustainer of grammar, who fiercely enjoyed themselves by throwing an increasing number of stones at us from the top of a rugged hill, Mount Kailas, considered the earthly abode of Shiva). What was before merely a fact (of relief, joy, certainly, but not more) was ritualized, and bathing there meant to be healed from many ills. In some way, then, that primitive religion—which the Indians there call Sanatam Dharma or the old road or the primordial way, as I interpret it (that is, it would not be a religion as we are able to understand it from the European scar)—which worships elements reestablishes, without forgetting Heraclitus, a link with life. With life beyond identity, beyond a cloistering in the "I." And beyond (or close by: in Girondo's masmédula) of anthropocentrism, which we must urgently revise, but which, for some reason (perceptual domestication?) our culture is not even able to focus on. Perhaps to meditate on language is nothing more than to be absorbed in that river: each word floating spirit, transubstantiator of energies belonging to all and, ultimately, to no one. (And, in an equally primeval way, the part about the name containing the qualities and even the essence of what is named).

S Recent experiments, in what concerns language and creation, in a way do away with the distancing and are indeed true oases of light. I am thinking now of Joseph Beuys and his ideas on *social architecture* in art, religio (reconnection), where the word "religion" comes from, understood as an attitude of return to knowledge, to the rebuilding of vital links, to primordial knowledge. The river in motion, the flux of words, the link with life, the ancient sovereignty of the I (Nietzsche), where the real is substance and language reveals more than a functional mechanism, a spiritual energy.

J Precisely, the expansion of the concept of art, where "every person is an artist," in Beuys's views and his actions related to the figure of the shaman (connector of energies, and therefore transformer of realities: even Christ as a shaman) added to the image of the *nomads of Nietzsche*, as Beuys himself stated, is one of the star points for these resplendent revisions. It must be underscored, even if it seems obvious, that Beuys does not say: "every person should be an artist"—but rather he assumes it, pointing only to the freedom to assume that capacity, of taking that ambiguous force by the horns, within the possibilities of each individual. That expanded concept of art would not be only the known practices, but it would encompass being and participating attentively, without the need of cumulative results.

In any event, I feel that the majority of artists (including the poets), rather than showing disregard for uses and abuses, have embarked instead into a cynical exploitation of socioeconomic structures, trying to stay on a column plinth as a safe niche, in some state or degree of life that would allow (as in the old Kingdom of Aragon), above all, to maintain a certain sovereignty, which results in an excessive accumulation of meaningless objects. And there is violence in this. It is a violence founded in the interference of the ego, precisely, which acts as a stoppage of energy (necessarily anonymous, and which remains momentarily fixed in the construction of the character-artist) through the fixing of personalities and the constant manipulation of mere effects, (for instance, the pathetic *hit* of the sawed cows preserved in formaldehyde by British artist Damien Hirst, and other appropriations of alienation in favor of personal figuration. All this regardless of the price, and without considering even for a split second, the spiritual consequences that any act—particularly a public one—entails).

And here is the question: is it that we are being devoured by effects? I don't think so. Or at least I think that it is necessary to take on optimism, in the sense of getting a glimpse of new attitudes in favor of that understanding of language as substance, which you mentioned. (Although this has been happening, anyway, very slowly in relationship to the urgent need for change at all levels of society.) And Beuys's idea—each one is, in him or herself—tends to dethrone the traditional artist the owner of a sector of power. Which, logically if seen from the point of view of those who support them, few artists care to even take into account. It is that reluctance to lose the alleged privileges of specialization, of the excessive partiality of power, which makes artists extremely conventional, regardless of what kind of transgressive or "cult" clothes they might wear, in the struggle against this emerging consciousness. Always a precarious struggle, but a continuous one, by necessity: because this consciousness is the body.

There is the case of the Peruvian Jorge Eduardo Eielson, a parallel to Joseph Beuys in his efforts to expand the concept of art. This Peruvian, a poet from the start, but who has gone through a visual poetry phase—simultaneous to Brazilian concretism, but with less publicity—to the knots (quipus of Inca writing), sound experiments, performance and installation, the essay and the combinatory action. (I can mention for example, his *Esculturas para ser desenterradas* [*Sculptures to Be Unearthed*] on September 16, 1969, which consisted in impossible constructions that Eielson had clandestinely buried in public places—parks, avenues in cities he visited during his trips—and which had to be dug up at the same time. A sign of common planetary ownership: in each place there was a different text in the local language, printed on a transparency of a different color, and all the projects, superimposed, were part of a palimpsest-book which confounded all lead roles: Scultura di marmo con fuoco interno, Sculpture lumineuse, Time sculpture, Skulptur mit comprimierter Stimme, Escultura horripilante . . .). Eielson also has not ceased to thrive on all influences, in an arch that extends from his early knowledge of pre-Columbian textiles, to his love for animals or the study of scientific thought, to his involvement with zen.

I would like to share with you a paragraph of his, describing the 1993-1998 installation *La última cena* [*The Last Supper*]: "In daily life we think of light and shadow as opposites and our own life appears oriented towards light, influenced as we are by the old rhetoric of good and evil. But in other cultures—in Oriental cultures, for instance—the borders of the mind, in the widest sense of the term, admirably coincide with that double nature of reality, made of shadows and light. In this extremity, which almost always escapes our perception, in this last limit of spiritual attention, is where the mystery of vision resides."

S It is very beautiful and appropriate, in relation to the "old rhetoric of good and evil," to return here to a previous question, the one dealing with the unity of being and of state, overcoming the old and bad Manichaean habit of body versus soul, making possible a third field, eros and logos in conciliation, where the mystery perhaps resides in the subtle encounter of light and shadow, in that instant when night plots day. When the words of the tribe are purified (Mallarmé), when we approach our perception in that sense, we exercise a sort of affective tautology, uttering many words that had been buried throughout time, lost in the layers of our intuition and sensibility.

J Yes, but notice that the "tribe" doesn't recognize itself anymore. Few people recognize themselves in that reborn word, that word of intuition. Intuition has been scorned so often, that the poets themselves seem to feel embarrassed by terms such as "sensibility" or they reject that purifying or curative action implicit in their task. I believe poets have slowly confined themselves to aestheticizing or hyperartistic specialization, in a one-dimensional way, the situations deriving from holding a certain knowledge-power, which, as such, delimits and excludes. Don't you think, Jussara, that language itself, has long ago—in terms of "humanity"—become the central code? And that this complex condition, precisely, would be the great obstacle or the great trigger—depending on how one looks at it—for the encounter with those other words in the words themselves?

S The tribe has abandoned, yes, certain essential practices in its understanding of language, be it in terms of creation, or in the articulations of the word as manifestation beyond communication, that is, the word with its original charm, the word as a practice not divorced from doing. Sensibility, intuition, emotion, the linking to the sublime, all give rise to a kind of formal pragmatism of the word, exclusionary, as you point out, and reductionist. Barthes, in his *Camera Lucida,* discusses the role of the gaze facing the image of a photograph, proclaiming the abandonment of all knowledge inherited through cultural codes. *"I am a savage, a child—or a madman"* . . . to cast desire beyond that which it reveals . . . not only for the ghost of a practice, more for the absolute excellence of a being, body and soul entwined. I also question some people who self-appoint themselves as "shamans" of our time, repeating that appropriation of the knowledge-realm, alienating and timely. The other day I saw documents about a primitive tribe, the Kingdom of Goa, I think in Indonesia, where they believe that beings all share a single idea of soul, and that the form, that is, being born as a lizard, human or water, are simply different choices made by the sacred divinities, and thus every word is elevated to a vast and generous code of possibilities and beauty, perhaps that encounter of words with words themselves. . . .

J And that common spirit, Tao, that source of life, shared presence, is transpersonal, right? And that it necessarily demands an offer, a gift or—to say it in drastic terms—a sacrifice (penance, in English, which would imply a willing sacrificial offering). In this pilgrimage one has to leave a bit of one's own skin, to surrender to the greater will of the path or the route. It's the itinerary of the mystics' souls, but also the process of individuation noted by Jung. And in relation to that I always return to this paradoxical feeling: only through the pure intention of individuation, can one break free from the exclusionary gravitation towards the ego, in terms of self-centering, so that the common spirit may manifest itself and flow. In other words: the search for one's own spiritual axis opens us to the transpersonal, to a "permanent center of gravity" which does not lie in the fixity of one's own character as owner of some domain.

With respect to all this, I'd like to ask you something, since you pass through both the media of the written word as well as visual art, and given what we've been saying so far, I believe that you are in one of those personal situations where the poetic may be open to other relations: How do you experience, in relation to your work, that joining of media in reciprocal directions? Could you talk a bit about that?

S It is simple, as you've now reminded us; Tao, the way, the universal principle, harmony. Language reveals itself as an asset to be explored, and we translate in this or that way the understanding of one. I believe that that change in reciprocal directions happens as a vital exercise, which originates from the basis of being, where images are stuck to words in a massive and very old block, which the poet reorganizes, giving it a body. Images generate words which generate images in a chain where author and viewer create a story that is the story of one and all. If it produces a poem or a drawing, it is a mirroring of reality, infinitely rich in symbols, in signs, teeming with organic matter. And regarding Jung still, I remember a passage from a text about the spirit of the poet, where he affirms having had the creative attitude of an essentially feminine nature, because creation emerges from the depths of the soul, lunar and generous. And since we were speaking about the common spirit, I think that the various languages also share that aspect of the *transpersonal*. To sacrifice? It means to make holy, sacred, in the origin of the word.

J And once again, we go back to the interstices.

Translated by Odile Cisneros.

M. KASPER

Re-Search

RESEARCHER *approaches the Library Reference Desk:* You busy?
LIBRARIAN: Um, nothing I can't interrupt.

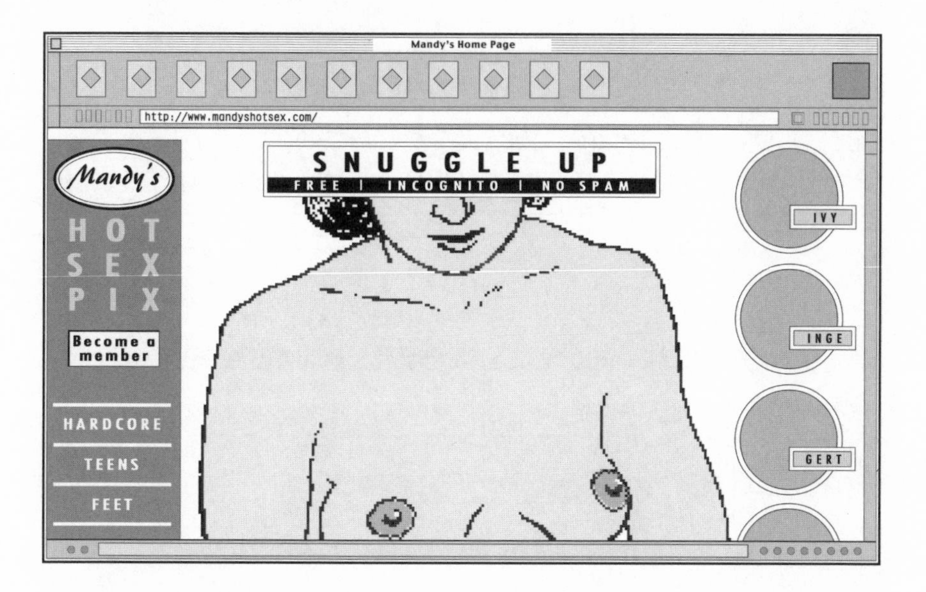

RESEARCHER: I have a kind of stupid question.
LIBRARIAN: Ask away. We're paid to be tolerant.
RESEARCHER: Ok, I've been trying to find material on the relationship between information and knowledge.
LIBRARIAN: Hm . . . you may need to narrow that. Like, from what standpoint? Popular culture? Philosophy? Communications?
RESEARCHER: I'm not sure yet, but I'll know when I find it.
LIBRARIAN: What have you found so far?
RESEARCHER: Not much. I started with dictionaries, encyclopedias, but they're contradictory. Can you suggest online sources?
LIBRARIAN: Sure, if you want. Try a natural-language search engine like "knowitall-dot-com." But come back if it doesn't help.

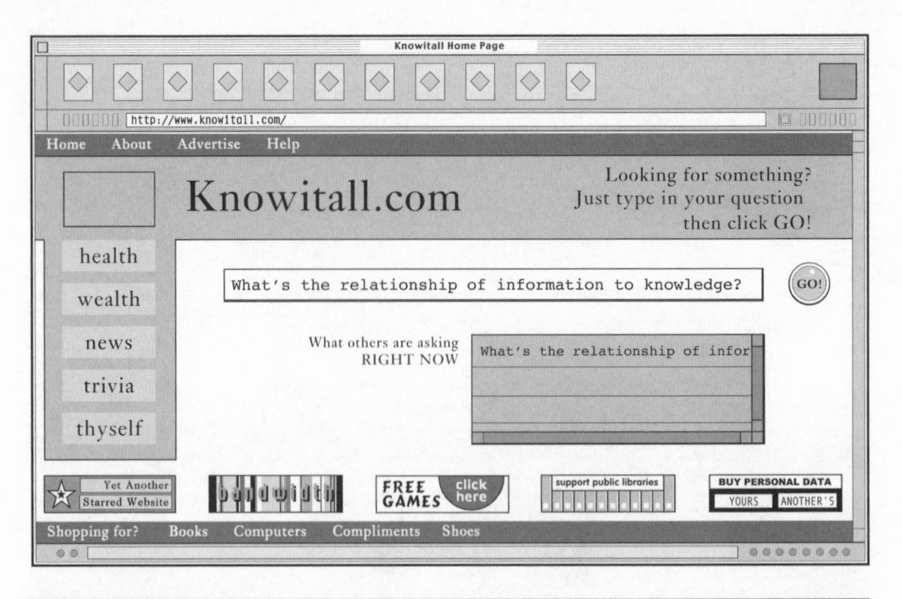

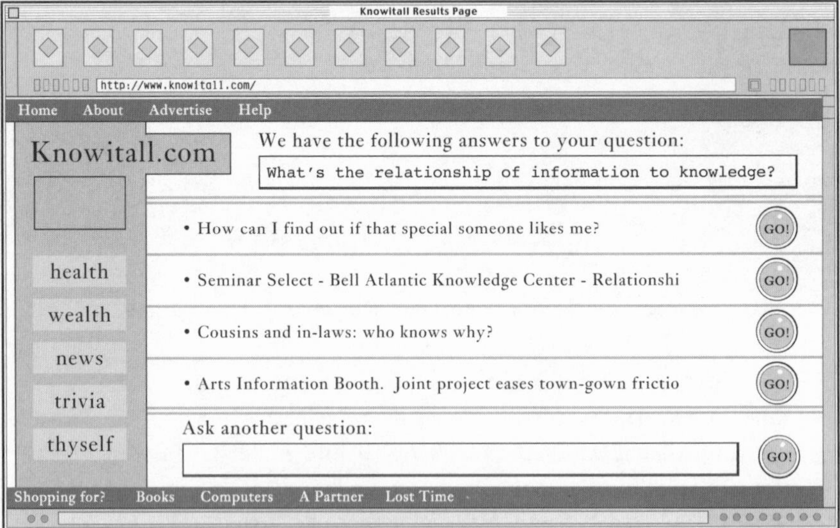

RESEARCHER: Yikes!

returns to Reference Desk: You busy?

LIBRARIAN: How'd it go with "knowitall"?

RESEARCHER: Not so well.

LIBRARIAN: I was afraid of that. Keywords with multiple meanings *(shakes head)*, they're trouble . . .

RESEARCHER: How about online newspapers? When we were painting the den, my partner said newspapers cover everything.

LIBRARIAN: "The den?" . . . Well, anyway, we subscribe to "Deadline," lots of papers, searchable and full-text. Here, I'll show you how to tie words together with proximity operators.

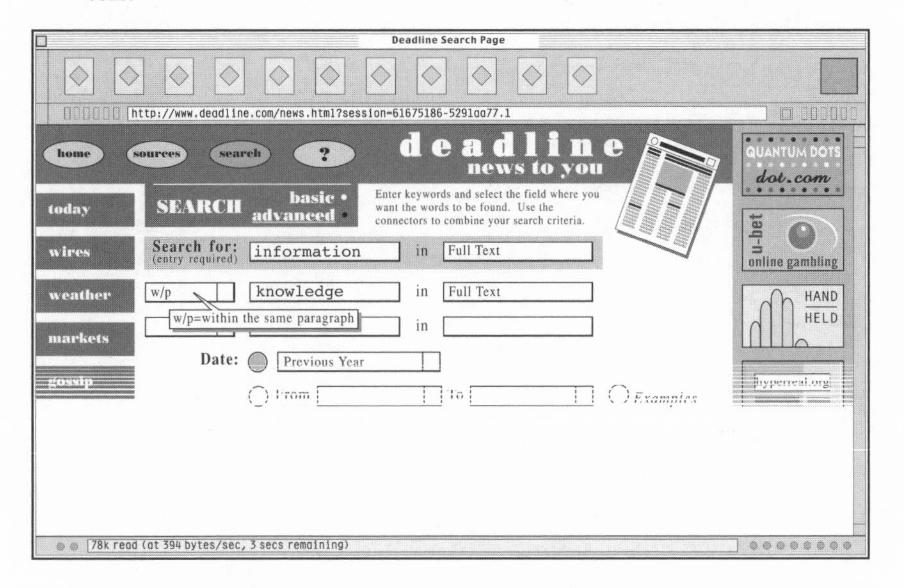

LIBRARIAN: While we're waiting for the page to load, y'know, I'd suggest you also try dictionaries and encyclopedias again, because definitions and synonyms are crucial for relevant results.
RESEARCHER: But there are so many different definitions.
LIBRARIAN: But maybe that means you need to focus.
RESEARCHER: How dare you?!
LIBRARIAN: It's difficult, but part of the job.
RESEARCHER: So you do this to everyone who approaches your desk?
LIBRARIAN: People think we're here to provide answers *(shakes head)*.
RESEARCHER: So you're saying I have to ask my question in your terms?
LIBRARIAN: Not necessarily, and they're not so much "my" terms as commonly acknowledged ones, but yes, it's a useful tactic.
RESEARCHER: What if all I want is *some* result, good enough, but not necessarily the best?
LIBRARIAN: *(shakes head)* You and lots of others, we've noticed.
RESEARCHER: Look! Results . . .

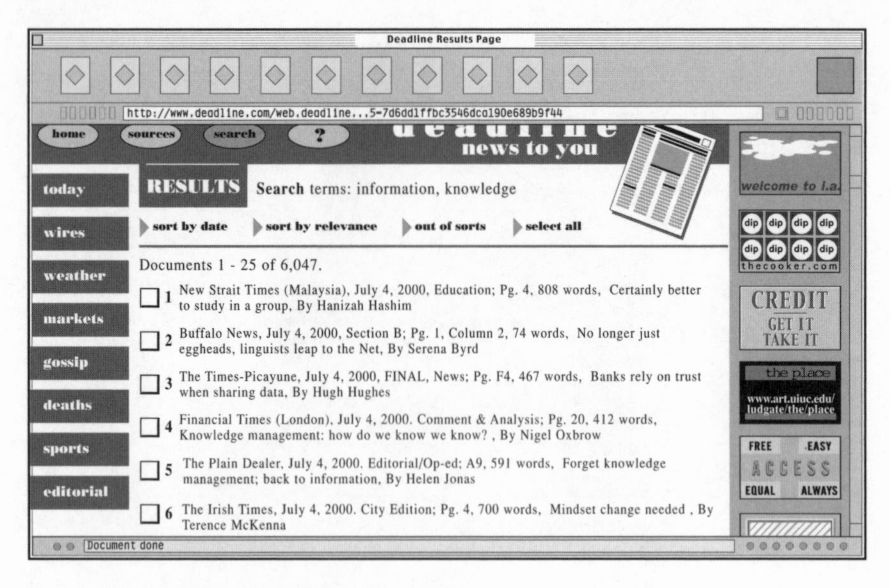

Researcher: Six thousand articles!
Librarian: You could browse a few.
Researcher: It's like I'm driving in a strange place, with arcane traffic laws, sadistic cops.
Librarian: You think the difficulties are intentional?
Researcher: Intentional or not, the effect's the same.
Librarian: Well, I'm no cop. Nor are computers law-abiding.
Researcher: Though they should be helpful for solving this sort of research problem.
Librarian: Maybe this problem isn't a scientific one, but a muddle felt as a problem, as Wittgenstein said.
Researcher: I can't go on.
Librarian: Look, it's called research because you search, then do it again. It's tedious sometimes.
Researcher: But sometimes not?
Librarian: It ends in erudition. They say that's a beautiful country.
Researcher: So you think I should go on?
Librarian: I think that's for you to know.
Researcher: But I don't.
Librarian: With more information you might.
Researcher: I know your job depends on promoting it, but maybe more and more information doesn't add up to knowledge.
Librarian: If that's your angle, let's try a philosophy site . . .
Researcher: Yikes!

LIBRARIAN: . . . trust me, an academic site, where content also tends to be better selected and organized. Here's "Xenophanes," a limited-area search engine with full-text links.

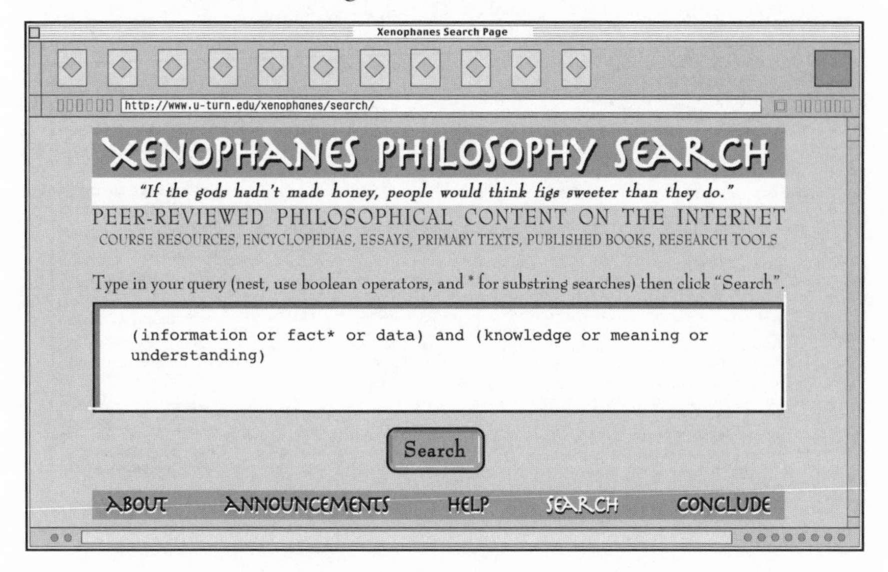

RESEARCHER: This could be interesting.
LIBRARIAN: Look at the next page.
RESEARCHER: Some of these look good!

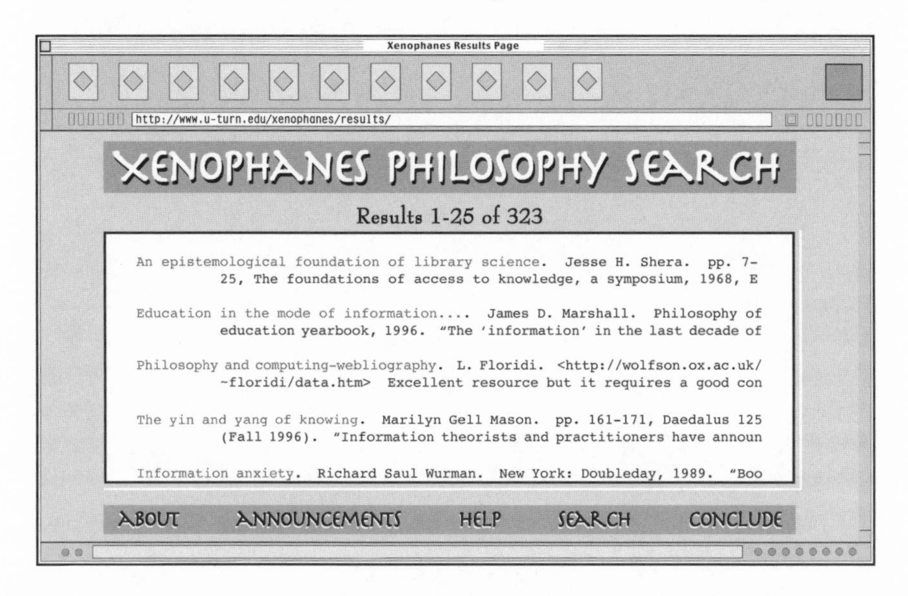

LIBRARIAN: To help judge quality, try to identify each site's sponsor.

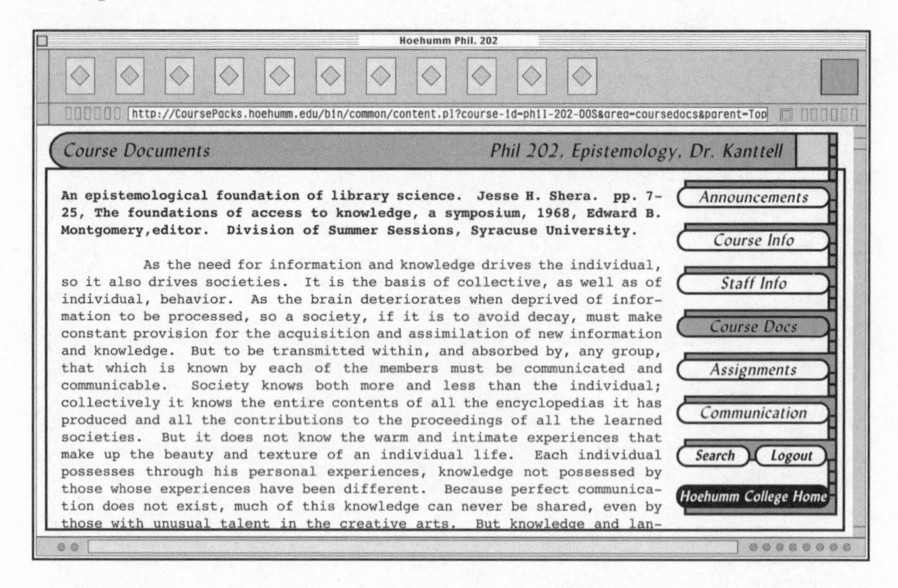

An epistemological foundation of library science. Jesse H. Shera. pp. 7-25, The foundations of access to knowledge, a symposium, 1968, Edward B. Montgomery,editor. Division of Summer Sessions, Syracuse University.

As the need for information and knowledge drives the individual, so it also drives societies. It is the basis of collective, as well as of individual, behavior. As the brain deteriorates when deprived of information to be processed, so a society, if it is to avoid decay, must make constant provision for the acquisition and assimilation of new information and knowledge. But to be transmitted within, and absorbed by, any group, that which is known by each of the members must be communicated and communicable. Society knows both more and less than the individual; collectively it knows the entire contents of all the encyclopedias it has produced and all the contributions to the proceedings of all the learned societies. But it does not know the warm and intimate experiences that make up the beauty and texture of an individual life. Each individual possesses through his personal experiences, knowledge not possessed by those whose experiences have been different. Because perfect communication does not exist, much of this knowledge can never be shared, even by those with unusual talent in the creative arts. But knowledge and lan-

RESEARCHER: Thanks for your patience. I'll take it from here.
LIBRARIAN: We're paid to be patient. Good luck.
RESEARCHER: Not paid much, I don't doubt.
Librarian shakes head.

JOHN KINSELLA & MCKENZIE WARK

Landfill

Date: 28/09/99. Place: British Airways aircraft, flying between London and Toulouse.

KINSELLA . . . There was actually a rubbish tip there and they went in and "reclaimed" the ground—reclamation and reoccupation are two quite different things! It's worth noting that they also reclaimed sections of the Swan River to build the Kwinana Freeway, which I find darkly amusing because it's the Perth tourism trade's number one asset (closely followed by King's Park). They filled it in to develop other aspects of Perth . . . using landfill, of course. A paradoxical act in the eyes of the local balance of payments, maybe. And two things are interesting . . . where the landfill comes from and how they reclaim an area in the first place.

WARK It's characteristic of human activity particularly in the New World. You dig a hole and then you fill the hole in from somewhere else. You notice it in my part of the east coast in the freeway (that used to be the tollway) between Newcastle and Sydney. This huge gash is gauged through hills, the rubble from which of course you then use to fill in the valleys so that the roads create this whole new, this geological feature that is 100 miles long and much the same level from one end to the other. This smoothness is a great characteristic of New World topography. A smooth straight line connecting property to property.

K So what you do is you strategically locate your places of extraction. For example, take the Daweswood Cut, an engineering "feat" in Western Australia near the "tourist town" of Mandurah, where they cut a channel between the ocean and the Peel Inlet so they could flush it out because it used to get algae-ridden in the summer, making the area fresh and wonderful and consequently more attractive to residents, investors, commercial enterprises utilising the resources of the inlet. The cut is quite massive, and as a consequence a massive amount of landfill was extracted—stone, soil, etc. One might assume that they took that extracted material to other places for building purposes. So, if they plan wisely, they can turn the whole loss/gain thing into a true profit-making capitalist enterprise. But lack of planning leads to unwanted holes and too many piles.

W Yeah I'm thinking this loss/gain thing even transcends the space of the continent. I remember as a teenager growing up in this house where there were these quite distinctive stones that were the walls around the edge. And they were a very, very dark blue stone. Newcastle is mostly sandstone, so this igneous rock was really distinctive. I remember having it explained to me that the blue stones were ballast stones off the ships from England. So you can imagine: ships bringing rocks all the way across the other side of the world for no particular reason, other than to load up with cargo to take back to the other side . . .

K Upsets the equation that reads: natural produce and materials go out of the Antipodes, minerals and so on, to the industrial centres of the world . . . manufactured goods back. One of those neat and highly fallible equations economists love to use at press conferences and that primary school teachers fob off on the kids. Of course, in the early part of this century, the equation was quite specific to Britain. There wasn't quite the same random variable there is now. Or, indeed, even when Pig Iron Bob did his notorious deals with Japan just before the war. I found it fascinating going into Australia House in London for the first time, as people pointed out the various hardwoods had been brought in from Australia to timber the place. It was built during the First World War, and even stone used there was from Australia as well. Now here's this massive war going on and they were concerned about bringing building materials from Australia so they were occupying valuable cargo space with a vanity product.

W That's my whole approach to modernity. I think it always starts from the periphery. When you look at the construction of modern Europe it seems to me to be made from the materials of the periphery—made from the landfill of somewhere else. The gold was from somewhere else. Even the tea that stirred the metabolisms of Europe's labouring classes, as they laboured with the materials from the colonies, was from the colonies. Modernity is shifting landfill on a global scale.

K What's interesting is that centre/fringe construction, and that peripheral construction is an interesting entry point into British society. When we first moved to Cambridge, Tracy and I attempted to construct all our conversations in terms of "this is the fringe come to the center," and we're going to occupy it and take over as a defensive mechanism. As the last few years have passed, that centre/fringe construction is entirely gone and as far as we're concerned our centre is in fact the place we've left and we now live on the fringes. And really and honestly in many ways that's quite the case. That whole peripheral construction is something that can be manipulated according to personal perspective.

Landfill is also a kind of cultural filling in. In Britain, in trying to promote Australian poetry or Australian literature, the idea is that we're filling in a space that they don't occupy—but the potential for reception is there. Historically, they made the hole long ago. But rather than a law of diminishing returns they're getting something rich and complex back, that has outgrown them and that flows over into other spaces. This spreads all over the world—it grows and represents the complex amalgam of voices that constitute Australian "identity." The trick is, once you start occupying the space they allow you to fill, you start rhizomically spreading through their culture and affecting the centre's "culture" as well. So landfill actually becomes something quite dangerous (in the centre's eyes) and mobile, and it doesn't just get moved from one space to another, it actually spreads above and below the surface in a rhizomatic way.

W Can you fill that space in the landscape and still occupy one in Australian landscape? There's a danger in the Australian cultural space of being constructed as either/or, as one of us/not one of us.

K Yeah. There's two things one could say to this. First, in the removal of raw materials from Australia, particularly minerals and for example the smelting of the iron ore, be it Japan or the States or Britain, you change the nature of the materiality of place. The material might represent Australia in the same way a souvenir does, but they no longer have the complex set of references (i.e. comparisons) that make landscape. They are denuded of that meaning and given others. Though, of course, they can still symbolise aspects of the landscape they're extracted from. Of course.

Second, if we send satellites into space and pass a particular barrier—leave the earth's atmosphere and consequently what we define as "ours," won't it affect the whole structure of the earth? Won't it affect the way the earth's held together? Even the symbolic value is lost—that is, there are no points of reference relative to the individual and cultures. But maybe that's what science fiction's for! And the eternal "our universe" type shows that saturate television. Patrick Moore's Night Sky program has been going for decades in Britain. He's tolerated because he's speaking about something entirely disconnected from most people's reality. The man is an absolute bigot and misogynist. His racism would not be tolerated under any other circumstances in so public a position. (Though one sometimes wonders about certain members of the police force/s in public relations positions.)

In the same way, the removal of Australian raw materials has always bothered me, to put it mildly . . . that it would cause a total unbalance . . . Interestingly, most indigenous peoples invariably say that the removal of any of the materials of place . . . of the land, causes distress and disrupts it . . . the Ranger uranium project is a good example . . . that the elders of the area said at the time that any interference with that particular space would cause an imbalance and poisoning.

W Well it's the difference between a traditional and a modern relation to space. The modern idea is that space can be abstract. That anything can be in any one place or it can be in another place—it can be moved. You can construct any relation whatever between one place and another, or one resource and another. Or in other words, in the modern world, there's nothing outside the vector. There's no outside-vector. Things only exist in their productive relations to other things. Which is why I wonder about the grand plan to put traditional, indigenous communities on a self-sustaining economic basis. I sometimes wonder if outback tourism might be more of a curse than mining, in the way it makes the most intimate parts of traditional culture "sustainable" only at the price of being a useful "resource."

K You know, talking about spatiality. . . . Have you read Jan Appleton's "Darwinian" theory of prospect and refuge? Extending the notion, within the context of landscape theory, prospect is what you can see in many different points in a landscape—your vista, your horizon, and actually what exists in between the point of seeing and the point of absolute perspective. Refuge is the "shelter" or hiding place within the landscape—it's the place you go internally that you can't see out of and consequently can't be seen within. Now, we're talking about processes of extracting, taking materials from a particular place and using them as landfill elsewhere.

Well, in terms of that model, by taking something that's part of an entirety, a complete picture, a "wholeness," and with respect to traditional uses of land versus modern uses of land, you're actually destroying any ability to gain refuge. Landscape becomes pure prospect. You're actually destroying the internal space of the land—its interiority. Your creating an increasing perspective of prospect then equates with productivity and absorbs refuge. Refuge becomes a marketable idea. The house, the swimming pool. Refuge as marketing concept. Check out Barnley Heights, our prospects offer a variety of refuges . . .

W Refuge as prospect—how perverse. Or as Paul Virilio says, there's nowhere left to hide. If the whole surface of the earth . . . is mappable then in a sense the line of sight becomes a line of force. The vector of perception doubles as a vector of exploitation. Although of course Virilio has never been in the Western desert, so his thinking doesn't really fit. He's too much of the centre, he doesn't see things from the periphery, which to me is the point of view from which you see how things move. You see the prospect in Australia, at a time when in Europe there's a lot more loose talk about losing a privileged refuge, I think.

K There's two interesting points to bring up here—one is that we're in an aircraft that is actually a composite construction of global components . . . and certainly global technology; the second that as we shift from English-speaking space to French-speaking space, the crossover of languages and the removal of languages, and using languages of landfill in the construction of new languages should come into consideration. Should always be under consideration!

Moving "back" to Australia: There's also—thinking about the Western Desert and the making of sand paintings that dissolve after a period of time and represent a particular, not only in a symbolic sense but also in a quite literal sense, mapping of both physical space and conceptual space. The plane—and the aircraft!—in some very abstract sense, almost hijacks mobility and fluidity and precision in crossing particular spatial zones.

W Yes, now you've got me thinking about the way Stephen Muecke thinks about the difference between Aboriginal space and white fella space, in his book *No Road*. In white fella space you can connect any point to any other point. But what makes this possible is the ability to divide any point from any point. This is the instrument of private property: any point can be closed off and owned, and having been made distinct, can be seen as potentially connected, along any available vector, to anything else. Or in other words: roads and fences. Abstract, meaningless relations.

As I read Muecke, he's saying that Aboriginal space is one where you can't automatically connect any point to any other. It has to be negotiated, every movement is singular and meaningful. But there is no private property—nothing is blocked off absolutely, everything is a site of rival and related claims. To effect movement in this landscape, you have to negotiate, and negotiate again each and every time you want to effect a relation. It's a brilliant system for preventing abstraction from taking hold, the abstraction that allows power and wealth to accumulate.

K I'm also thinking of ownership, say, along the Canning Stock routes, and using that as a closed European construct of that particular area. But you see a gnamma hole becomes particular watering space and a signifier of voice and identity, a mythical exchange point where different stories move in and out of each other, which anthropologists then usurp and impose as registration. One of the things that came up in Daisy Bates' investigations of mythologies and customs revolving around gnamma holes is that distinct sense of "ownership" and space. That it didn't exist anywhere else. (I'm reconstructing an argument almost not made to make the point, making utility where it shouldn't be made, but . . .) Because in that particular region water places were the only reserve of life. Particular peoples did feel strongly about their usage and there was a kind of debt incurred when a particular place was "invaded" or used. And this goes against the whole notion of nomadism and so on . . .

W Well yes and no. I think Deleuze and Guattari's *Anti-Oedipus* has not been well understood on the subject of nomadism, particularly in the centre. It takes a "peripheral" writer like Stephen Muecke or Eric Michaels to find the still-workable materials in their work and release them. What you often don't get in the celebrations of nomadism is an understanding of debt. Deleuze and Guattari talk about the savage relation of debt—only the French could use language like this in this day and age! But there is something in the way they distinguish the privatised, monetised, abstract debt of modernity from what they call a debt to the earth. A debt that is always quite particular. It could be owed to quite particular places, to quite particular symbolic figures.

Besides this so-called savage debt there is despotism, where debt is accumulated and subordinated as debt to the sovereign. The sovereign could also be the dictator—Kim Jong Il or Saddam Hussein. In comparison to despotic debt, private debt really does seem more conducive to liberty. Debts are contracted singly and abstractly, always in the same coin. But while the cold war was won by the system of private debt, which really was I think much more conducive to liberty than debt to the sovereign, the state, the party, the relation between private, quantitative, abstract debt on the one hand, and social, qualitative, particular debt on the other, emerges from under the shadows of the cold war as a more fundamental problem.

K Interesting subtext to this—I'm thinking of processes of reterritorialisation for example . . .

W Which is exactly what debt does—it reterritorialises. It connects a prospect, a potential, a resource, to something that limits and directs it. Or in other words, the problem of "reconciliation" can be seen as a problem of conflicting practices of debt. To what does who owe what? Only once you see it as qualitatively different kinds of obligation, it's no longer so easy to talk glibly about reconciling them. There's no middle road between landfill and a sacred site.

K There is a wonderful analogy I can make with the draining of the fens in the south-east of England. They brought drainage engineers across from Holland to put the canals and ditches in to drain the area, to make it fertile and profitable to farm. It had been primarily under water and was occupied by eelers and people who hunted wild fowl. By gradually releasing areas, "reclaiming" them, by draining and by setting up wind pumps and dykes to keep the water under control, the Crown and Parliament and others stimulated the processes of accumulation and profit—the potential increase in material wealth became very specific and measurable.

So as each place was cleared, its value obviously increased. But more interestingly, because the "mythological map"—that of spiritual and cultural identity—was being changed, instead of overlaying, landfilling, covering things up, they were actually exposing, unearthing In many senses, a dual process took place. Drainage literally revealed a lot of lost items. From potlatch to missing treasures. So some people reclaimed that history—they gained wealth because they were able to claim the lost and forfeited, the offered and the taken. But they lost their identity in the same process of revelation. So this kind of revelation/enclosure thing was constantly going on. There's a huge metal detector craze in Britain—this obsessive reclaiming of the past, or getting lost wealth back. Of exacting "rent" from invaders, particularly the Romans.

Enclosure worked in the same way. Works in the same way! Getting control over the usage of public land, of the unobtainable—say so-called Crown Land in Australia, as opposed to returning it to its rightful custodians. Obviously wealth was increased in a general sense through drainage and enclosure, but there was also a diminution of the local peoples' individual prospects, of their capacity to earn, to maintain control over the negotiation and reception of their mythologies as well.

I don't know how you translate that in the whole gnamma hole context, and, in fact, it may be undesirable to do so. But there are certain obvious theoretical correlations that can be made.

W Well, maybe one has to make the attempt, even if only as conversation, to connect these things. In the New World there's a kind of repressed similarity in some way to things that have always existed in English space and the Old World in general. There always were these pockets of traditional property right, there's always been something like "native title" in England. There has never been an absolute form of private property—it's always negotiable at some point . . . with things like right of way and so on. So we suddenly rediscovered that—that, ah hello!, here are all these previous complex, quite subtle, unreadable and in a sense non-negotiable rights. How do you negotiate between them?

K We're talking about the genocide of people and landscapes. The two become indistinguishable. The destruction of one leads to the destruction of the other. A "terrible" symbiosis. Thinking of the fens, they actually removed the landscape, they altered it, they changed it. Theoretically if all the pumps stop, and the dykes overflow and so on, and no-one repairs it, Cambridge might return to something like its previous form. But the people who were part of it have long gone. But that's not completely true, fenlanders always claim difference and speak against outsiders. The threat of flooding, of water, makes them different. Those on the Norfolk Broads in particular, but also in Cambridgeshire. They always remember the great floods!

I find this interesting, Lionel Fogarty, the great Murri poet, actually gets inside the English language and dismantles it from the inside out. Mudrooroo has called this his guerilla tactics. Instead of using a kind of Pidgin English or a construction of a hybridity, he is actually taking words and dismantling them through using his Murri tongue as the colonising language, and not the colonised language. He reverses the hybridising relationship. He's remapping a landscape that has been entirely removed from his people. He's reclaiming it through speech, through words. The "control" of language is power. He's rejecting the coloniser's linguistic claim on that space. . . . He's saying that you've come into our space and we're fighting you with your own language. So he's entirely reversed that victim/coloniser binary. He's reclaiming space.

W In a less "literary" way, that's the story of Aboriginal country music and of "settlement rock." A sort of oral guerrilla culture inside the language and harmonic language. We were discussing earlier whether modernity begins on the periphery or the centre. Or whether these terms make any sense once you explore the play between them. Likewise, I think there's a sense in which colonialism begins at the centre and not the periphery. So 1745, before Australia's even "discovered," the colonisation of Scotland gets going full bore. There's a sense in which, seen from without, you tend to think about the Old World as the centre from which modernity radiated. But without the resources set free in the periphery, the whole process would never have got off the ground. The whole process began at home already, already in Cambridge, already in Scotland, this process of internal colonisation had already been going on.

What an act of colonisation does is deterritorialise and reterritorialise. Land and people are broken free from their debts and set loose, only to be subordinated to a qualitatively new kind of grid. Only in the process, some resources, particularly people, are set loose to colonise again. The Scots were great colonisers in the New World, having been set loose by the dispossession of their traditional relation to land. My ancestors and probably a lot of yours were themselves "landfill."

K One thing that shocked me when I first moved to Britain was the reference to Australia as the New World, uncritically. New to whom? Using an old term for a new process without question. Any comment on that?

W I still like the expression in the sense that it has been used in the Americas. The New World has a sense of hope, something that has yet to be constructed. I think it's hard to have that optimism in the face of the continuing existence of the Ancien Regime in Europe, but it's something that Australia, in a more low-key way, does share with America. That sense of constructing the world—and still trying to get it right. An open modernity rather than a closed—and enclosing—one, perhaps.

K We're flying in over the fields and roads of a Euro heartland right now. One thing that's interesting about this particular conversation, because we're in a plane, and because we're about to land, it induces stress. I'm certainly finding that my thought patterns aren't as linear, I'm reacting under a kind of stress to answer a question I've been asking myself about what constitutes the occupation of place and what do you take away from place when you physically leave it. If we weren't about to land would I ask such a question? What your obligations are as a human as a citizen in movement?

You've come from Sydney to London and then to Cambridge and back to Toulouse, then you'll go back to London and back to Sydney and you'll do it all over again. And what are your obligations in the removal of cultural discourse or whatever cultural participation into that space and then to the next space. Acts of appropriation. The tourist thing. The destruction of regional boundaries. In the same way we criticise those who make the holes in order to fill other ones they no longer want, what are your responsibilities?

W Interesting question. Though why is it the movers rather than the unmoved who are supposed to have a responsibility? What are the responsibilities of people who don't move? There's a sense in which you're supposed to be exempt. I'm curious as to why. It is always so-called "globalisation" that is called upon to justify itself. It's amazing how old leftists and the far right share this totally uncritical sense of the rightness of the national boundary nowadays. And the left can't even see how defending protectionism might be just as racist as restricting immigration. At least the right aren't hypocrites! They know they are against foreigners prospering, whether by coming to "our" space or selling their goods into "our" space.

So, perhaps perversely, I wonder why staying put and valuing staying put should be exempt from ethical questioning. "Cosmopolitanism" was a term of abuse used by the Nazis, and sometimes by Stalinists, too. Sometimes "cosmopolitan" was a code-word for Jew, but sometimes I wonder if Jew might not have been, and still be, a code-word for cosmopolitan. It's a refusal to accept identities constructed on the run, on the move, along the vector, rather than within the territory.

K Exemption? My grandmother on my father's side never, ever, ever left the south of Western Australia. Her husband was a state forester of Western Australia, and there is actually an area called Kinsella in the south west named after him. The naming was a reward for his services in the forests to the State. Such namings are all about usurping and totally obliterating indigenous occupation and ownership. And for him it would have been an honour. I don't know if he thought about its implications.

My paternal grandmother's heritage was Irish and Scots and she basically went through a process of denial. She felt there was no point, say, returning to visit her "roots" as it would be destroying identity a lot of people had gone to a lot of trouble to create. She was a Western Australian, and that was that. Time was not the issue, presence in place was. Immediate family was the signifier, the marker of presence and place. So she felt it was morally bankrupt to travel, to leave one's space, and she criticised my mother when she took my brother with her to Bali when he was 13. She was indignant, absolutely outraged. I stayed at home so I could sell more stamps, actually. She respected my profit-making enterprises, I think. Not sure though. We didn't really discuss it. But it kept me "home," so I guess she did. Home was actually Geraldton then—five hundred kilometres north of Perth—but still in WA! She was indignant because she felt that by travelling, especially at such a young age, he would be corrupted and turn against his home, that he would weaken the ties of place.

What's interesting—my brother travelled overseas before I did but has never left the region and never will. He's stuck in the country of Western Australia, he's a shearer, he wants to be there and it's a conscious choice. He talks occasionally about going across to the eastern states but he'll never, ever get into an aeroplane . . . [*end of tape*]

TOM LA FARGE

from *Kiarostami Series 5: Underground*

GRAVEDIGGER.
I've been digging this
trench two weeks. I have
to make it straight. In
places I have to tunnel
under roots and rocks.
Four meters deep.

GIRL.
He was afraid of falling,
coming down the stairs. It
was dark to him. He
didn't know where the
cow was. He didn't know
where I was. I had the
lamp in the storeroom in
back.

The stones are the
hardest. I have to dig
around them, like carving
them out of the earth, till
I can pry them loose.
Then I have to get them
out.

He called me again and
again. My aunt told him
my name. Even after I
answered him he went on
calling. I told him I'd be
right there. I told him to
be careful. Wait by the
cow.

Then there are the bones.
The earth is packed with
them. I can't dig without
hitting old bones.
And skulls.

But he hit his head.

So? It's a cemetery. What
did you expect? You
probably put them there.

No, they're older than
that. Older than I am.

Older than anyone now
alive.

There are jars down there
put up before I was born.
I was wiping off old
sealed jars, counting
them, but I lost count
when he began to yell.

A root in the roof of the
tunnel. I was burrowing
under it and hit a rock. I
started to scrape around it.

I asked if he had come
for milk. I put the lantern
down beside the stool.
He was startled to see the
cow so close.
I kept as much in the
shadows as I could. I
couldn't hide my hands. I
could tell he wanted to
see me.

It was too big for me.
There was no end to it.

Did he have his camera?

No, but it was like that.
He had dark glasses in
the dark! He was behind
them. I kept my face
down. Instead he watched
my hands on the udders.

I had to go up instead. I
had to cut the root.

The root of this tree?

It has others. I've dug
around a hundred of
them. There's a root in
every grave. The village
feeds the tree.

That's a pleasant thought.
I began to milk the cow.
I began to milk, and he
began to talk.
He talked in poetry. The
cellar was warm and
damp, the cow's flank was
warm and flies were

The root was tough.
Tougher than I thought.
I sawed at it. I pulled at it.
It was as thick as my arm.

Clamped on every rock
in the hill.
Old, twisted, gnarled,
scaly.

I dug and I cut but in the
end there nothing to do
but to take it between my
hands and pull it out.

Pull and pull.
I'm sure they weren't love
poems.

Fingers about the root. I
was impatient. I pulled
too hard.

The whole wall fell on
me. I heard a roaring. I
was pinned, my head
against the rock.
I couldn't move. I didn't
know what bones were
broken. A rock sat on my
back between my shoul-
ders, my face was pushed
against the immovable
rock. There was a little
space where I'd been
digging. A pocket of air
near my nose. My mouth
was full of dirt, I couldn't
spit it out to call for help.

walking on it. Her udders
were warm and full, the
milk steamed into the
pail.
His words were cold. I
shivered. Old poems, so
he said. They twisted
around my head.

Don't you want to know
what sort of poems?

No, not love poems. No. I
don't know. Old poems
about women. Words
about beauty.

Cold words about beauti-
ful women twisting around
me in the warm cellar.
Words packing the air.

I had to move closer to
the cow and breathe her
smell.

But I could hear.

Mountains and panting gazelles. Lilacs and white doves rising, wheeling. Running water, waves on shore, the changes of the moon. Cedars. Sunshine. Ripe round fruit.

I was afraid. I could not move but I was moving with everything. I was pulled into the earth by the weight of that rock below my head, and I was spinning, spinning.
[*He sings wordlessly with her.*]

A mine of sparkling opals. A bowl of rose petals, jasmine. An arrow. A tortoise with gold eyes, crawling. Moss, a well, an orchard of almond trees in flower. The desert in winter, the wind. A scattering of ducks from a marsh, a pen on paper, a pair of cupped hands.

Spinning, spinning.
What?

That was what he said. Those were his words.

Oh. Metaphors.

Even the cow was restless. I pulled my headscarf down. I wished I had no breasts. His voice was everywhere.

"Hello! Hello! Hello!" Through the dirt I heard him calling.

He was calling you?

No, he was calling the boss! On the telephone! "Hello! Hello!" I couldn't make a sound. The earth was in my mouth, I told you.

Fragrant orange blossoms. Honey, the song of bees

making honey, and bees
dancing and bees flying and
bees pushing into flowers.
Even the cow shook her head.
At last the pail was full.

Talking to his boss.
"Yes. No. No, not yet.
Please give me three
more days." I wanted
three more minutes.
The strange thing
was I felt my fear
leave me. I listened
to him talk to his
boss and I felt
released. His speech
came through the
dirt. It made some
space.

Talking blind.

His words do not come from
a place. He speaks into empty
air, holding a telephone.

The excerpt printed here is drawn from the conclusion of a libretto, Talking to the Earthquake*, loosely based on the Iranian director Abbas Kiarostami's film* The wind will carry us. *A gravedigger and the girl who keeps him company are talking after the departure of a photographer from the capital. They are remembering the ways in which the photographer affected them.*

ROB MACKENZIE & LEE A. TONOUCHI

This dialogue took place by email in December 2001.

TONOUCHI Howzit Rob,
I like kickstart our Chain Dialogue wit one question to you about your work. I nevah read all your stuffs, but da little bit I read I wen notice dat you incorporate planny different languages insai your work. So my question is—who is da audience you envision reading your stuff? I imagine you gotta be writing for more than just yourself cuz you publish, yeah, so dat means you like share??
K-dens Rob. Look foward to hearing from you.
Write on brah,
Lee

MACKENZIE Good to hear from you. I attach a few more things, more grist to the mill. If you could pass on some stuff of yours too, that'd be great—I like the idea of getting to know you, your criticism, and your work, simultaneously and at some leisure.

Who I'm writing for, though, that's to start with one of the hardest questions. Seems easy first of all: in the UK there's a small, but reasonably self-sustaining, community of people interested in writing that's come to be known as "linguistically innovative," really meaning a negative identity—"not like Larkin, Heaney, and Hughes." So, not in thrall to the lyric voice of the 'sensitive' poet (I know there's a black hole here—let's step over it . . .). This community seems willing to listen to macaronic poetry from me—publish it, etc.—and in the maybe ten years since I've become aware of this community I'm sure it has influenced what I write as much as provided an obvious first audience. Why they are willing to listen to what I write I'm sure comes down to a load of different aesthetics-building, some of which'll maybe come through in what we talk about here.

That's probably not enough for you, I guess: serving the interests of a few culture vultures disenchanted with the current, easy, "mainstream" poetics. Different poetry for its own sake. I'd hazard that you want to speak to those outside the ivory towers, and that writing in pidgin is a political choice that you want to act to empower people—

your people? And I want a similar justification too, the justification I used many years ago when an editor said my practise showed a disdain for—or downright hostility towards—"the readers." But this is to take the identity of the readership for granted. I envisage another readership, outside the primary small magazine circulation. This, largely imagined, readership is Scottish or Scotophilic, and hence familiar with the languages of Scotland, at least to the rudimentary level that I use scots and gaelic. Speaking to this readership in macaroni echoes everyday speech, and so privileges the demotic over the arch, the aristocratic, and the barrenly academic. I hold to this line even though my writing is not demotic—people tell me that they would never say what I write in the way I write it—but the connection to everyday speech is there nevertheless, I think, and it acts to align the writing with a Scottish democracy of intellect rather than an English meritocracy.

I wanted to mention something you've discussed in other places (can't see where now, but somewhere in the interviews, etc. Juliana passed on): that pidgin needs to be used for serious purpose in literature, not just comic effect. Because, of course, it's used for serious purpose every day outside literature. That's an argument well won for 'pure' scots and gaelic, and fine, I admire much single-language work in english, scots, and gaelic. It just happens that my upbringing leaves me unable to write comfortably in 'pure' gaelic or scots. And my politics/aesthetics leave me unhappy writing in 'pure' english. Wresting what I can write in from comedy is worthwhile not only for the link to the demotic I was talking about above, but also as an antidote to the romance of "the wisdom of the old languages"—Celtic twilight kind of stuff that's much more prevalent in Scottish letters than the commentators would like to admit (because they do not recognise that it is connected to the "sensitive poet" malaise from which we currently suffer in the UK). Pidgin is maybe spared the worst excesses of linguistic ring-fencing and romanticism, but I can see from the discussion around "Pigin Wawrz" that it's not exempt. Is there an argument here for going beyond mimicry of the demotic? I mean mimicry here in a very positive sense. I mean the powerful use the everyday's put to in William Carlos Williams and Tom Leonard as well as yourself. But d'you think you'll always be able to find an existing pidgin construction to fulfil your literary requirements?

Best wishes 'nat,

Rob

T Sorry for da delay. I wuz in Queens hospital da last few days. I wuz da passenger in one car accident. Jus got discharged dis afternoon. Still kinda busted up. But will respond soon.
k-dens,
Lee

M Dear Lee, I'm sorry to hear about your accident—hope you're healing fast and firm. I'll be away until January 3rd or so (difficult for a Scotsman to be precise about when New Year ends . . .), but hope to talk to you some more after that. I'm anxious that my last email may have sounded high-handed, when that was not at all the intention. Maybe because I was replying in straight english? Or maybe something about the peculiarly blank context of email—somehow more difficult to contextualise than almost any other text I can think of. Evolution of "smileys" (:), etc.) was not purely for decoration I think, Best wishes for a happy holiday and speedy recovery,
Rob

T Rob, Howzit, howzit. My lung pau puka so I can breathe bettah now. Hope you guys is having one good New Year's celebration. I'm jus glad for be alive.

K, continuing wea we leff off . . . Nah Rob, no werries can handle da "hybolics." Da ony big word I nevah know wuz "macaronic." I tot might have someting for do wit pasta. Dictionary sez it's one mixture of two or more languages. I get 'em, I get 'em. I wuz talking in macaroni all dis time and I nevah even know. Cuz Pidgin is one mixture too.

I like talk about dis imagined readership we both get. Da idealistic me always hoped dat Pidgin would allow me for crossover and reach da kine people who normally wouldn't be exposed to Local literature. I went through da whole public education system and I nevah even know had such ting as Pidgin stories, Pidgin poems until I went college. Da funny ting I found out wen I went college wuz dat lotta da kids who went private school had da exposture to Darrell Lum's Pidgin stories and stuff, but most of da kids who went public school nevah. So da schools wea had da most Pidgin talkers nevah get for see demselves in writing, in "literature." Kinda backwards yeah.

Anyhow, getting back to da audience ting . . . sometimes I get discouraged cuz da people who I tink I writing for, dey not so interested lotta times in reading wot I writing. Da major reason is cuz dey jus no like reading. Lotta my friends, das da people I cruise wit, da people I grew up wit, dey not really interested in reading my stuff cuz not ony dey gotta read, but dey gotta read Pidgin and das someting dey not used to seeing so das like twice da effort. (Pidgin is one oral language and no mo' one set standardize orthography so writers usually jus spell 'em phonetically. Some writers go more crazy wit da spelling.) So my friends not into my stuff. Sad yeah. And my grandma, whose one full-on Pidgin speaker, she absolutely cannot read my stories. Seeing Pidgin in writing is totally foreign to her. I always tot wit Pidgin I would be able for crossover and reach academic peoples as well as da non-literary types, but I dunno. Jus da fack dat I get one "book" turns lotta people off. I tink so if I made MTV pop songs or Hollywood movies den would be one easier sell. Once in awhile I reach da regular peoples I trying fo' reach, da Pidgin Hoi Polloi, but da instances is few and far between. Sometimes I get 'em interested wen I do readings. People gotta hear my stuff first—hearing my work makes 'em pick up my "book," someting which dey usually wouldn't even consider looking at.

I wuz jus curious . . . Juliana sez you teach Atmospheric Science. Wen you doing stuff das not creative writing, stuff in da "serious" halls of academia, how do you write? You write in "pure" english? You use one mixture of Scots, Gaelic, and english? Wot's accepted and wot's not? How much does your language politics/aesthetics carry over into your everyday life?

K, for answer da question you wen end wit. Hod one. Not sure if I fully get da question, but correck me if I misunderstand, k. "D'you think you'll always be able to find an existing Pidgin construction to fulfill your literary requirements?" Dis implies dat get one set usuage for Pidgin. And da majority of da people probably tink dea is. People say you cannot use Pidgin fo' dis, you cannot use Pidgin for dat. As one exercise I made my freshman community college students make me one list of tings dat people toll 'em ova da years of wot dey cannot do wit Pidgin. Get planny stuff. Try go look dis group poem we made.

Dey Say If You Talk Pidgin You NO CAN . . .
by da Fall 2001 PCC of Kapi'olani Community College
as edited by Lee A. Tonouchi

Dey say if you talk Pidgin you no can . . .
be smart
be important
be successful
be professional
be taken seriously

be one teacher
be one doctor
be one lawyer
be a government worker
be big businessman
be da Pope
be the president
be the wife of the president

Dey say if you talk Pidgin you no can . . .
communicate
eat at fine dining restaurants
enter a beauty pageant (and win)
flirt
function
go out tonight
go to job interviews
go mainland
go mainland school
go opera or someplace elegant
go forward

Dey say if you talk Pidgin you no can . . .
get good grades
get one good education
get good job
get a smart guy
get a sophisticated guy
get chicks

Dey say if you talk Pidgin you no can . . .
give public speeches
join the military
look high class
make it in Hollywood
pray to God
read
run for governor

Dey say if you talk Pidgin you no can. . .
score
sound intellectual

survive
talk straight
talk proper
talk to da phone operator
talk to da judge
talk at funerals
talk to da haoles
talk to tourists
talk in European countries
talk in the classroom
take tests
teach
understand

Dey say if you talk Pidgin you no can . . .
work customer service
work at Neiman Marcus
write a proper sentence
write letters
write formal essays
write papers to pass this class

Dey say if you talk Pidgin
YOU NO CAN.

And if you axed me, wen I wuz one college freshman, I probably would've sed all da same tings. Cuz das how we's raised. We get 'em from da teachers in school, from our parents. Basically da message is in order for be one successful, career-minded adult, you gotta lose da Pidgin, brah. I wen add da "brah" cuz lotta times da message is delivered from adult to child in Pidgin. My faddah talk Pidgin, but to him, da less Pidgin words I knew da bettah. I always wanted for know more, but he nevah like teach me. Da turning point for me wuz wen I took Rob Wilson's sophomore lit class at UH Mānoa. Das wea I saw Eric Chock's "Tutu on da Curb" poem, one Pidgin poem. First time I seen Pidgin in writing. So das wot got me started. I took one creative writing class so I could write in Pidgin. Den later I took playwriting in da theatre department cuz I wanted for write more stuff in Pidgin. Den later I wuz all like eh, if I can do my creative stuff in Pidgin den hakum I cannot do my oddah writing too. So I started doing my response papers in Pidgin, den eventually I did my full-on thirty page research papers in Pidgin too. But I gues I wuz lucky dat I took classes from da

cool people who would "let" me do dat. Da teacher get a power so I'm shua if any teacher along da way threatened for give me one "F" if I nevah write 'em in english, den I'm shua I would've caved in. Well, maybe not. I might've protested. Yeah, I probably would've. So getting back to your question, da ony restraints for Pidgin is in people's minds. If some people tink dat Pidgin is ony da language of small kid time, den their Pidgin probably not going grow, so das why to dem, in their reality, Pidgin is one simplistic language, but das ony cuz dey wen turn 'em off ass why.
K-dens,
Lee

M Hi Lee, Yeah, I suppose I did mean something else with my last question. I agree completely that pidgin and other 'minority' languages have been repressed for political ends—I come from the generation between the active discouragement of gaelic in schools and the active encouragement of it. In my parents' adolescence it was still common for school children to be beaten for speaking gaelic in the playground and classroom. So there is a strong subconscious reflex in older gaels to consider their native language as barbaric and unsuitable for government work, big business, education, etc. (You no can . . .) The turnaround in the political status of gaelic has changed all that. If anything the problem now lies with those who think that speaking gaelic gives them an automatic authority: I have called this "guddling the salmon of wisdom" previously.

The schools in Scotland now carry scots (and gaelic to a lesser extent) writing from pretty early on in the curriculum. This is done best in scots, so far's I know, because there is a well-trodden path from "bairn sangs" to MacDiarmid. I'm not sure the legitimacy of non-bardic "low" literature is quite so well established for gaelic in schools.

So I think that much of the argument for legitimacy you face with pidgin has been won for scots and gaelic (some will think me glib at that, but the situation is not of the same scale as in Hawaii). But for a macaroni of scots, gaelic, standard english, and scientific english? I don't think that the question of legitimacy arises. Although I argued earlier that the macaroni I write has one root in everyday speech, I'm not arguing for its use in all aspects of our lives. I'll argue for its legitimacy as a poetic mode—more than that, I'll argue for its power—but I wouldn't expect to be able to teach using it, nor would I have the faintest chance of publishing a scientific paper in it. The scientific arena is a very special case here: even when you have pidgin teaching in schools, pidgin TV, and legal representation in pidgin, Tony Clarke and his students in U. of Hawaii will not be allowed to publish atmospheric science research in anything but scientific english if they want to be published in an international journal. This is a kind of imperialism that, as an english speaker, I find difficult to gauge and analyse.

Which kind of converges my question on "literary requirements" and yours on "wot's acceptable and wot's not?" towards "why write in a mode that is not, and never will be, of broader use." There's an easy appeal to the "high-falutin' language of poetry" here, but it's not very interesting. What I think is more interesting is the double edge that macaroni can (i) undercut poetry's implicit claim to moral authority; and (ii) criticise assumptions of power and meaning in more standard speaking/writing. Point (i)'s back to the salmon of wisdom, or the english lit. equivalent of the smooth and unified poetic voice that claims for the writer a privileged sensitivity. All kept writing is privileged by its being kept, but there can be a creep towards believing that only a certain 'smoothness' is valid, and there can be a creeping erosion of self-criticism. Point (ii)'s more like what a lot of the L=A=N=G=U=A=G=E stuff seems to be about: I can't say that I have a strong grasp of the economy of aesthetics, but I can appreciate that the power and implications of words like "I," "are," "love," "got" (my favourite), etc. are often forgotten. I'm doing L=A= . . . a disservice stopping here, but this is a dialogue, not a paper.

So, feeling brave now, I'll ask again, is there an effect you can imagine wanting from your writing that you think won't come through in from-the-street pidgin?

To end with some more on our imagined readership. You sound despondent about the effects of your writing in pidgin, that it has not brought in a new readership. I recognise the situations you describe (I could count the readers I have in the Highlands on one hand, I'm sure), and they are dispiriting, but I don't think they mean your efforts are in vain. Even without acclaim—which, of course, I hope you receive sooner rather than later—your effect can be significant even if subtle. I despise the Thatcherite economics of the "trickle down" of riches, but maybe there's something in the "trickle through" of cultural values,

Orra best 'nat,

Rob

T Interesting how people's minds about Gaelic wen switch li'dat. I wondah if Pidgin get chance too. I can forsee dat might get one similar problem too wit da automatic authority deals. Local people is very protective about their Pidgin. Wenevah haoles or outsiders come ova hea and try talk Pidgin, lotta Local people get upset—dey's all like no, you dunno how so no even try, brah. But to me, so long as da effort stay sincere den ees cool.

But wot if Pidgin Powah became one reality—wot if we lived in one world wea Pidgin wuz encouraged in Hawai'i—would dis position of Pidgin/Local supremacy start for take ova? Would people make one fuss about da head of da university not being from ova hea? Would people complain if da head of da Department of Education wuz somebody from da "mainland"? Would we become totally Locals Only and rejeck all tings foreign?

To me, das like da antithesis of Local. Da way I see 'em is dat Local is based on da concept of being accepting. Accepting of diff'rent ideas, diff'rent people. (But of course Local is one idealized concept so critic peoples make da argument dat Local is a buncha bull and we live in one society das egocentric and cutthroat.)

Like Local, Pidgin is accepting and open. (Of course get people who disagree wit dis. Get people who tink dat their particilar Pidgin is mo' bettah cuz ees mo' country sounding and townie people Pidgin is not real Pidgin or wotevahs) But . . . To me da danger is tinking of Pidgin as jus ONE ting wit ONE set of rules. Da beauty of Pidgin is dat get planny kine Pidgins. Get grandma-grandpa kine Pidgin, get Moloka'i kine Pidgin, get Nānākuli Pidgin, Hawai'i Kai Pidgin, Filipino Pidgin, Hawaiian Pidgin, and even haole Pidgin. So, so long as we remembah dat get ukubillion varieties of Pidgin in Hawai'i den I tink so das how we can avoid da situation wea talking Pidgin gives somebody mo' authority ova one noddah somebody who talks diff'rent from dem. (But wot about people who talk standard english? Is da Pidgin talking peoples going accept dem too? I no tink get such ting as standard english so no need worry about dat one.)

K, I gathering da courage so I going try for answer your question again even though I wen miss da boat da first time. You wen ask is dea one effeck I can imagine wanting from my writing dat I tink not going come through in from-da-street Pidgin. K, I guess my answer is yeah and nah.

Yeah, cuz lotta times I like make people TINK in my writing. But I face da barrier dat jus cuz I writing in Pidgin so muss not get anyting fo' tink about insai dea. Da stereotypical prejudice is dat dis person dunno how write english so gotta be he stupid and so dis not worth trying fo' read. But nahting I can do about dat.

Nah, cuz to me, from-da-street-Pidgin is jus one kine Pidgin. If I writing academic papahs den I like try buss out da college edumacated Pidgin and use da kine terminology and discuss da kine ideas dat critics and theorists use. But again, jus da fack dat it's not in 'standard english' makes some intellectuals dissmiss 'em. And I suppose get some Pidgin purists who might argue dat Lee's hybrid creation—Academic Pidgin—is not really Pidgin. It's really more englishy wit funky Pidgin spelling and little bit of Pidgin hea and dea kine. (Get some linguists who been analyzing my Pidgin. Da verdick is still out. Dey say ees real diff'rent from da kine Pidgin from 20-30 years ago kine.)

So maybe I pretty much alienating eh-rybody. And da effeck dat I like have for get people fo' tink and question their belief systems ain't going happen. One ting dat turns pretty much eh-rybody off is da orthography. Pidgin is one oral language so no mo' one standard orthography—therefore people is not used to reading Pidgin. Even da most hardcore Pidgin talkers get hod time reading Pidgin cuz dey not used to.

Getting back to da question—is dea one effeck dat I find wanting from my writing dat no can come out using Pidgin in terms of expression? No. Both creatively and critically, Pidgin is how I most comfortable expressing myself. People who get hod time expressing demselves wen probably stop using Pidgin somewea along da way so their Pidgin nevah grow and das why dey find 'em limiting.

Da mission is for blend creative/critical, literary/mainstream worlds. Wenevah I write reviews or articles for Local newspapahs, I try get 'em for take 'em in Pidgin. Da hope is dat if people see articles wit intelligent insights das written in Pidgin den dat might get dem for re-tink wot dey tink dey know about Pidgin.

K, I get one question for you—if you wanna write in your particular macaroni cuz you wanna criticize assumptions of power and meaning in more standard writing, den why limit 'em to da realm of poetry?
Shoooooots den,
Lee

M Dear Lee, We've got to an end, I think, by virtue of other demands on our time rather than for lack of things to say. But I feel much the better for looking at the complementarities in our angles.

It's as well we've stopped, because I think I was about to get into deep water around the idea of "scientific language." I guess I'm interested in the way macaroni and scientific terms interrupt the poetic 'discourse.' That's because I don't want poetry to be a discourse, to have fixed the meanings of important words. I want the thrill of different meanings sliding across a poem as you read it, to point up where we are falling into circumscribed discourses as a result of class, race, gender, education, and cultural background. My own preference in writing is to keep quite a tight conscious hold on where I think the poem is, but I'm interested too in reading those who obviously allow something of the subconscious (or chance) in somehow.

Which is not, I hope, to eschew meaning altogether. Poetry must communicate or it's nothing (I'll step glibly over any potential black hole related to "communicate"). So the trick of poetry gets to be slipping your gaolers without altogether skipping the country.

Does this explain why I'm not talking macaroni to you now, or in this morning's lecture? I think so: I have the energy to attempt the trick in poetry (and have garnered one or two of the other crowd-pleasing turns too), but I don't have the inclination or facility to attack the discourses in my teaching and scientific writing. To do that I would need a different set of weapons, and probably a different job. I'm happy talking *within* the discourse because I can see that the science has worth to itself, and to the world outside science. If I want to criticise some aspect of the superposition of scientific discourse on the rest of the world, that's a job for poetry. I don't use macaroni in my standard writing precisely because that writing is conforming to standards.

But for your work in the humanities (including politics) I can see why your use of pidgin is so successful. I think the same arguments to the value of the "old" critical "discourse" could be raised, but with less impact because so much of the discourse centres on the re-evaluation of meaning, and so is self-obliterating.

All of which is a long way, I'm sure, from the day we simply put the pidgin or macaroni in there because it fitted. It was many days in my case, since I was very unsure of having permission to use the language I wanted to use. It seems a one-way gate now—I can't imagine arguing now for a pure language of poetry—but it does put you up against the problem of finding an audience. My personal preference is for footnotes, but I know that there are many in poetry vehemently against such foreclosing. But if it's footnotes or shouting in the desert, I'll take footnotes every time.

Yours aye,
Rob

ADDENDUM

ROB MACKENZIE
Incipient myth

'Se fear a bh'ann, calendrically blind,
agus ise, anxious to lock, lost keys.
So their marriage unfolded terrae incognito
and oceans of bestiary.

A lion scourged the worktops.
A tiger sat gauging the sun.

Syne bha ise's esan gan càraideach;
she rubbed to lodestone,
he oiled escapement.
The map remained in Latin.

'Se fear a bh'ann—there was a man
agus ise—and she
Syne bha ise's esan gan càraideach—then himself and herself

LEE TONOUCHI

Grandpa's Ancient Medicine

Wen da jellyfish wen go sting me
  my Grandpa toll me make shi shi on top.
Da times I had stuck doo doo
  he gave me some prune juice fo' drink.
And wheneva I had mosquito bite
  jus spit and put tsuba he sed.
He toll me fo' eat da fish eye
  for bettah vision
  but I nevah like cuz gross ah.

Wheneva my Grandpa had itchy rash
  he rubbed vinegar.
Da time he wen go cut his leg
  he wen put aloe from da backyard.
Doze days wen he had sore throat
  he wen gargle salt water.
And wheneva he burn himself on da stove
  he jus smear on some
  Arm & Hammah Baking Soda.

Doze wuz not bad
  you should see da hardcore kine
  treatments. Unreal.
Wen he caught one cold
  he wen cure 'em wit his formula—
  twenny year old garlic
  soaked in whisky
  in da brown kim chee jar.
Wen his body wuz all achin'
  he lit one senko
  from his bottom dresser drawer
  and did yaito
  on da proper pressure point
  burning away da pain.

Now my Grandpa stay hospital—
   Brain Hemorage.
Da doctors wen operate
   but dey no tink he goin' be da same.
If he could only eat da fish brain.
I once toll my Grandpa
   he should write down all his recipes
   so he no forget 'em.
He sed, "No can depend book.
In case lose, wot?
Mo' bettah leave in head
   den stay inside
   foreva."

MARK MCMORRIS
from *The Alphabet of Wounds*

CAROL: A B C Vestibule Pipe Baton.

BASIL: Who are you?

CAROL: A gnome inside a footlocker. *Thump. Thump.* Tiny fists beating on the lid of it.

BASIL: Right jab.

ANTOINE: It was one fine day in July, and I sat across from her in the Bois de Boulogne, in a telepathic embrace. Madame N must have said: "The relentless parabolas of discourse: I have been crippled by my metaphors. I put my ear to the labia of a vowel. The task: to translate a shadow. To make a tactile ark from the theories." Or perhaps it was I who said it. Well, it was years ago. But still, something in her bare shoulders, some beneficent aspect in the greenish light that fell from the oak trees.

CAROL: Others say that it is unthinkable, that they stumble down hill when the Earth looks so flat.

BASIL: So flat.

CAROL: Sent semaphores, sent a signal by sparrow. So flat.

BASIL: The professor had a theory: he said that the universe was actually an Apple in the outstretched palm of a Demon. *Jab. Jab. Jab.* But this Demon was like a one-celled microbe encamped on the rear of a Sheepdog. And the Sheepdog, in its own turn, was a mathematically-determined cross-section, without any width, of a piece of String unwound long ago. String, Dog, Demon, Apple—our chain of being.

CAROL: *Tap* *Tap* *Tap*

BASIL: The unpronounceable name of a scandalous enigma.

ANTOINE: *N N N N N N N N N N N N N N N N*

CAROL:
Sundays   demon   oscilloscope   alphabet
needle   Jupiter   colophon   oyster
stampede   Catullus   footlocker   dunce
signal   bitumen   naked   Cleopatra
microbe   snowfall   tumble   heretofore

This snowfall. The brown earth.
And the interior pressed on the back of the
neck, my eyes be open.

ANTOINE: Dread Aggressive Nymph

BASIL: Intended Energy

CAROL: Left Languishing Error

ANTOINE: Cleopatra's Needle in a plaza at sunrise, across from the train station—to set my eyes upon that chiseled stone.

RUTH MARGRAFF WITH SA'DI AL-HADITHI,
AYAD RAHIM, & KANAN MAKIYA

Colossal Woman At The Well

loosely surrounding modernity & antiquity incidental texts toward imagining a more non-western modern American opera

•

Oh Monsi well, to your waters came gazelles.
They were guided to your sighs by the eye
For the sake of the camels and pilgrims to Mecca
Let the well always be full of water
Let the blonde plaits float in the wind

•

He went down to the brook to make his filly drink.
She does not drink with a vessel
She only drinks from his palm

•

Oh my gazelle, come down, you who are carrying the jar.
I am thirsty. The water this year has not once passed by me.
Oh brother, my protector. I do not want a man who already
has a wife.
I want a house for myself only, to live happily

•

I will sit a while at the well waiting for you
You fine girl with the black eyes
I will climb up and throw you a cluster of grapes
And some dates from the garden

Excerpts from Desert Songs translated and archived by Iraqi singer/folklorist Sa'di Al-Hadithi in his book The Choobi Songs of the Upper Euphrates In Iraq, *The Arab Gulf States Folklore Center, Doha, Qatar, 1986.*

Maxfield Parrish, "The Garden of Allah," 1918.

DIALOGUE:

RUTH MARGRAFF My dear, dear Sa'di. I always see a woman at the well when I listen to your voice. There is such a heavenly and lyrical sense of her for me in your bedouin songs. I have heard a thread of your singing behind me ever since I drove from Minneapolis to Detroit in 1996 to meet you. You have influenced every opera I have written since then. In *Night Vision* the Dysney davids, the vampyre 'Ajlinna id-Dibayih—whose name is from one of your desert songs—and the stray poodle/nativity lamb in *The Cry Pitch Carrolls.* And now this woman at the well I keep trying to write somehow. If I can only have any say in what I get to write about this time as it always gets dictated by those who control the means of production. I think you were there in my writing even *before* I met you! The psalm that Chaucia sings to decorate her hysteria in "Matte the Powder" . . . This is because you have a voice crying in the mediterranean wilderness that was so familiar to me in my imagination growing up hearing my father preach. The same fertile crescent of the middle east from biblical history. So, Sa'di . . . is there such a thing as an Iraqi opera, historically speaking?

SA'DI AL-HADITHI No. There are no traditions of Iraqi opera singing. The Egyptians tried to present *Aida* but the Arabs did not pay much attention to that. It may be because most people do not know this art, which is not popular even in the European countries. There were some endeavors to present some dialogue singing on radio but they were not developed to be a sort of opera. Some of the Bedouin singing styles which have the dialogue and the dramatic atmosphere can be developed into some form of operatic singing.

RM How so? If we were to re-define what opera means in relation to the Arabic tradition of singing epic story lines well-known to the people singing. How would the dialogue be heightened and the atmosphere to become viewed as opera to an American audience, for example?

A-H Again, desert songs are multi-form, multi-function. It is as if we have a heap of beads and our job is to make the best wearing-beads of them, not forgetting the dramatic progression. Saying this, I think a fresh fieldwork of archiving these bedouin songs as I have started to do . . . this is needed. As for the American audience I think they are like any other audience.

RM Could an Iraqi water well or the Euphrates River be seen as a natural Monument or operatic in any way?

A-H The space around the wells in the deserts can be ideal for a stage. It gives the director full freedom to plan the positions and the movements of the characters. The constructions around the well, if any, do not make any problem to the director. They can be used to complete the stage setting. As for the river, it always constitutes a natural stage for singing across its waves. If we think of the basic elements of opera the answer would be yes; the simple forms of singing dialogues, which usually performed indirectly across the river or while taking the water from the well, have dramatic elements in them. Although the songs are basically lyrics some fragmented epic pieces are sung too. The bank of the river or the area around the well make an ideal stage for action. There are stories, characters, dialogue, singing, time and space.

RM I remember the story you told me long ago of the Iraqi girl who slept late until the sun burned the jewelry on her ankle. She was very beautiful and everyone let her sleep late. They had already gone to the well together, so she had to go alone and was afraid of the evil spirit in the well. So she brought the outcast of the village along with her. They go to the well and he goes down into the well to draw water for her and the story ends with him looking up to the mouth of the well at the girl. She has loosened her hair. I remember thinking how non-linear and yet linear this story was. How it had a landscape of time to the events but there was no need to resolve in the western tradition. I loved this possibility of what seemed to be a simplicity of syntax and yet there was little sense of capital there—the tight dramaturgy packaging that we have come to sell in American theater as art. I was reading 35 or so classical western libretti over the summer and realizing how sprawling the operatic narratives are there. Wagner for example would never be produced with an unruly libretto like the Ring cycle. Have I remembered it right? Over all these years?

A-H Well let's see . . . the Iraqi girl could be a bedouin girl and she was born years after the youngest child of her parents, which makes her in the position of a grand daughter! The parents spoiled her and dare not wake her up. She arrived at the well to find everybody has already fetched water. The darkness inside the well made the outcast see the mouth of the well like a white disc, which appeared as if it is a picture frame.

RM But how strange that I remember this storyline so clearly. I don't usually remember sequence in this way. I've been thinking again of the colossal characters in opera, characters that Kanan Makiya might be able to see as monumental. Could you talk about how you see the desert songs as both classical/ancient songs archived in an oral tradition and as modern? Are these songs still sung today in Iraq?

A-H Bedouin songs are forms. Text can be changed or adjusted as long as we have plenty of them. We are not introducing them as documentary because the traditional life in the songs still survives in many forms which makes the bedouin song still popular in most countries but with some local differences. The choobi songs for example, were the popular songs of their day. They have even been considered the "hit" songs of the youth.

RM Do you think the story lines of the bedouin songs are monumental in this way, or colossal at all?

A-H Bedouin songs are epic in nature. The difference is that each single song represents an isolated sub-theme of a larger theme which has never been brought together to make one body, like the Greek's colossal epics. It depends on the way we gather the songs that can be arranged into a harmonic narrative line. We have the freedom of choosing a "third world" line of new opera if we want because nobody has tried this before us.

RM I wonder if you can describe what a modern Iraqi water well would look like?

A-H They exist in certain areas in the desert yet they are not the same wells as the classical wells of the Bedouin desert songs of the Upper Euphrates region. Most of them are fitted with pumps to produce water now. If there are some of the traditions left, they serve as tourist places.

RM Dear Ayad, I've been browsing the American painter Maxfield Parrish lately and am struck by some of his more obscure works like "the Garden of Allah" and "the Lamp Seller of Baghdad" and "the Light of Egyptian Nights" which were produced circa 1918-1923 by the General Electric Mazda Lamp calendar and decorated boxes of Cranes chocolates all across America. The "Arabic" women portrayed are neo-classically reclining in American landscapes with their water vessels beside them looking, now, to my mind—Greek. I've been trying to understand the Balkans lately as a crucible of modernities and antiquities of east and west and trying to understand why I grew up thinking of Greece as European. Which after traveling there, I see that it is not. And thinking of the 1001 Arabian nights and this sort of colossal woman at the well in my mind as biblical and yet also American biblical in such beautiful for spacious skies. I realize that you were only 9 years old when you left Iraq, but I wonder if you could imagine . . . if a modern Iraqi woman were drawing water from a well, what would she feel?

AYAD RAHIM Well, I doubt that there are many women in Iraq today who draw water from a well, except in the far hinterlands. I'm sure she would have a hard life—she'd be concerned for making do with the work of the day which would be quite laborious. She'd have a hard day—and long, too, no doubt. Drawing water, finding wood, probably working in the fields, cooking, minding the children, cleaning the primitive house, mud or reed. She'd be struggling to survive—never mind having the luxury to think or feel about anything. She'd be thinking about all the things she has to do—maybe having a memory here and there—something pleasant, I would hope—but probably just as likely, something unpleasant—about her children, or about her childhood. Maybe to offset the difficult and strenuous work she has to do, she'd want to have something pleasant in mind. Maybe she'd sing a song, too, to pass the time away. Some lament—sort of like the slave songs of America's past. Or Sa'di's desert songs.

RM What do you imagine the Iraqi desert to look like?

AR To be honest—to be sure . . . my images come more from movies than from reality. I'm thinking of *Lawrence of Arabia,* in which there's the striking well scene in which an intruder on one tribe's well is shot dead by a member of the tribe that possesses the well. And there, the well is in the middle of the desert, just a hole in the ground. It's in the middle of a vast expanse of sandy . . . plain . . . flatland—as far as the eye can see. I just remembered seeing a well in the West Bank. It was low. Actually, a couple of wells. It had stone on its lips, around the hole. The hole was covered by something like a man-hole cover. And all around the well's hole, the surrounding area was paved—with cement, and it was slightly inclined. That covered an area, about the size of a medium-sized house—the area that was paved—a light brown, beige color—that surrounded the well. That was near a big-sized town in the West Bank.

RM What is the landscape like around a water well?

AR Well—when it comes to desert . . . on second thought, there are so many—it's hard to know where to start. There is the rocky mountainous, and sometimes hilly, northern Kurdish region. And that tends to be lush, with waterfalls, and you have Amadiya, a town on top of a hill. Sort of rests atop a table, the top of a volcano. Then there's a variety of desert landscapes. I remember on the western plane, it's rocky, almost charcoal-gray. On the road to Najaf and Kerbala, I recall very salty fields, with a woman dressed all in black hoeing the field. She looked very fit—probably in her teens or twenties. We drove by this scene. But the salt made the brown earth speckled in white. It was quite thick, quite apparent—the salt.

RM How do you imagine the Euphrates River?

AR Well—you know, they say the Euphrates's water is sweet—I can't speak to that. I do remember driving by some lovely scenes—with bends in the river, and trees overhanging it—could've been eucalyptus, or weeping willows. You know that kind of small-leaved, hanging branched tree. And it's very lush on the banks of the river. Nice place to picnic. It's not necessarily surrounded by trees—not far inland—but right at the edge of the river, at the immediate banks of the river, it's green and leafy . . .

RM Do the images of Afghanistan in the news recently resonate for you with other desert lands?

AR No. Some, such as the mountainous regions—remind me of Kurdistan—a bit. The deserty parts—or, I should say, the beige parts—it's a similar color. Around Najaf and Kerbela, you've got that same color, with the same sun, unbearably hot, beating down on that blank palette.

RM Have you ever seen or visited an American desert?

AR Yes. In Arizona and California. Very different, those. Along Interstate 10, I think it was. All that cactus, and shrubbery. And you've got so much built up—well, I should say, a lot of greenery implanted in the desert—you know, suburban homes with lawns, golf courses, etc. I'm thinking of Palm Springs, and the like.

RM Do you think traveling can provide any sort of cultural mutuality?

AR Absolutely. I guess, it also depends if you get out of the hotel. Out of the areas that cater to tourists—a bit off the beaten path, or just walk around, into the neighborhoods, into the shopping areas, the markets, the bus stations, etc. I'm thinking about my recent trip to Turkey—and how much I got to experience, and see, walking around—through the streets, seeing what the police did to the Senegalese workers, seeing. . . . And the same applies to my travels to England, walking about London, or going around in the countryside. You can certainly tell a lot about the people, its history, their tendencies, proclivities, likes and dislikes, passions . . . . On second thought, even the tourist spots provide a great deal of historical and cultural information, insight, into the society, its ways of thinking, ways of operating, values, mores. I'm thinking about the palaces of the sultans we saw in Istanbul, and all there was to learn and see about the way they lived—their priorities, the segregated living quarters, the way the slaves and eunuchs were treated—you name it.

RM Do you think romanticizing or exoticizing other cultures is more an American convention or is it human?

AR It's very human. I think that Americans are actually more down-to-earth than Europeans, and thus more prone to see the humanity in others, the ordinariness in others, and less prone to stereotype. But that's a natural human instinct, in any case.

RM Do you think of Greece as European or Balkan?

AR European, I guess.

RM Do you think of Turkey as European or Balkan or Middle Eastern?

AR Middle Eastern, definitely.

RM I think you and Entifadh [Qanbar] both forwarded to me a *New York Times* article from December 20, 2001 on "SECRET SITES: An Iraqi Defector Tells of Work on at Least 20 Hidden Weapons Sites." It is about an Iraqi civil engineer who personally worked on renovations of secret facilities for biological, chemical and *nuclear weapons in underground wells*, private villas and under the Saddam Hussein Hospital in Baghdad as recently as a year ago.

> Adnan Ihsan Saeed al-Haideri gave details of the projects he said he worked on for Hussein's government and said that several of the production and storage facilities were hidden in the rear of government companies and private villas in residential areas, or underground in what were *built to look like water wells* which are lined with lead-filled concrete and contain no water. He said that he was shown biological materials from a laboratory that was underneath Saddam Hussein Hospital, the largest hospital in Baghdad. [emphasis mine]

When I met Judith Miller at a Council on Foreign Relations and the Iraq National Congress last Friday, she said Adnan is still in the custody of the CIA and that she was surprised I had read this article as it passed so quickly away. What if . . . we were to find out that a surveillance image of Iraqi waterwells was set up to look like a Woman going to a well to draw water when in reality the woman was a chemical weapons engineer in women's dress.

AR Wouldn't put it past Saddam. Although he tries to banish "backwards" images, types, from . . . wipe them off the map. The cultural map, the identity of Iraq.

RM What if . . . Americans were fooled by a "doctored" media story and bombed real water wells with smart bombs and found out later they were just plain water wells . . .

AR That, unfortunately, is part of the picture. Part of the game.

RM Do you think Saddam uses the presumed antiquities of Islam as a mask for his own modernity?

AR I don't think he is. That's not what I got from that article. The wells there are probably quite modern water aqueducts, or water reservoirs. Need to ask an engineer, maybe a water engineer. And that field—irrigation engineering—is quite developed in the Middle East.

RM Is Saddam perhaps trying to use the western world's presumptions of the Middle East as "third world"?

AR I don't think so. He wants to keep things very modern—makes things look very modern. I don't think he's playing around that way. Now, that is, unless I've misread that article.

RM Dear Kanan, I haven't seen you since those days of my following the Iraq Opposition that was once in Boston when I was in grad school, but I pinned one of your Op-Ed articles from the *International Herald Tribune* to my door in November and I am teaching a few chapters from *The Monument* to playwrights at Brown and Yale this semester. I'm trying to apply some aspects of your analysis of monuments to characters in drama that are colossal or larger than life in such times of American redundant realism. I wonder if you have ever considered writing for the theater?

KANAN MAKIYA It is funny you should ask me this as I am just finishing a proposal to write a screenplay for *The Rock*.

RM I wanted to ask you a question about Judith Miller's article on "Secret Sites" in Iraq for possible chemical weapons building inside what look like traditional water wells. Do you think Saddam may be using modern technology to look like ancient or pre-industrial "third world" life in rural Iraq?

KM The "third world" is an ideology, not a real category. And it is the kind of ideology that perfectly suits someone like Saddam. He has since the late 1970s aspired to be the leader of this "third" world—that is why he launched war against Iran in 1980. Had he succeeded, he would have been crowned "leader" of the third world by none other than Fidel Castro in Baghdad (Baghdad had been designated the next site of the non-aligned nations conference). Since all Muslim countries today (with the possible exception of Turkey) are in the "developing" countries category of nations—and are not members of the first or second worlds whatever they are—under this banner of "Third Worldism," Saddam is able to fold the whole Islamic tradition under his wing. This fact alone is a measure of the worthlessness of this category in my eyes.

FIRST ADDENDUM:

Notes from our gathering in Bellagio, Italy at the Villa Serbelloni with Iraqi archivist/singer Sa'di Al-Hadithi and Jewish-American composer Joshua Fried in 1998 to draft the movement of a DESERT SONGS opera that we have been trying to produce for six years with absolutely no interest or support from any American theater or funding organization. (RM)

I. Cluster of Grapes

Mneef sings to Al-lya as she draws water. That night he goes to Sheikh Hammad to ask for Al-lya's hand in marriage. Hammad wants 500 camels for Al-lya's dowry which will cost Mneef seven years of labor. Mneef decides to run away, telling only his mother who packs food for him and kisses him. Mneef sings to Al-lya from the banks of the river as he leaves. Al-lya dreams of his promises inside her tent.

II. Monsi Shepherd

Mneef wanders in the desert foothills until he comes upon the Monsi well, where he asks the Sheikh Sla-man to be a camel boy, but the Sheikh says he must start as a shepherd for a few years. He works for a year very hard to earn a dowry for Al-lya, sometimes singing songs to the sheep about her.

III. The Rose Torment

Mneef hears the thunder of tribal conflict in the distance of the desert. He goes to fight for the Sheikh's tribe to defend the wells from an agressive caravan in the drought. They agree to let their flocks drink occasionally from the Monsi well. Mneef is injured in the conflict and happens to notice the Sheikh's young daughter Reem coming to the mouth of the well with the outcast David because she is afraid of a hanish (large snake) in the well.

IV. Chimi Truffles (wild brown mushrooms)
Mneef and Reem collect truffles from the cracked ground after a summer flash flood. He falls in love with Reem, forgetting Al-lya's dowry. Reem puts kohl on her eyes in her tent and sings, overheard by her mother.

V. Copper Jar
Mneef sings Mneef's Gisiid (a desert song wellknown by Bedouins in Iraq and parts of Saudi Arabia generally sung to the tune of the Saamri, a famous war dance, which is usually accompanied by the Tabl). Mneef dreams that he travels home to his tribe after seven years and finds only Al-lya's mother, Mariam, swimming in very deep water, shining like a copper jar. She sings to him about the Euphrates in the "fertile crescent," still flowing strong and wise and beautiful in the desert.

SECOND ADDENDUM:
"Sarajevo Carsisi" *(a draft of aria material written in June of 2001 in the Muslim marketplace in Sarajevo for a new opera I am writing about a classical woman married to a modern man which caused the impresario to say she'd rather I set the opera in Venice because there have been so many awful things happening in Bosnia that people don't want to hear about when they go to the opera). (RM)*

TASSOS *(draft of aria material)*
where is my little black dog, said the ingenue
her dresses are closed, her mama's name is Jasmine
"Welcome here for copper kava and a perfect dress for you"
(you'd be damn'd romani jealous of this Ottoman boutique)
where Jasmine's son is spilling the piano Sarajevo
knock on wood to keep them out of poverty so byzantine
the lace grown thick across the blown out windows
ghosts still flung across the Carsisi
and blood still rushing in the bookstore
cursored past my periwinkle screens
for such a gypsy traviata
as she pours her grappa aria
choking back her waterpipe agony

heirlooms pressed . . . into her bosom
as the land split open into three
"how do you wash these painted dresses?"
I drink, in broken sympathy
stepping on a little black dog underneath
"what is the size of her?" she winks
"I show you how your wife look twenty
and have a concert by herself"
and how she dip her bread
into the rancid looking meat
if you slip a little bit of gypsy
into virtuoso orthodoxy
strolling grim and dull as hatred
in the battle-streaked mahoganny
such a gypsy traviata
as she pours her propaganda
"what is your mother's song about in English?"
I ask the dervish (in your bodice)
what in English might be simply this:
that her father was maybe too old but a good man
that her mother maybe thinks this way about her father
that her mother maybe sings too much by ear but was a good Muslim wife.
and I feel myself in mortal danger here where the fathers' flowers once exploded in the birdseye deconstructed marketplace . . . Once bewailed as "how can such humanity survive its sufferings in the back of such boutiques?" . . . "How can sorrow's children both be twenty? and virtuoso and dirt poor?
and jack up the price of your dress ? (and summon the police?)
while snoring face down on the dressing floor?
strolling grim and dull as hatred
in the battle-streaked mahoganny
"It will ruin you in this day and age to stare full frontal at me wide-eyed all the time, without a little sidelong second guessing. It's shameful in this day and age.
To love this way."

Act 2, Sc 1 Heartsong Aria from Night Vision by Ruth Margraff ©1999
Music by Fred Ho
Intro: freely/menacingly
open
cluster-effects
open
ON Q
(horns)
8vb
open → vocal ad lib (see below)
I Ca-a-w'---Al-ll to you wild.
I Ca-a-w'---Al-ll you from my he-eart.
I Ca-a-w'-al-ll (mejana) to you wild.
I Ca-a-w'-al-ll (mejana) from my he-eart.
If you reach me deeply to my he-eart and
grasp it lightly as I quicken limb to limb
you rest your warmth upon my...
the trees that cast a shadow to the carpet
(back of the wireless) whe-en...
the circuit breaks you stumble to my he-eart
to nurse my outcr-y... lay your weary head
and with your fingers parting, with your mouth.
to letter A (dance tempo)
A dance tempo

CLAIMING TO PRESERVE US AS THE SACRIFICE GOES LIMP
YOU KNEW A THOUSAND YEARS AGO MY PULSE
WOULD STIR YOUR FOETUS
TO THE THRALL SEALED SHUT AGAINST THE
WIDE-EYED GLOTTIS
(DRAGGING ME DOWN LIKE AN ARROW)
*SO EAGER TO BE CIRCUMCISED SO **Y-OU** COULD WITNESS*
***Y-OU** COULD DRIVE THE WOLVES BACK BY THE FANG*
*SO **Y-OU** COULD FEEL MY (SO NIGH) DYING*
WITH MY SLIT VOICE CRY-YING TO YOU. CRY-YING WILD.
GIVING WITH ABANDON UP THE GHOST
THE WALLS OF MY HEART THICKEN WITH YOUR TIMING
(SLOWLY TO ENSURE THE EXCITATION)
WHEN I OPEN UP MY HE-EART.
WHEN I OPEN UP MY HE-EART.
WHEN I OPEN UP MY HE-EART.
MADE LIKE SLAUGHTER IN THE DARK I SEEM TO YOU?
MY LAMB SHORN TO THE BREAST?
STRIPPED TO THE MURMUR?
THUS YOU LUST THE SAVAGE BY MISTAKE

BREAK IT NOW. PLEASE (OH GOD)
BREAK IT AGAIN.

Act 2, Sc1 Heartsong Aria
13
G–
G–7
Ab–
G
(8vb)
Chorus
Ah
(horns)
Chorus ♀
Aj- lin- na
Id-Di-bay-ih
(OPTIONAL ♀)
♂
8vb

FOURTH ADDENDUM

Handwritten notes to Sa'di from Austin, Texas in Spring, 2001. An attempt to write in a narrative as simply as I possibly could muster, trying to restrain any of my usual American impulses toward the more decorative, neo-biblical language I tend to write naturally. (RM)

I lean toward the well. With the water vessel there. I am born to its stones, built around her face. I brush away the long hair from her eyes. Her breath stirring the ripples. Sweet with her tongue. I want her to stand behind me again, looking to the deep. Press my thighs when it is dark and we travel home. I ache in my bones to carry her lambs across my lap. In the psalms, curl into the wool. She would put the grapes into my hands every morning before I go, carry my seed in her loins as it stood itself into a man. She would wash my grandmother's body as she stiffened on the mat. Put the grain to her dry lips. I will meet Battat's rose torment in the South, where the mouths of the Tigris and Euphrates ravage each other, a cradle spread like thirst. My betrothed kneels down to pull back the curtain, to go in unto me. Waits for me 6 years and then 6 days of fasting and kneeling, bathed in myrrh and henna. Lain all day in the rocks' heat. My face filling her mind, walking, towards her face. She sees my body in the cleft of the rock. She sees me walk against the sky. But she is too quiet for my liveliness. I take her sister and work in the fields, a wild gazelle, torn with longing. I lower myself to her sister's shoulders as she sleeps. She suckles me as a breast, drawing out the seed like milk in blazing sun. Nothing moves but a damp scorpion into the wool, drawing slowly up the moon. The second wife is pale and speaks in riddles, naked children tangled in her weeping, closing her eyes, the village suckling her. Her sheep fall down the steepness. The brother running. Our mother comes to the doorway and sighs. In my brother she sees my face but a distant wool for his feet, he tries not to step on as he walks. Her children run rampant in his legs, her womb shut to the noise. He moves into my face in her mind, but she does not turn to him in the dark. You came here, her mother would sing. But we pulled her from her sadness out of my womb. Why does she cry so often. Nothing monstrous in the well. No evil, just slowness of walking. It will slow down her thoughts and feet into the bucket. I will vanish as the shepherds do, in the mouth of the well, quick as a knife in a brother's face. She will reach for the likeness of me with her eye falling into him, wherever he goes. The wrong brother, no. "No. No. It would slip behind him." Something missing in the eyes. "The monuments of water scent the reeds" they say. The heaviness of me will keep her sturdy in the wind. So she won't blow away too, like the brother. Everybody sings about the brother who blew away with the sand and a small stone inside, they say. He would have grown into a heavy stone. Lain on top of her ribcage. They would have blown away together with the time. But I left you underneath my brother barely able to breathe in his monstrous snoring, arisen as a scarlet demon in his sleep.

My heart finds no enjoyment but in you, my homeland.
You, who always straighten up what is leaning
When people ask for a drink, they get water
But you drink the red blood of the enemy.
—The Choobi Songs of the Upper Euphrates In Iraq *(Al-Hadithi)*

FIFTH ADDENDUM

www.liberateiraq.org

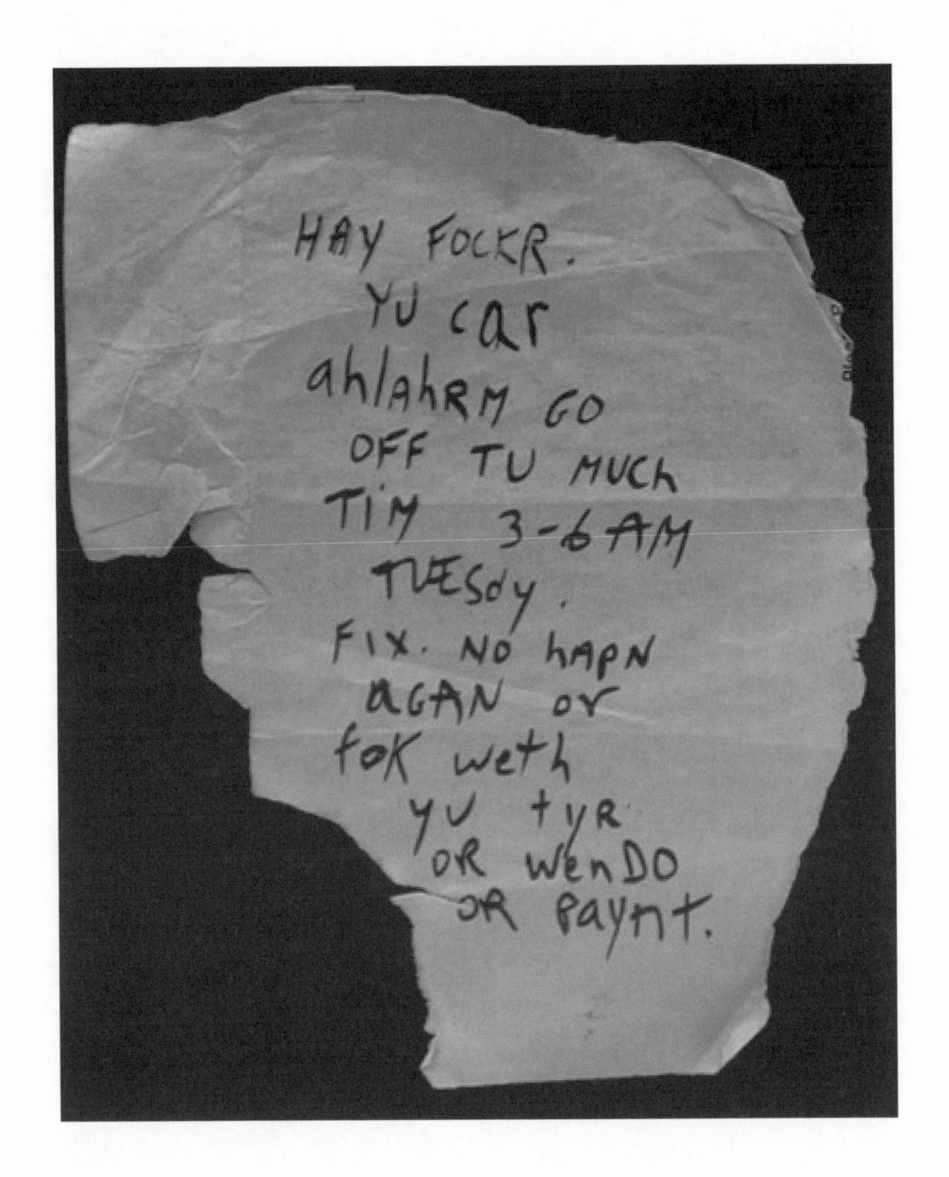
HAY FOCKR.
YU car
ahlahrm GO
OFF TU MUCh
TIM 3-6AM
TUESdy.
FIX. NO hapN
aGAN or
fok weth
yu tyR
OR wenDO
OR paynt.

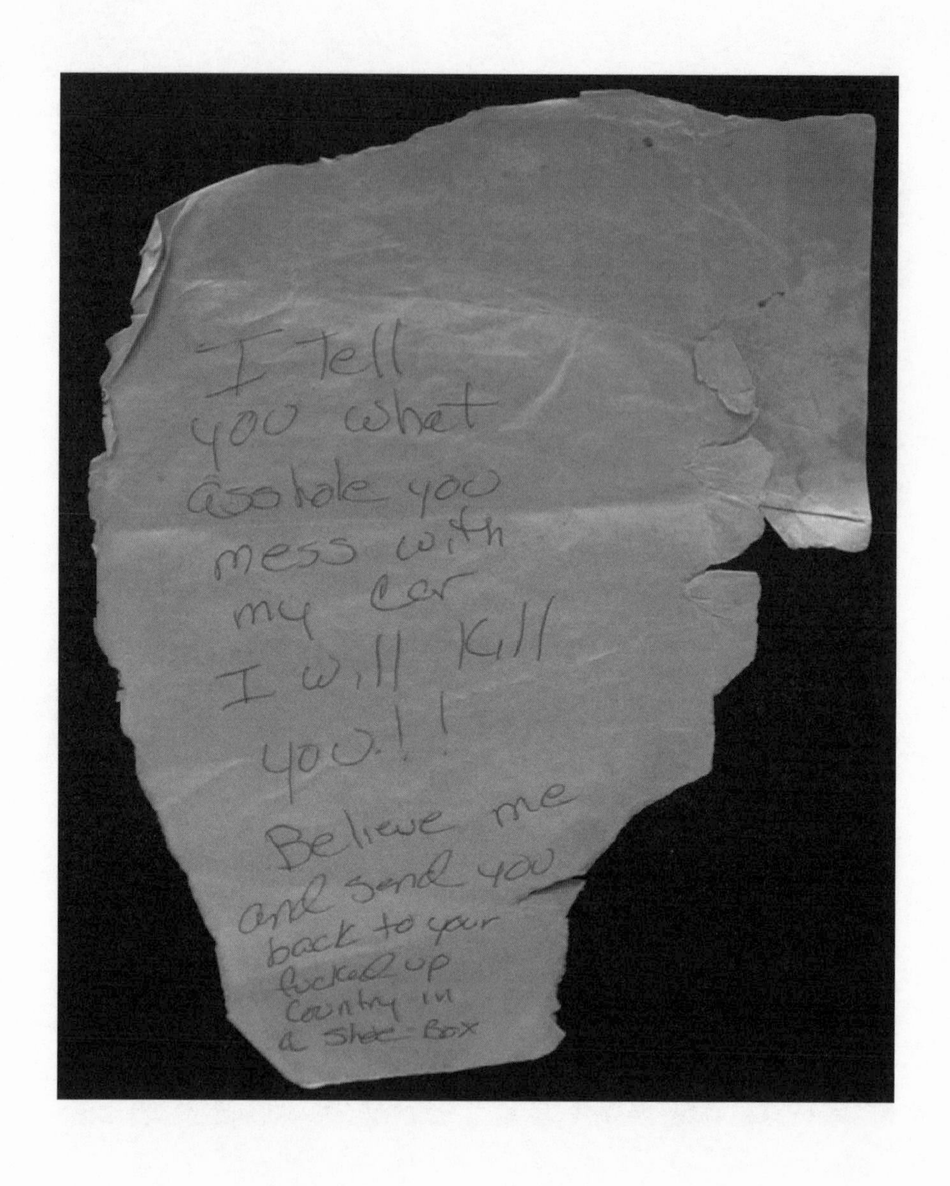

I Tell
you what
asohole you
mess with
my car
I will kill
you!!
Believe me
and send you
back to your
fucked up
country in
a Shoe Box

Found May 7, 2001 at 47th Street in New York City.

SEAN MEEHAN & MICHELLE SPENCER

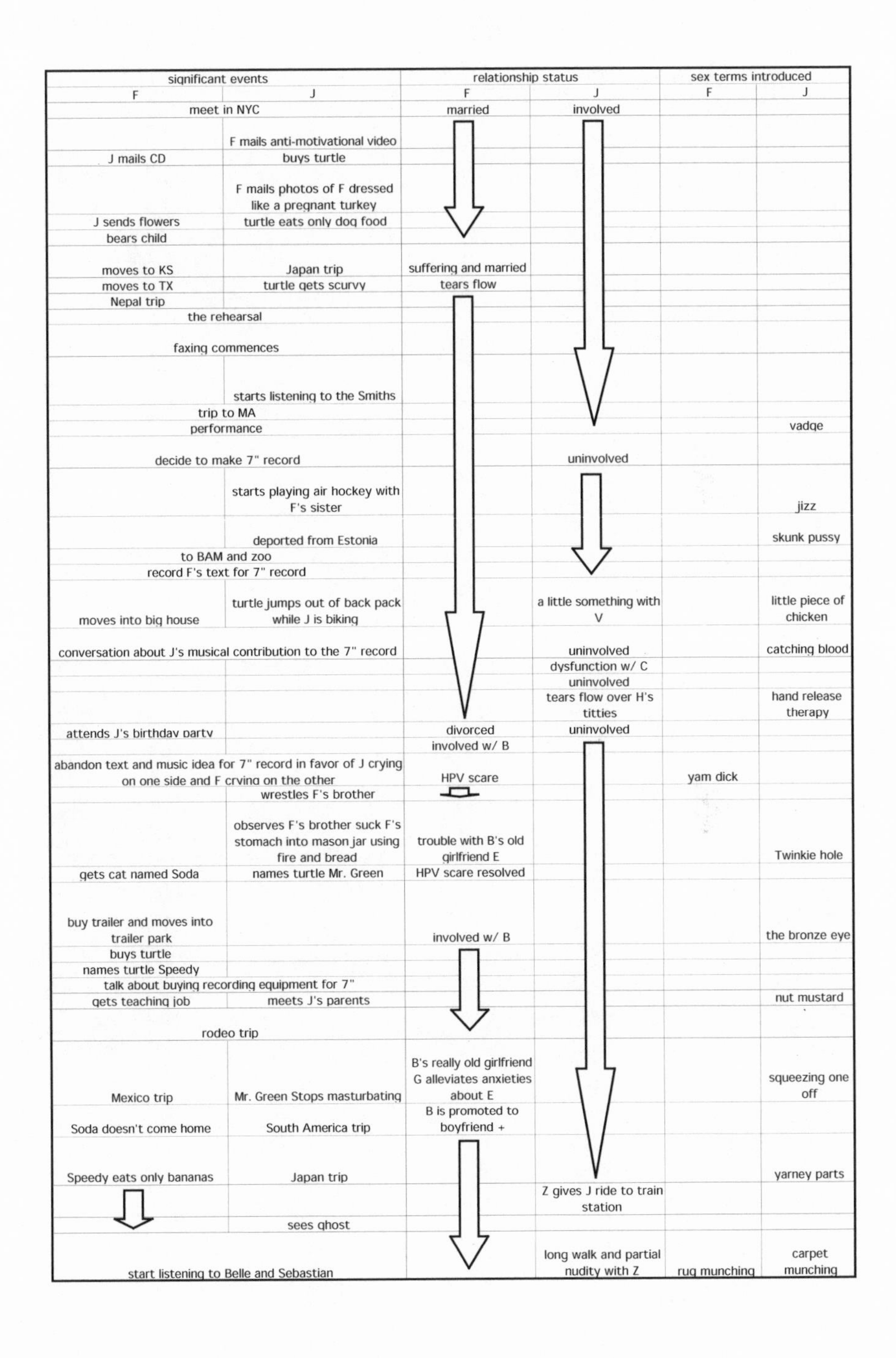

significant events		relationship status		sex terms introduced	
F	J	F	J	F	J
meet in NYC		married	involved		
	F mails anti-motivational video				
J mails CD	buys turtle				
	F mails photos of F dressed like a pregnant turkey				
J sends flowers	turtle eats only dog food				
bears child					
moves to KS	Japan trip	suffering and married			
moves to TX	turtle gets scurvy	tears flow			
Nepal trip					
the rehearsal					
faxing commences					
	starts listening to the Smiths				
trip to MA					
performance					vadge
decide to make 7" record			uninvolved		
	starts playing air hockey with F's sister				jizz
	deported from Estonia				skunk pussy
to BAM and zoo					
record F's text for 7" record					
moves into big house	turtle jumps out of back pack while J is biking		a little something with V		little piece of chicken
conversation about J's musical contribution to the 7" record			uninvolved		catching blood
			dysfunction w/ C		
			uninvolved		
			tears flow over H's titties		hand release therapy
attends J's birthday party		divorced	uninvolved		
		involved w/ B			
abandon text and music idea for 7" record in favor of J crying on one side and F crying on the other		HPV scare		yam dick	
	wrestles F's brother				
	observes F's brother suck F's stomach into mason jar using fire and bread	trouble with B's old girlfriend E			Twinkie hole
gets cat named Soda	names turtle Mr. Green	HPV scare resolved			
buy trailer and moves into trailer park		involved w/ B			the bronze eye
buys turtle					
names turtle Speedy					
talk about buying recording equipment for 7"					
gets teaching job	meets J's parents				nut mustard
rodeo trip					
Mexico trip	Mr. Green Stops masturbating	B's really old girlfriend G alleviates anxieties about E			squeezing one off
Soda doesn't come home	South America trip	B is promoted to boyfriend +			
Speedy eats only bananas	Japan trip				yarney parts
			Z gives J ride to train station		
	sees ghost				
start listening to Belle and Sebastian			long walk and partial nudity with Z	rug munching	carpet munching

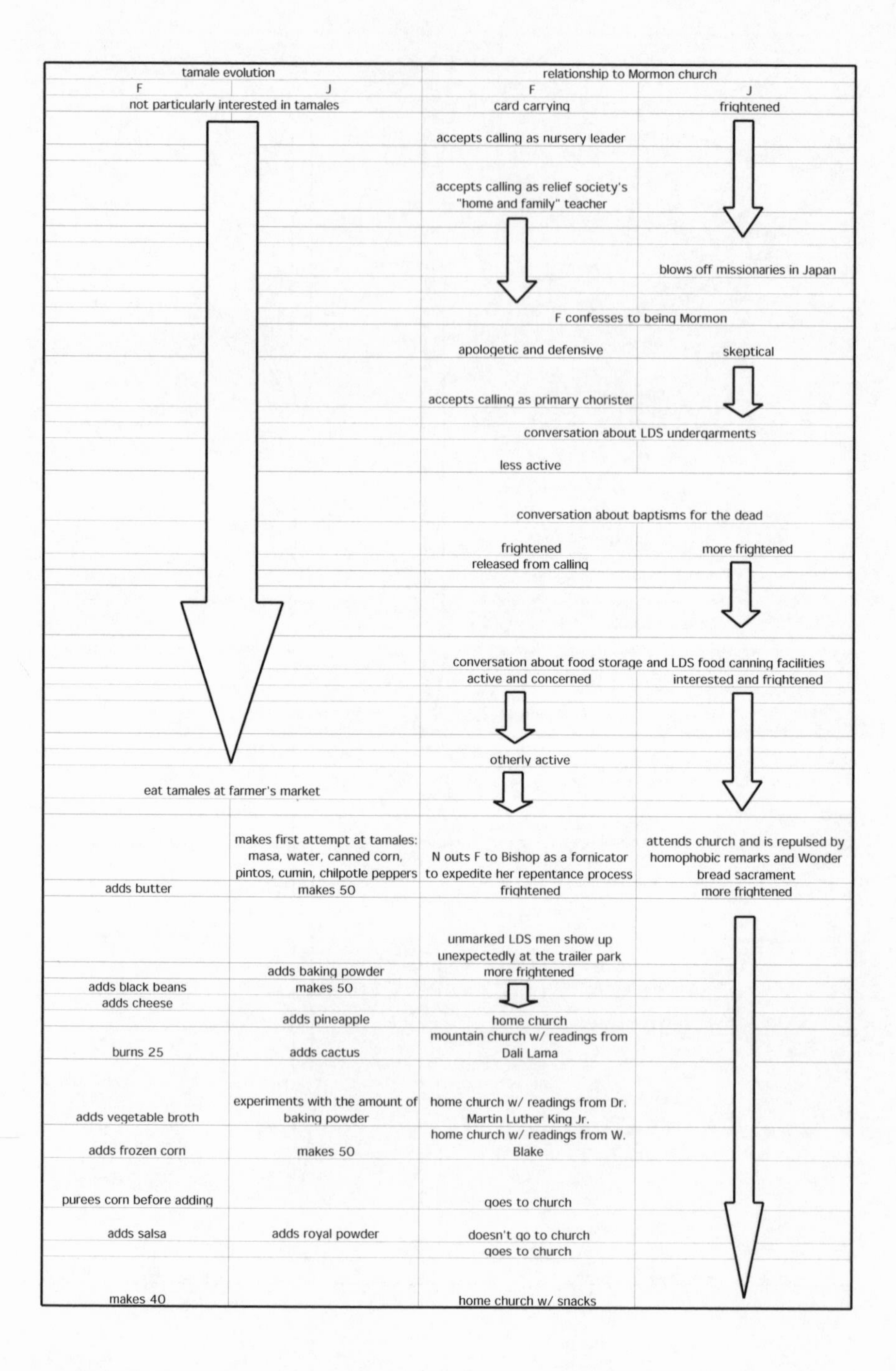
tamale evolution
relationship to Mormon church
F
J
F
J
not particularly interested in tamales
card carrying
frightened
accepts calling as nursery leader
accepts calling as relief society's "home and family" teacher
blows off missionaries in Japan
F confesses to being Mormon
apologetic and defensive
skeptical
accepts calling as primary chorister
conversation about LDS undergarments
less active
conversation about baptisms for the dead
frightened
released from calling
more frightened
conversation about food storage and LDS food canning facilities
active and concerned
interested and frightened
otherly active
eat tamales at farmer's market
makes first attempt at tamales: masa, water, canned corn, pintos, cumin, chilpotle peppers
N outs F to Bishop as a fornicator to expedite her repentance process
attends church and is repulsed by homophobic remarks and Wonder bread sacrament
adds butter
makes 50
frightened
more frightened
unmarked LDS men show up unexpectedly at the trailer park
adds baking powder
more frightened
adds black beans
makes 50
adds cheese
adds pineapple
home church
mountain church w/ readings from Dali Lama
burns 25
adds cactus
experiments with the amount of baking powder
home church w/ readings from Dr. Martin Luther King Jr.
adds vegetable broth
home church w/ readings from W. Blake
adds frozen corn
makes 50
purees corn before adding
goes to church
adds salsa
adds royal powder
doesn't go to church
goes to church
makes 40
home church w/ snacks

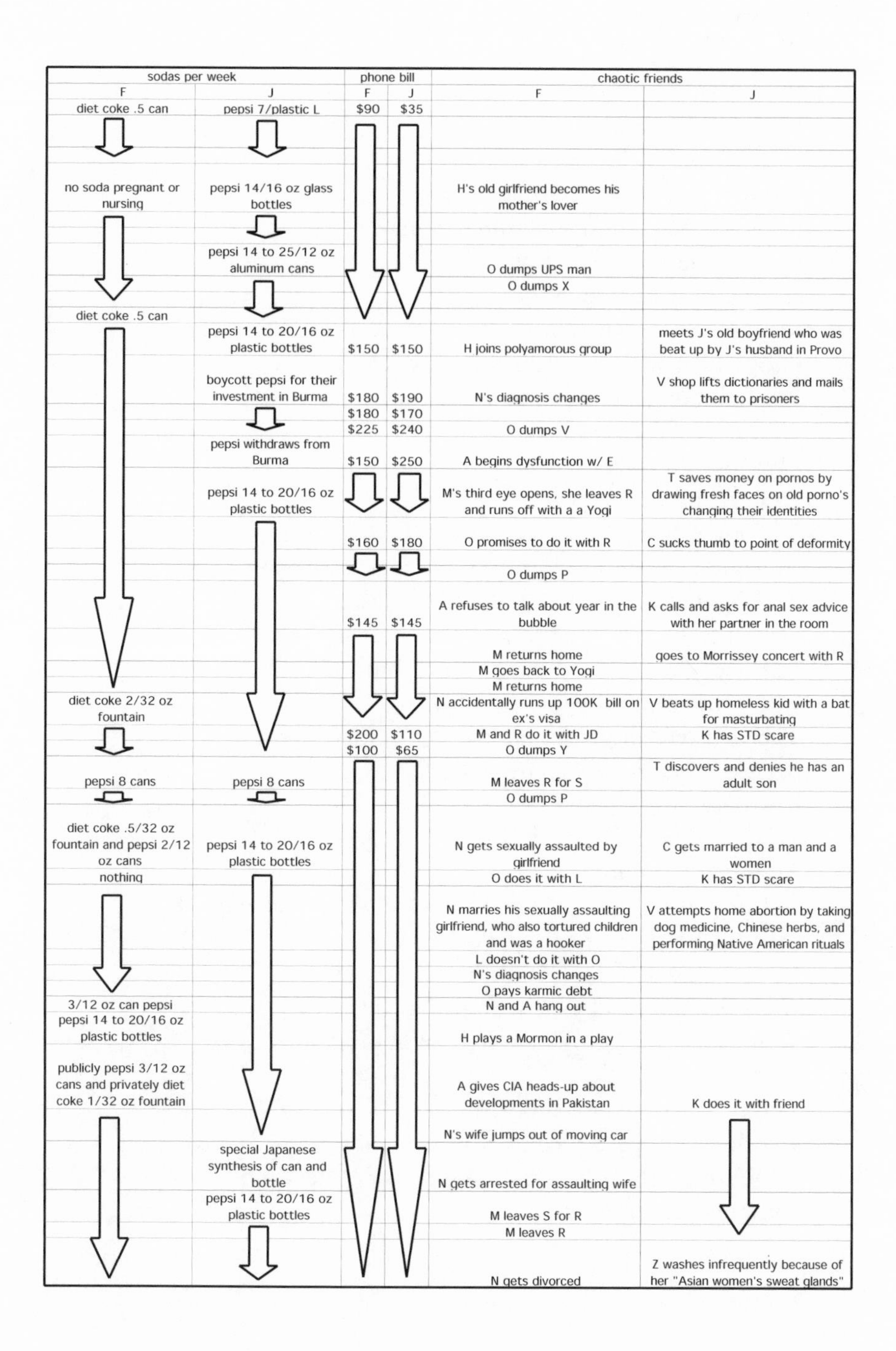

sodas per week		phone bill		chaotic friends	
F	J	F	J	F	J
diet coke .5 can	pepsi 7/plastic L	$90	$35		
no soda pregnant or nursing	pepsi 14/16 oz glass bottles			H's old girlfriend becomes his mother's lover	
	pepsi 14 to 25/12 oz aluminum cans			O dumps UPS man	
				O dumps X	
diet coke .5 can					
	pepsi 14 to 20/16 oz plastic bottles	$150	$150	H joins polyamorous group	meets J's old boyfriend who was beat up by J's husband in Provo
	boycott pepsi for their investment in Burma	$180	$190	N's diagnosis changes	V shop lifts dictionaries and mails them to prisoners
		$180	$170		
		$225	$240	O dumps V	
	pepsi withdraws from Burma	$150	$250	A begins dysfunction w/ E	
	pepsi 14 to 20/16 oz plastic bottles			M's third eye opens, she leaves R and runs off with a a Yogi	T saves money on pornos by drawing fresh faces on old porno's changing their identities
		$160	$180	O promises to do it with R	C sucks thumb to point of deformity
				O dumps P	
		$145	$145	A refuses to talk about year in the bubble	K calls and asks for anal sex advice with her partner in the room
				M returns home	goes to Morrissey concert with R
				M goes back to Yogi	
				M returns home	
diet coke 2/32 oz fountain				N accidentally runs up 100K bill on ex's visa	V beats up homeless kid with a bat for masturbating
		$200	$110	M and R do it with JD	K has STD scare
		$100	$65	O dumps Y	
pepsi 8 cans	pepsi 8 cans			M leaves R for S	T discovers and denies he has an adult son
				O dumps P	
diet coke .5/32 oz fountain and pepsi 2/12 oz cans	pepsi 14 to 20/16 oz plastic bottles			N gets sexually assaulted by girlfriend	C gets married to a man and a women
nothing				O does it with L	K has STD scare
				N marries his sexually assaulting girlfriend, who also tortured children and was a hooker	V attempts home abortion by taking dog medicine, Chinese herbs, and performing Native American rituals
				L doesn't do it with O	
				N's diagnosis changes	
				O pays karmic debt	
3/12 oz can pepsi				N and A hang out	
pepsi 14 to 20/16 oz plastic bottles				H plays a Mormon in a play	
publicly pepsi 3/12 oz cans and privately diet coke 1/32 oz fountain				A gives CIA heads-up about developments in Pakistan	K does it with friend
				N's wife jumps out of moving car	
	special Japanese synthesis of can and bottle			N gets arrested for assaulting wife	
	pepsi 14 to 20/16 oz plastic bottles			M leaves S for R	
				M leaves R	
				N gets divorced	Z washes infrequently because of her "Asian women's sweat glands"

METTE MOESTRUP

Mnasidica

Today I picked up the fragment
in which Mnasidica has a prettier figure
than gentle Gyrinno. Nothing
about her is known. She's a name
in a fragment. Mnasidica. Dicka. Mica. Bind dill
into your hair. Don't slam the car door like that.
You shouldn't be there, in pencil,
on a note, all crumbled.
My note. My handwriting.
Dear Dolores. Dollie.
The men, here, are so beautiful—it's
contagious. Is he too beautiful for me, you think?
And how about him? He doesn't believe
in beauty, he says, then there's a pair of us,
and pop! then we are three. Does your child play
with a fish behind your back, too?
The mackerel has a mouth
but we don't eat it. We are hungry.
It is because the child
ate the entire fish.
All but the mouth
and now the mouth is lying there. Right there: Mnasidica
Mnasidica it sighs to the dolls
for they speak, too. 7 Afghani children
are presumed dead. Apart from that, all is well.
Tonight we are going to watch an abnormal
twin fetus on TV.
There will be many problems
and they will be difficult to solve.
It will be in the 15th week of gestation, and almost totally
without a head.

Mnasidica

Today I picked up the fragment
in which Mnasidica has a prettier figure
than gentle Gyrinno. Nothing,
about her is known. She's a name
in a fragment. Mnasidica. Dicka. Mica. Bind dill
into your hair. Don't slam the car door like that.
You shouldn't be there, in pencil,
on a note, all crumbled.
My note. My handwriting.
Dear Dolores. Dollie.
The men, here, are so beautiful – it's
contagious. Is he too beautiful for me, you think?
And how about him? He doesn't believe
in beauty, he says, then there's a pair of us
and pop! then we are three. Does your child play
with a fish behind your back, too?
The mackerel has a mouth
but we don't eat it. We are hungry.
It is because the child
ate the entire fish.
All but the mouth
and now the mouth is lying there. Right there: Mnasidica
Mnasidica it sighs to the dolls
for they speak, too. 7 Afghani children
are presumed dead. Apart from that, all is well.
Tonight we are going to watch and abnormal
twin fetus on TV.
There will be many problems
and they will be difficult to solve.
It will be in the 15. week of gestation, and almost totally
without a head

I mailed the poem to five people. It was a test (I planned to repeat the experiment in a larger scale with 500 persons). I found the names in the phonebook. I chose at random among names with the initials M. M. I asked the persons to inscribe or rewrite the poem and return it to me in an enclosed stamped envelope. Three out of five did not respond. One rejected in blue capital letters on the back of the letter: "Dear M. M. I am an old lady of 82 years and unfortunately I can not write poetry so unfortunately I have to return your material. Yours sincerely Molly Møller." One wrote the letter in black pen on white paper. He or she had chosen to be anonymous.

The statistics don't overwhelm me. How would 100 handwritten versions of "my" poem look? For they would, I suppose, really LOOK different. And on several levels interfere with the original/ printed/ single/ final poem. I think of it as an experiment with reading and (re)writing: A correspondence or dialogue between poet and reader which can change the poem.

Translated by Thomas Schødt Rasmussen.

CARLOS NAVARRETE

Two Forms of Dialogue in Relation to Landscape: Marking as Absence, Memory as Presence

On last Monday, July 20—as I was developing a project in Como, Italy—I received the following e-mail from my colleague in New York, Eduardo Larrea, which read more or less as follows:

"Hello, If you can, look at this image. You will find it interesting, it is the explosion of the gas towers near where I used to live . . . I remembered that you took some photographs of them . . ."

Before ending his message, Eduardo attached a link to a website so that I could access the event. But I was unable to do this and see the images of that explosion.

Days later—back in Santiago, Chile—I asked Eduardo to explain to me in more detail the purpose of that explosion, as I had been unable to access the image. In his message of August 6, Eduardo made an eloquent attempt to describe the event. His message read more or less as follows:

"*The towers had been unused for a long time and there are plans to use the land for something. The cheapest way to get rid of them was using dynamite. They fell like two gigantic trees and now rest, one over the other, like two whales aground on the sand . . .*"

After reading that e-mail I began to rethink and reflect about the series of ephemeral actions I did during the New York summer of 1997 in the areas of Brooklyn and Manhattan.

Perhaps motivated by curiosity or by the fascination of trying to mark my presence in this determinant urban landscape, I concluded that a series of dialogues had arisen between a domino piece—intervened using color—and the city as backdrop. I had been doing this since the nineties (in different parts of the world) using various objects or markings that I considered emblematic, for my visual work: but which in the city of New York acquired a new cultural and geographical sense for my plastic concerns.

As I recalled at that time, this series of ephemeral interventions of landscape came about as a result of the need to establish a dialogue between objects and identity. This need led me to seek out some kind of object that would transmit or outline that "*need for identity*."

With the passing of time and the accumulation of experience, this activity became a plastic game where cultural, cartographic and even biographical elements intertwine. These elements gradually determined a *modus operandi* in relation to landscape understood as a theater of operations (multiple and stimulating) where these interests may be visualized.

A few days ago, I revised the image file containing visual records of the series of ephemeral actions carried out that summer of 1997, perhaps as a way to seek for an explanation for the sudden transformations suffered by that urban environment. But, also, trying to establish possible correspondences in this absence/presence dialogue that the concept of identity draws from landscape and memories.

September of 2001

I want you
more than I
have you I

want to be
you more than
I want you

If I'm
rocking back but pulling
where
you're leaning toward the
point where
we'll balance if you'll
just
hold me still everything
will still
be the same for
you—agreed?

One two three, two two three
One two three, two two three

I'll sing you the tune of
a genre I know:

It goes when you know two three
I'm touching you two three

That much we know two three
No? two three? You two three
You're holding me and we
call this activity
will accidentally
for the world to see
the genre of poetry

Exploring the space where terror and comfort, pleasure and pain are overlaid, I have done a series of 52 paintings using three small figures, two per painting, in various provocative and ambiguous poses. The figures are familiar toys: a bendable person (either a male or a female), and a plastic dinosaur. The paintings are done in a light style similar to ink brush drawings, in blue paint on high gloss white, reminiscent of Delft tiles. The paintings are metaphorical in that each gesture or pose suggests an often contradictory variety of emotional meanings. The relationship displayed can be read as between 2 figures or between different parts of oneself. At the same time they are clearly paintings of toys. The 52 paintings as a whole do not form any narrative progression; instead, each painting poses a variation of some basic questions: is this play or struggle, or both at once, who is carrying whom, who is in control? (FS)

Francie finished the series in 2000. We had been planning to renew our collaborative work for some time, and as I saw the paintings emerge, I kept wanting to write poems to them, but didn't begin until the Fall of 2001. I tried to do justice to the exhilarating and terrifying primal meanings that I see the paintings display with such passionate wit. (BP)

JOSÉ PÉREZ DE ARCE

Dying Ancient Tongues

SONG OF THE BIRD BECOMING EXTINCT

9000 years ago, the loica, the tortolita cuyana, the zonal, the peken, the turca, the diuca, the chincol, the tenca, the cherkan and the cachudito would sing the following concert every morning in the small valley behind my house, in the quarries of Colina. Now there is a condominium being built there. Soon the space will be silent.

chip chip chichi chipiu piuu tuiiii chip chip chiu chiuuu
chuit chuit cchiu chiu pirr pirrrrr chit chit chuirr
chuirrrrrrrr chhio chip chip uet uet chip chi chirri
chirri chip chip chichi piuu pirrrrr chip chuit chuit chit
chuirrrrrrrr chip chuit chuit cchiu cchiu cchiu chip
chiu chiuuu chuit chuit cchiu chiu pirr pirrrrr chit
chit chuirr chuirrrrrrrr chhio chip chip uet uet chip
chi chirri chirri chip chip chichi piuu pirrrrr chip chuit
chuit chit chuirrrrrrrr chip chuit chuit cchiu cchiu
cchiu pirrrrr chit chit chuirr chuirrrrrrrr chhio chip
chip uet uet chip chi chirri chirri chip chip chichi piuu
pirrrrr chip chuit chuit chit chuirrrrrrrr chip chuit
chuit cchiu cchiu cchiu chip chiu chiuuu chip chuit
chuit cchiu cchiu cchiu chip chiu chiuuu chuit chuit
cchiu chiu pirr pirrrrr chit chit chuirr chuirrrrrrrr
chip chuit chuit chit chuirrrrrrrr chip chuit

FOUR-EYED TINY TOAD BECOMING EXTINCT

The four-eyed tiny toad has been singing in Chile's central valley consistently for the past 10,000 years. Today it is becoming extinct, relegated to isolated ponds. Recorded in Cachagua in September, 2001.

cre cree cree crecre crecre
crecrecreecrecrecreecrecrecrecrecrecrecreeecrecrecre
crecrecreecrecrecreecrecrecrecrecrecrecreeecrecrecre

crecrecreecrecrecreecrecrecrecrecrecreeecrecrecre
crecrecreecrecrecreecrecrecrecrecrecreeecrecrecre
crecrecreecrecrecreecrecrecrecrecrecreeecrecrecre
crecrecreecrecrecreecrecrecrecrecrecreeecrecrecre
crecrecreecrecrecreecrecrecrecrecrecreeecrecrecre
crecrecreecrecrecreecrecrecrecrecrecreeecrecrecre
crecrecreecrecrecreecrecrecrecrecrecreeecrecrecre
crecrecreecrecrecreecrecrecrecrecrecreeecrecrecre
crecrecreecrecrecreecrecrecrecrecrecreeecrecrecre
crecrecreecrecrecreecrecrecrecrecrecreeecrecrecre
cre cree cree

KAWÉSQAR
BECOMING EXTINCT

From time immemorial, the Kawésqar or Alakalufe peoples have wandered the canals of southern Chile. Now there are only a few remaining, living in Punta Arenas. Recorded by Margarita Molinari, Alberto Achacaz, Maria Luisa, Jose Ramon Paterito and Julio Tonko in September, 1994, in Punta Arenas.

walakial, charlakeyo, jetarkté stocksó workwá keorro afsaiar jaguarájar frichi kse chalás, keiyero stayekan achar akar ienap layiep kesáu akiar akiáu skoi iepcheyo chajok atala itaksta shafkás akchague iaftes kuonoks papéchapana guasrrok ápala ataiyesap yefayejar tajlar chapakana agulke tala urka laaks cherekstayek katoustkal asoi laák tau chapá at kolaf alíjar yakshal chowalchok arrás kinés yetana shaftas erkocsta asar enkstás ajuákar taskar tantar calas skéna, iekshal carwoch, kolak ayarak sharrak anata shersaloja saltajar asar kayak apalá eskiená yahánar kawas kenchhéjal tajaite awana chtáwuech chalá ikulka cham ati yekstaste arkiawe iofita layep melchek tajarieks llabrapu acherksta pakakar acúlator aculaia sectiser acatieser shiuiali yeyaye'afté ufiéli lukaï o lekeurk affiry til'he o li-a-a tash-shelabé uruchkech

Carlos Vega Delgado, When the Sky Grows Dark (samán arkachoé Life History), *Alacalufe testimony of Alberto Achacaz Walakial, 1995.*

KUNZA
EXTINCT
Unknown Sound
The Atacameñan people spoke Kunza from the beginnings of time until 1900.

sima-ninchies balkatur yockto haabu ppáputur yockontur hatratchatur c'locjmaia beu-nítur saarsitur yébitur ckolbacktur ttacktur khûro ckaacka haaru tackackntur ckomal ttutur ckomallechaque hebitur chópar chaickai tchuckun tchicknar hackamur pputo ttusune tacktacknatur ckomuraimir cósco ckaipi tarcktur ckori ckuckuntur kúhri ckatur tchipnatur tcheckuntur hackmur sáamus i saamis tultaptur ckumi kúhri pani hockoltur ckaickai las-si herabuntur yocon-tur ckaipi hay-ps-ckuntur hónanar tússutur cca q´yoconama ckapckitur ckunsa hebíutur licancáur ckeutur!tchatur! hammatur lulantur malckar tussumar ckuri herck-ckar cappin ckocktur ttackatur

Francisco San Román, "The Kunza Tongue of the Indigenous Peoples of Atacama," Magazine of the Secretary of Public Works, *Mining and Geography Sector, reprint Nº 288, Gutemberg Press, Santiago: 1890.*

Pbo. Emilio Vaïsse, Félix 2º Hoyos, Anibal Echeverria Reyes, Glossary of the Atacameñan Tongue. *Cervantes Press, University of Chile, Santiago: 1896.*

CACAN
EXTINCT
Unknown Sound
The Diaguitan people spoke Cacan for millennia, until 1590. One of their chants, of unknown meaning, survived in La Ligua until 1800.

Aliquitaña pelucha anganú anganú angañe chipapalallica numantimayé amomorimeña miracuraye enenante pelucha y más pimeo eñomitaña chipapa

fragment of a chant of unknown meaning, circa 1800.
Between Swords and Basquines, *Ed. Hermelo Arabena W., Zig-Zag Editions, Santiago: 1946.*

SOUNDISMOVEMENT
MOVEMENTISLIFE
SILENSEONLYEXISTS
INLIVINGSABSENSE

EACHSPESIESHASASONG
DIFFERENTFROMANYOTHER
RINGINGOUTEACHINTURN
INNATURALCONSERT
ALLKNOWHATOSING
ALLKNOWHOWTOLISSEN
EXEPTMESOLONELISSENING
TOTHEGREATSITTYBUSSELING

EACHSPESEISDIFFERENT
INITSWAYOFLIVING
HUMANSTANDOUT
ASABLETOANALIZETHINGS

SPESIESDISAPPEAR
LITTLEBYLITTLEFOREVER
CULTURESFADEAWAY
SUDDENLYGONEFOREVER
NTHECULTURESOFTHEWORLD
AREWAYSOFHEARING
EXEPTMESOLONELISSENING
TOTHEGREATSITTYBUSSELING

THEYSAYGODCREATEDMAN
NGAVEHIMAPARADISE
ASLONGASHEDIDNEAT
FROMTHATREEOFSIENSE

NFORHISDISOBEDIENSE
HESLOSTHISINNOSENSE
ALLOFASUDDENIREELIZE

THEPRICEWEEVHADTOPAY
STHATWERESPONSIBLE
FORGOVERNINGTHISWORLD
EXEPTMESOLONELISSENING
TOTHEGREATSITTYBUSSELING

ICANTACTLIKEMDEAFANYMORE
INTHEABSENSEOFSILENSE
ASITSOVERYNESESSARY
ANDCANTBETRANSMITTED

EACHNAMESASOUND
INTHISIMMENSECONSERT
NAMETHEBIRDTHATSINGING
NAMETHEWINDWHENITSBLOWING
NAMEPEEPLEWHENWEERSPEAKING
INSOMANYDIFFERENTWAYS
EXEPTMESOLONELISSENING
TOTHEGREATSITTYBUSSELING

OURGRANDPARENTSCONVERSED
WITHALLTHEANIMALS
UNDERSTANDINGSTRANGELANGUAGE
NLISSENINGALITTLEBIT

EVERYTHINGHADITSONGS
EACHTHINGINITSOWNMOMENT
INJUSTALITTLEWHILE
THEYLLNEVERHAVETHEMAGAIN
THOSEWHOKNEWTHEMHAVEDIED
BUTNOONEREELIZEDIT
EXEPTMESOLONELISSENING
TOTHEGREATSITTYBUSSELING

NAVIGATINGTHEDESERT
FROMEVERYHORIZONPOINT
PRESERVINGTHECUSTOMS
THOUGHSOLITTLEREMAINS

LETSGOTHENBIDDINGFAREWELL
MOVINGTHROUGHIMMENSITIES
SOMANYTHINGSWEUSETOKNOW
BEFOREWEKNEWHOWTOSPEAK
ANDWHENWEDIDLEARN
THENHADTOFORGETHEM
EXEPTMESOLONELISSENING
TOTHEGREATSITTYBUSSELING

Translated by Jen Hofer.

Hear these poems at http://www.temple.edu/chain.

JANE PHILBRICK
Common Prayer

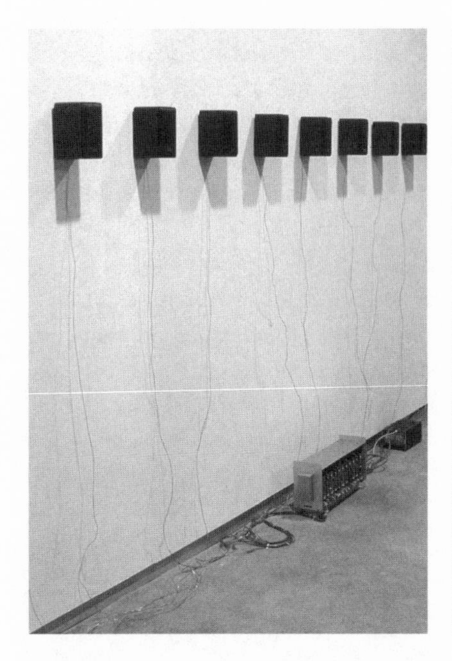

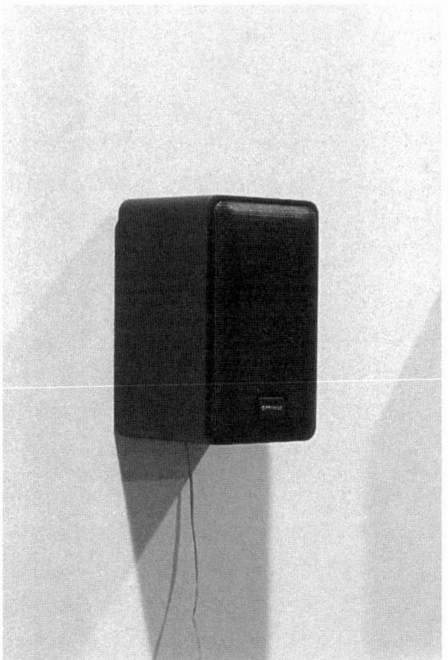

In July 2000, Rudolph Giuliani, his eight-year mayoralty coming to a term-limits-mandated close, was laying the groundwork to reinvent himself from an "only in New York" politician to a mainstage, mainstream national candidate for US senate.

Throughout his controversial, no holds-barred tenure, New York had flourished, but for many of the city's liberal constituency, especially people of color and the working poor, the Mayor remained an extremely polarizing figure.

Notoriously abrasive to those who challenged him, he brooked no dissent in a city of perhaps the greatest diversity of voices in the world. Every New Yorker, as a US citizen, has a constitutionally protected right to freedom of speech. Was this, vis à vis Mayor Giuliani, a right to speak, but not necessarily to be heard?

In her book *The Other Side of Language: A Philosophy of Listening*, Gemma Corradi Fiumara conflates these two speech acts, "Speaking is itself a listening. Speaking is listening to the language we speak." To speak, to think, to dream—all, writes Fiumara, are language-based activities. Being itself, both concious and unconscious, sleeping and waking, is experienced in language, specifically dialogic language, an event of speaking and listening.

Like any public figure, Giuliani is (at least) "double-voiced," on the one hand, symbolically, an elected official representing "the voice of the people," on the other, inescapably himself. The opportunities for personal and public dialogue are manifold; for the mayor of the Greatest City in the World, they are writ large and yet were largely unavailed. It is no coincidence, in pointed contradistinction to his own unhearing rules of engagement, that the central and defining pre-campaign strategy of Giuliani's (ultimately successful) opponent Hillary Rodham Clinton was a statewide "Listening Tour."

To govern with a single voice is antithetical to the workings of a people's government, and presumes as well a delusionally monolithic construction of self, from which authority and power issue. As Richard Azcel discusses in his article "Understanding as Over-hearing: Towards a Dialogics of Voice," self is a multi-voice phenomenon. "[W]hat is heard in voice," he writes, "is not presence per se, but an echo":

> . . . If, as Bakhtin suggests, every utterance is permeated with *heteroglossia*—the tongues of others, with which every utterance is "overpopulated"—every act of speech is an act of ventriloquism, and the source of the voice can never finally be fixed in the presence of the speaker.

In the famously deaf speech of Rudolph Giuliani, there were other voices to be heard; despite his iron will to mute them, other voices speak.

In spring 2000 I visited the Andy Warhol Museum in Pittsburgh, to be captivated once again by the serial silkscreens, the Elvises, the Marilyns, the car accidents. "[T]he painted thing speaks if we listen," John Berger writes in a discussion of the dialogic relationship between painter/model and viewer/work in his essay "Steps Toward a Small Theory of the Visible." What had my ear caught in looking at these works?

Take, for example, the line up of Elvises. Is each canvas saying something different? Or, as in Greek tragedy, are they a chorus, speaking as one? Do they all say the same thing, but individually? Are they speaking at once, or in turn, randomly, or in sequence? Is what is said different heard a second time, a third? How is what the viewer hears looking different from what the artist heard with his eye, from what he heard in the painting, from what he said? "Listening" to the Warhol multiples yielded my own work, *Common Prayer*.

In his book *Dialogism: Bakhtin and His World*, Michael Holquist writes, "there is an intimate connection between the project of language and the project of selfhood: they both exist to mean." As an artist compelled by issues of identity, I am necessarily engaged with language. Now with the advent of digital audio technology, in which sound can be plastically manipulated within thousandths of a second, it is a formal, material engagement with the language-object, voice.

> Thank you. Thank you very, very much. I am a very fortunate man. God has given me a lot. And whatever obstacles are placed in your way I think the way to deal with it is to try to figure out how, how to make it make you a better person. The reason I am such a fortunate person is that I have people who love me and I love them. They care for me, and I care for them.

Opening with these words at a hastily called press conference July 19, 2000, Rudolph Giuliani officially withdrew from the US Senate race, citing health concerns arising from his recently diagnosed prostate cancer. He was hestitant, reflective, emotional, his faltering voice as if "ventriloquized," so discordant was it from the camera view of a battle-hardened politician, whose modus operandi was popularly likened to a pitbull in attack mode.

Words such as these said at such times reverberate with subtexts of fear, of regret, of hope. But for me, they formed a faultline through which a mono-vocal Fortress Giuliani might speak the contesting voices of choatic lived experience.

I brought these words to twelve clergymen of a range of denominations in the Judeo-Christian faith and asked each to speak them for me. Giuliani's plainspoken address had had a kind of plaintive, secular grace and I was attracted to the compounding parallels of voicing the one within the other.

Many of the clergymen commented on the simplicity of the text, relieved perhaps that the recording wouldn't be difficult or in anyway controversial, regretful maybe that it wasn't "better material" to work with, curious perhaps that such humble fare would be the basis for a work of art. With each of them I had thoughtful discussions on art, politics, and religion. One rabbi showed me an Old Testament tome from the library of a 16th-century monk, which he had acquired in Europe. It had handwritten notes in the margins and psalms nested in printed columns of commentary, recording the ongoing dialogue with the sacred texts. He demonstrated with a contemporary volume and much more densely bordered texts that this continues today. The parish of one Methodist minister had recently been a campaign stop on Mrs. Clinton's circuit, and we talked presidential politics as well. With another minister, who had been a philosophy major focusing on Wittgenstein as an undergraduate, we discussed language and the dialogical experience of the Divine, from the speech act pronouncement of Creation ("And the Lord said . . . ") to its mirror re-enactment in the format of call-and-response prayer.

Each of the twelve voices of *Common Prayer* plays through a handsized, black, rectangular speaker hung in a horizontal line across the wall. They are randomly sequenced to play two voices, eight, five, twelve, three, and so on. Sonically, the texts alternately compete with, yield to, support, obscure, reinforce each other. Their differing speech patterns present a diverse breadth of humanity, and the associative interplay of their assembled voices works narratively through strictly formal means.

As part of the ongoing project of meaning making, in which the dialogical is engaged, it is interesting to note a shift in the experience of *Common Prayer* post-9.11. The words Giuliani spoke that millenial July appear now almost prophetic in anticipating the role he would play in the tragedy to strike 14 months later as spokesman for a wounded city, united in grief and mutual care.

With thanks to Reverend Roosevelt Ewell, Reverend Richard Gilchrist, Reverend Frank Greer, Father John Giuliani, Rabbi Geldafayah Jeremias, Rabbi Jon Haddon, Reverend K.P. Hong, Reverend Daniel O'Connell, Reverend Stephen Philbrick, Reverend Barry Rosenberg, Reverend Joseph Washington, Reverend Randolph Weber, and Bob Beliecki.

Hear this piece at http://www.temple.edu/chain.

NICK PIOMBINO & BARRETT WATTEN

The Flag as Transitional Object

Poetics Listserv, September-October 2001

WATTEN "Action/Language," 15 September 2001

I'm grateful for the recent writing about experiences of being in New York. I've also found valuable the sources of analysis and information—the position of the War Resisters League, the information on asbestos in the WTC—that have been sent out on the list. The question I am asking myself now is how to put this material to work—making use of one's perspective, resources, and experience as a poet. Which are incredibly valuable, which we have variously schooled ourselves to do for a reason, for years.

I remember well being at what felt to be at a center of concern, and opposition, to the last national crisis of similar proportion—the Gulf War. In the San Francisco Bay Area, as the date for American attacks approached, and the attacks began, tens of thousands hit the streets as they had many times since the beginnings of the anti-war movement. But this time, the acts of opposition were drowned out by the yellow flags of jingoism and, as Bush [senior] said, roughly, "There are those who oppose this war, but you can't hear them." I think he said "you" rather than "we"—in other words, there was a directive not to hear them, even if one could.

Now that I'm located in one of the areas of the country that wanted not to hear any opposition to the politics and tactics of the Gulf War, I'm concerned to listen for similarities and differences to that time. There are many. From what I understand from people who were here, Detroit—where the capacity for automated production was a major factor propelling America to victory in WWII and afterward, and people now drive Humvees as recreational vehicles—there was a steely solidarity and dumbed-down rhetoric that completely stultified, wiped out any alternatives. And even now I see the same dumb rhetoric in the Detroit papers—of good vs. evil, etc.—that is always less analytic, more invested with an assertion of who we are than even the national norm.

There are differences, even so. The impact of the news, of course, was total. There was a delay, then a somewhat orderly shift to a response. The Big Three let off employees, and there was a calm but intense stream of traffic out of the city center. People who had jobs to do did them. There was not, however, any sense of civic authority to direct this response—it was a seemingly ingrained notion of appropriate action. The only untoward event I noted was a brief episode of gas profiteering ($6 a gallon the night of the attack), which ended in a day or so. The media was the source of trauma—but this is now interpretable in two ways. We know what a media disaster is, by this time, and we also know that the referent is real. If there is a dissociation between the two—that we do not identify media trauma with the referent—that could be a hopeful sign. This is why particular accounts are so important—to dissociate the two experiences of trauma.

Neighborhoods around Detroit have always flown the flag. During the Gulf War, from what I have heard, this was particularly intense. Afterward, however, there was a shift in the practice. Many of the flagpoles that adorn suburban houses started to fly flags that were more fanciful—flowers, panda bears, pumpkins, an innocuous happy-face iconography. Not monolithically the Stars and Stripes. So I am watching for the return of the practice. Gas station flags are at half mast (there are enormous ones). Small flags often line the roads. I have heard of women in malls wearing flag dresses, recently purchased. Where the insignia of the Red Wings hockey team have been flown on plastic attachments to SUVs, I have seen some American flags—when driven at speed, evoking a cavalry rescue, John Wayne style. You can almost hear the charge being sounded. And of course there is the reinforcement of the Battle Hymn of the Republic being sung on TV.

But this is not the whole story. It seems to me there is another attitude—of evaluation, and desire for alternative perspective. Students in my classes at Wayne are interested in unpacking the discourses, rather than suturing them together. There is considerable discussion of not stigmatizing Arab students and residents in Detroit (a large population, from all over the Middle East, which has been here for decades). The university has explicitly addressed this concern.

All night long, when commercial air traffic was halted, one could hear the roar of jets, I assume from Selfridge AFB, in nearby Macomb County. Troops and equipment are being moved up.

I want to keep open the place of alternative analysis, as we are obviously entering into a period of war rhetoric and its military objective—to stultify and paralyze analysis and criticism. What I want to do in response: build up a set of references that can be used in thinking through the present. Yesterday, because I'm teaching the 50s and 60s, I went back through some of the writings of Paul Goodman, for example. An anthology he put together of articles from *Liberation* magazine in 1964 (*Seeds of Liberation*) contained Albert Camus's "Neither Victims nor Executioners"—a title that has to seem quite evocative at present. Some of it is dated, but some entirely true of the post-WWII period that is the framework we are in: "Modern nations are driven by powerful forces along the roads of power and domination. I will not say that these forces should be furthered or that they should be obstructed. They hardly need our help and, for the moment, they laugh at attempts to hinder them. They will, then, continue. But I will ask only this simple question: what if these forces wind up in a dead end . . . ?" Camus advocates an individual act of choice—not to join the party or accomplices of murder—that at least asserts that such an alternative is possible.

I don't think that an act of choice is sufficient, although it is important to think that there is such a thing as an act of choice. There are also the logics that we are embedded in, and cannot choose. Here action also needs to be understood as possible in another sense, and undertaken. Toward that end, I am interested in what Goodman, in another book, says about the role of the writer:

> Writers are linguistic analysts and know the folk wisdom and superstition that exist in common vocabulary and grammar. As General Semanticists, they are critical of the rhetoric of the street, the mass media, and official institutions. They understand, more than most people, what cannot be said, what is not being said though it ought to be, what is verbalized experience, and what is mere words. They can detect when there is really an idea and an argument rather than a cloud of phrases. They can date a passage and show a forgery. As psychologists of language they are sensitive to how people come on when they talk or write, the ploys they use, and the postures they strike. They can hear the personal that is expressed in habits of syntax, and the personal inhibition or freedom that is told by the breathing and rhythm of sentences and the quality of metaphor. They can judge the clarity or confusion or spurious clarity in an exposition. They are sociologists of language and can recognize the social background in vocabulary, pronunciation, and routine formulas.

> At the same time as they know all this, however, in their own writing they must let their speech come spontaneously: it is free speech, though they monitor it critically. (*Speaking and Language: Defense of Poetry*, 1971)

Goodman's political alternative is spontaneity, which solves the question of internal censorship and external valuation of the authenticity of speech, at the same time. While everything in this passage is, I think, baseline politics to many poets, there is also an understanding that the social character of "language" is precisely what makes spontaneity not an automatic alternative. And we have continued to explore that tension between the call to authenticity and the experience of being embedded in contexts, being spoken, being subject to discourses outside and beyond oneself.

I would like to build up some resources that would help think through the present. A more recent title that came to hand is Roy Gutman and David Rieff, eds., *Crimes of War: What the Public Should Know* (Norton, 1999)—lucid discussions of acts of war, rules of engagement, war crimes, international law, and so forth. I would be grateful for other such resources, and also for specific urls (War Resisters League, Chomsky, other perspectives, asbestos reports, poetic responses, and so forth) that could then be brought together in a single place.

Thanks, Barrett

PIOMBINO "The Flag as Transitional Object," 18 September 2001

Like many other listees I am grateful for this opportunity to read the (mostly) carefully considered statements on this list during such an agonizing and frightening time. It seems to me that this is the most important time in recent history to remember that all viewpoints and responses are partial; each has a point of view; no one point of view reflects the entire situation or reality. This, of course, is the essential purpose of rational discussion and debate. That said I want to add one point coming from my experience as a psychoanalyst. A patient of mine was able to get close to Ground Zero. He was shocked and disappointed to see some people taking snapshots of their children sitting on the rubble. In this regard I spoke to him about Winnicott's theory of transitional objects. To paraphrase and greatly generalize: Winnicott discovered that from early childhood on, people sometimes have a need for an object to hold on to at times of loss. The fact that a lost object (person or thing or experience) can continue to exist in the mind, sometimes by means of a physical reminder, might explain a lot of behavior that otherwise might appear incomprehensible. A young child might get very frightened if mother is absent, but feels better when hanging on to a blanket when she is not there, an object deeply associated with her presence. This is one way that we develop the psychological function of memory. This may help to explain why people need to hold on to things like flags. I realize that there is a darker side to this, that flag waving can represent symbolic support for acts of war. Like many others reading the poetics list, this horrifies me. But the psychological fact remains that during times like this we need our "transitional objects" as Winnicott termed them. These might be headline pages that people save, a photograph of a loved one, or an object that belonged to someone lost. It might be a poster, a book or a poem or an otherwise meaningless piece of rock. It seems best, at least to me, when the object is also some writing which enlightens me, such as that written by listees or forwarded by them. I try to remember this idea of the transitional object when I hear of people's need to hold on to certain things which upset me, like flags, which seem to imply support for war. We can strongly disagree with one interpretation of someone's behavior, while understanding other aspects of it. It seems to me quite possible to express a desperate hope that in the process of protecting innocent people other innocent people will not be destroyed, without condemning people for expressing their feelings by means of flags. We are fortunate to have this forum for considered discussion; others may need to further learn about and value such precious democratic freedoms. And finally, exchange and comprehension of crucial ideas calls not only for intellectual brilliance and force but empathy.

Nick Piombino

W "Transitional Object or Ego Ideal," 20 September 2001

The notion that one's changed feelings toward the flag might involve the need to be comforted by a transitional object seems to me not a good psychoanalytic account. A transitional object is a cat or blanket or thing to suck on that mediates the absence of the caring parent. Freud, in *Group Psychology and the Analysis of the Ego*—part of his meditation on the psychology of nationalism post WWI—lays out a more relevant set of terms. A flag is the symbol of a nation or group. What is the relation of self to this symbol of the nation? It seems to me this is precisely where the question of the flag rests—whether I identify with it or not. A terrific account of aggressivity and group processes, with implications for the nature of national identity, is Bill

Buford's *Among the Thugs*—on soccer fans in the UK, but by extension, on the lack of self that leads to aggression in numbers. I do agree, however, that the flag has been displayed in a way that has more to do with mourning than with aggression this past week—the flag is a substitute for a lost object. What, precisely, is the nature of that object? Our sense of well-being in the world? A transitional object is not primarily described in the context of mourning. Rather, as Freud saw it, there is a need to reencounter the things of the world, one by one, when faced with a catastrophic loss. A process of reintegration. Perhaps the flag is a step in that direction for some, and the act of forgetting other political valences a part of the process as well. BW

P *"Re: The Flag as Transitional Object," 22 September 2001*

> Nick Piombino's post earlier on the flag's role not as an icon of war-mongering, but as a transitional object in the grieving process, makes perfect sense to me.
> —Ron Silliman
>
> As I've written elsewhere, the flag is not a transitional object but a symbol of national identity. I cannot dissociate American history from that symbol. While I do not see the same aggression in flying the flag as was evident in the Gulf War, I think the innocence of its use as a symbol of human, rather than national, solidarity is a precise desire to forget that history.
> —Barrett Watten

I did not say what I said about transitional objects in order to be an apologist for war. I am trying to draw a distinction between the usual employment of the symbolism of the flag in leftist or pacifist terms, especially as it was critiqued during the Vietnam conflict, and its current, immediate function as a transitional object for those in mourning. When I burnt my draft card as part of the war resistance movement in 1967, it was at a time when I was already deeply depressed and mourning over the dead on all sides. Barrett is right in preparing the way for rational pacifism at the outbreak of this conflict. However, timing is everything in gaining public support for a cause. It is the very media power of the terrorists' acts that we have to find a way to combat. To show impatience towards the millions of people in New

York who feel terrified, at this very moment, of a follow-up attack, in giving up their rage and mourning would be, I feel, risking a setback for an effective and rational anti-war movement. We veterans of 60s peace efforts may be in a position to go about the effort of winning public attention for potential innocent victims abroad, as well as American victims of further terrorism here, as well as our soldiers abroad, or here, but any such movement must also deal empathically with the entire situation of loss, mourning and with any coordinated governmental manipulation of those feelings into a justification of further killing.

To view the function of the flag as a transitional object at this time I think might be one effective way to begin to short circuit the terrorist goal of creating chaos, divisiveness, confusion, especially among those in a position to try to decrease the tone of bellicosity. Certainly we do not want to engender a tone of bellicosity among each other here on the poetics list. For example, I don't think it was helpful for George Bowering to ask Tom Bell, when Tom said he would buy a flag, if Tom would now buy a gun. Nothing Tom Bell has said, or for that matter, anyone has said in support of using the concept of transitional object in understanding some of the reasons people want to display flags, in this context, has been employed, as far as I can tell, to support war.

It is also very clear to me that Barrett Watten (and I wouldn't expect him to) does not have very much knowledge about Winnicott's use, at least fifteen years after the death of Freud, of the concept of the transitional object, which emerged along with the increased knowledge of the human psychological development via the work of the British Object Relations school of psychoanalysis. (It is important to note that Winnicott gained much of his insight into childhood developmental psychology in treating, as a pediatrician, children during the London bombings of World War II; see *Winnicott* by Adam Phillips [Harvard, 1988], pp. 61-97). Much of this work was confirmed later in experimental work via Margaret Mahler's observation of infant and early childhood development. The idea of a symbol is a concept quite different than the idea of a transitional object. A symbol is entirely understood as a function of a cognitive experience alone. In the concept of the transitional object the physical presence of the object has a special meaning in combining with the physical, emotional and cognitive experience of its function. When people wrap flags around caskets and drape them on buildings or children hold them in their hands they are utilizing a physical holding presence of support during the grieving period. This can only be temporary, because in order to work through mourning, we must eventually let go of this emotional struggle for holding, or we could not get on with life by accepting the finality of the loss of the dead. Essentially, then, a transitional object supports a necessary, but also temporary, period of (unconscious) denial, during an emerging set of very frightening and agonizing feelings, including an awareness of mortality itself. It is virtually impossible to process such immense anxiety and loss instantaneously, or even rapidly, and this is why the mind gives us denial, and mourning, to give time for the absorption of the shock and the personal and social significance of the trauma. My hunch is that Barrett is for very good reasons (having to do with considerable knowledge of political history) impatient with this period of necessary denial. There is other work in front of us, as the denial gives way, and the complete terror of our vulnerable situation comes home to us in the naked anxiety of the threat of war. Barrett is warning us about the potential furious destructiveness that could be unleashed when the stunned period of mourning and denial ends, and the new cycle of destructiveness and counter-destructiveness begins. Nevertheless, I feel that to confront a very traumatized, confused country, many of whom are undergoing various degrees of Posttraumatic stress syndrome, with a premature expectation of empathy with future imagined loss, is unrealistic, and at worst, dangerously divisive. Although for reasons of national defense, we all posture strength, in reality we are mostly feeling not only some degree of loss, but also a sense of humiliation at having suffered a defeat. This blow is a narcissistic blow to our national self-esteem as much as it a physical loss of people. This vulnerability and the ensuing confusion, as well as ambivalence, must be part of the calculation of any rational emerging anti-war movement.

Finally, a distinction must be made between the experience of those who have more directly witnessed this event—someone might like to write to James Sherry about this—and those who have witnessed it on television. There are greatly varying degrees and types of Posttraumatic anxiety. Those who have witnessed the destruction of the WTC, or were in or near the building, or have been directly affected in losing a loved one are undergoing kinds of experiences and are in need of kinds of help not usually needed by others. Posttraumatic stress disorder can lead to prolonged feelings of alienation towards others, to a need to avoid ordinary enjoyments and contacts with other people, and easily triggered rage, anxiety and depression. There is often a tendency to withdraw from others and a tendency to withdraw from enjoyment of any type. We must try to be sensitive to the numbers of people involved and the fact that here, in New York, they are everywhere around us. This must also be true at the seat of our government in

Washington, DC. Victims of Posttraumatic stress syndrome are often dazed and emotionally volatile and don't even realize the full extent of their psychological debilitation, which can rapidly get worse if not treated. I feel that enlightened political response must include empathy for human psychological needs for recovery and a varying range of emotional response. But again, Barrett is right to warn us, to challenge us as to our rapidly emerging responsibility to understand the plight of potential future victims. At the same time, we must recognize that our country has not killed anyone in response to this specific atrocity yet.

Perhaps we should consider the possible significance of our national grieving over the bombing of the Oklahoma office building. At that time no physical response was possible, except the arrest, trial and final execution of the terrorist, one of our own citizens. Possibly our collective awareness of the fact that virtually no physical punishment of anyone, or for that matter any other than symbolic physical responses was immediately possible, and that no punishment could be much of any help in our national mourning may be on some unconscious or subliminal level helpful in developing a cautious, rational response towards this devastating atrocity. But, of course, we had Clinton then. And now, we have Bush.

And finally, this quote from Barrett Watten's amazing book *Bad History*:

> Who will save us? Intellectuals—split off from the mass of revolutionary clouds returning from a daily fog bank? The fog moves back to reveal smoky haze rising over burnt-out districts of Los Angeles, ô intellectuals, you who speak as if there were no one to hear you! But this smoky haze has spoken again, as we knew it would. Save us from our instincts and deny our necessary acts of self-destruction; ô intellectuals!

Nick Piombino

W "Crisis Page," 23 September 2001

I've been working on my crisis page, and these are the results so far: *www.english.wayne.edu/~watten/crisis.html*. Obviously there is only so much one can do with the vast amount of information flooding in at the moment. Building a page like this may simply be one way to deal with it. I'm trying to be useful and representative, within my limits. There's obviously more to be done with the bibliography of poetry and war.

I'm interested particularly in more links to "aesthetic" response. What is that? It could be, but not necessarily, a topical poem. It could be a quirky detail or link to visual information. For instance, Michael Gottlieb's note on WCW's fire engine was the kind of "aesthetic" detail that I would like to find more of. Ditto Muffy Bolding's forward of a url to that horrific album cover. Ditto mez's web page, where her current poems are displayed, and George Hartley's "Saturation Bombing."

Barrett

W "Analyzing the Flag," 25 September 2001

Dear Nick: Thanks for the eloquent post. When I first saw flags coming out after September 11, I correlated that with the (it turns out) more aggressive display in the Gulf War. I also remember the half-time show of the Super Bowl, an important cultural document that ought to be studied for its object relations. In it, groups of children of servicemen were trotted out on center stage, in a virtually sacrificial presentation. "We" were to identify both with the child left behind (perhaps permanently) and the parents doing their duty leaving the child ("who is us"). This identification of the child—held hostage by the adult demands of uncompromising duty—with the potential space not of play but of mourning has been reinforced in many ways since then. The Columbine High School tragedy, as much as the Oklahoma bombing, is emblematic of the way the child is placed at the forefront of a process of mourning that is also definitive of group identity.

I haven't seen that discourse invoked particularly, but it bears on the question of the transitional object. The transitional object, as you know, is primarily related to the question of separation and hence normal development. It also is important in relation to traumatic experiences that in some way interrupt the normal course of separating from the care-giving parent. A signal use of the concept is to describe a space ("potential space" in Winnicott's terms) that is where play takes place. Winnicott sees this as a space of acting out, and the child can unload its destructive rage in this safe space because really, the potential space is defined by the presence not absence of the mother. This has great use in thinking about art of all kinds. For instance, Mike Kelly uses teddy bears in some of his pieces where he punches them out, shits on them. You could think of Jasper Johns's use of the flag, in that famous work where there are three of them stacked on top of each other, as a playful acting out around the national symbol. And because it's art (the context being the late 50s or early 60s) it's OK. No one is going to accuse him of insulting the flag.

The concept is very intuitive and I think many can easily identify it. Maria writes about her cat. I have my transitional object (or one of them) sitting on a shelf—Mickey Mouse, c. 1950. But does that really work with the flag? I'm trying to think how. I'm picturing the huge flag right next to the hole at Ground Zero from a helicopter, on the TV news today. That's the use we are thinking of.

Reaching for my psychoanalytic library, I find the following passage in Winnicott:

> The object is a symbol of the union of the baby and the mother (or part of the mother). This symbol can be located. It is at the place in space and time where and when the mother is in transition from being (in the baby's mind) merged with the infant and alternatively being experienced as an object to be perceived rather than conceived of. The use of the object symbolizes the union of two now separate things, baby and mother, at the point in time and space of the initiation of their state of separateness. [. . .] The mental representation [that results] in the inner world is kept significant, or the imago in the inner world is kept alive, by the reinforcement given through the availability of the external separated-off and actual mother, along with her technique of child care. [Hence, the mother is not dead in the creation of the object and its space.]
>
> It is perhaps worthwhile trying to formulate this in a way that gives the time factor due weight. The feeling of the mother's existence lasts x minutes. If the mother is away for more than x minutes, then the imago fades, and along with this the baby's capacity to use the symbol of the union ceases. The baby is distressed, but this distress is soon mended because the mother returns in x + y minutes. In x + y minutes the baby has not become altered. But in x + y + z minutes the baby has become traumatized. In x + y + z minutes the mother's return does not mend the baby's altered state. Trauma implies that the baby has experienced a break in life's continuity, so that primitive defenses now become organized to defend against a repetition of "unthinkable anxiety" or a return of the acute confusional state that belongs to the disintegration of

> nascent ego structure. (D. W. Winnicott, "The Location of Cultural Experience")

And Winnicott goes on to conclude that most babies don't experience x + y + z. "This means that the majority of children do not carry around with them for life the knowledge from experience of having been mad. Madness here simply means a breakup of whatever may exist at the time of a personal continuity of experience." In that situation, the child has a hard time reintegrating.

I believe that's the model. It's distinct from Freud in "Mourning and Melancholia," importantly because the parent is not dead. The object is not lost, but the continuity of experience has become traumatic. That I think is accurately what those of us who did not experience a direct loss have just experienced. The continuity of our experience—sense of well-being, its protension and retention—has been disrupted. There is a before and after, a traumatic shock.

A number of aspects of what we are observing bear on this model. Something is holding it all together in the face of trauma. Does this mean the flag posits a caring parent? That could be interesting in light of the Columbine High School discourse—a way to translate child, parent, and community into national identity. Then there are the questions of play and aggression. When I see people in SUVs flying the flag where there once was a hockey team flag (Detroit Red Wings), something of the playful use of an identity symbol is suggested. But I can't get farther than that. As for aggression of the Mike Kelley variety, I don't see that. Acting out on the flag because it's safe.

What strikes me as important is the way that Winnicott infers that our response to this circles back to the position of the child. And I think that is a powerful political discourse. It also powerfully separates the politics of nation states (and their aggressions) from the politics of community (and their concerns with caring). Perhaps you can see by this analysis that I think this is a terrible result. It separates, cordons off, our basic instincts from the political arrangements that protect them. We are all held hostage by forms of aggression that at any moment could disrupt our lives.

So the flag. We could look at it this way, yes. We could look at it as an identity symbol—that's my flag, I'm an American. And we could look at it as a form of duty. Salute the flag and do your duty. I don't think it's possible to dissociate any of these ways of seeing the flag. What is remarkable at the present moment is the overwhelming sense that we have been placed in the position of the child whose mother, a.k.a. sense of well-being that can't possibly "go away," has gone away. For the present time. This is the x + y + z situation Winnicott discusses.

The tragedy is that, given the total destructiveness of great power politics and terrorist responses, that is the only place for us.

I certainly did not mean to infer that concern for the human reality of the trauma that has occurred is an apology for all that might be done in the name of a national symbol. I also feel caught up in the same relation to the trauma that occurred. I notice it because I perceive the flag, right now, as more or less benign in precisely the way you and others have seen it. But I also perceive in it an ominous masking of the other forms of identity and disavowal that are to come.

Barrett

P "Posttraumatic Stress Disorder," 25 September 2001

[NP posted a long extract from the American Psychiatric Association's *Diagnostic and Statistical Manual of Mental Disorders* (DSM–IV), which, due to copyright restrictions, cannot be reprinted. It describes the essential features of Posttraumatic Stress Syndrome; defines the nature of a traumatic event ("military combat, violent personal assault [sexual assault, physical attack, robbery, mugging], being kidnapped, being taken hostage, terrorist attack, torture, incarceration as a prisoner of war or in a concentration camp, natural or manmade disasters, severe automobile accidents, or being diagnosed with a life-threatening illness"); discusses how the event can be reexperienced and/or how stimuli associated with the event may be avoided by the patient; and lists specific symptoms due to trauma, including difficulty sleeping, recurrent nightmares, hypervigilence, exaggerated startle response, irritability, outbursts of anger, and difficulty concentrating or completing tasks. A specific set of diagnostic criteria then follows.]

W "Violence and Rhetoric" [response to Anselm Hollo], 26 September 2001

The point can be briefly, and rhetorically, stated: violence is as American as apple pie. This includes genocide of native peoples, mass displacement of civilians and destruction of "infrastructure" on which the lives of civilians depend as a military objective in the Civil War, use of atomic weapons on civilian populations in WWII, and mass bombings that do not distinguish between civilians and military in Vietnam and the Gulf War. Some of these are in fact American inventions (think of the use of napalm and defoliants, for instance, in Vietnam; cluster and other antipersonnel bombs in the Gulf War), and some even basic to American "character." I would put the stockade mentality ("draw in the wagons") and manifest destiny in that category, leading to the rise of cowboy poetry ("wanted dead or alive"). Not too debatable. What is debatable is that to point this out is to diminish the acts of Genghis Khan, the Royal Air Force, or other horrors of war. BW

FANTASY (1994)
A sudden shift in intensity . . .
Triggered by . . .
Bogged down . . .
Nearby . . .
Upset . . .
Incomplete focus . . .
"Continued build up of troops in the area . . ."
Took it out of fragments . . .
Blocked empathy . . .
Short circuited connections . . .
In pieces . . .
Could have been . . .
Out of . . .
Habituated . . .
Now for a stroll . . .
Climate control . . .
What in an image could illustrate . . .
The state I am trying to describe . . .
At the border of a fantasy . . .
I have internalized . . .
Clink of utensils in a dining hall . . .
Now can almost remember . . .
He or she had built it out of snatches . . .
Of memories none of which were intact . . .
Not only the memory but the event itself . . .
Was composed of such small parts . . .
Yes, I have drawn it to their attention . . .
That's the sound of a plane going by . . .
Primordial interruption . . .
Yet the assessment was out of control . . .
Not only those aspects our office was responsible for . . .
Also, I could only hear a few words . . .
Of each exchange because the radio was on loud . . .
I couldn't say anything . . .
Previous to its being seen . . .
A bridge from the beginnings . . .
To this part . . .
Somebody wants or wanted to start explaining . . .
Naturally I couldn't take over at this point . . .
Something moving through here . . .

By no means certain . . .
Like a few frames in a moving picture . . .
I stood there embarrassed . . .
More feeling than I would like to admit . . .
Her way of presenting a kind of self-conscious understanding . . .
Yet no one could have been sure . . .
It would turn out this way . . .
America—the land of sleep walkers . . .
Tuned continuously to the latest dreams . . .
Intricately constructed from tragic facts . . .
Now hear this . . .
No one must awaken . . .
You heard it first right here . . .
The nascent sound of a motorcar . . .
Yes, that voice was emphatic . . .
The first was indifferent . . .
Moved here as soon as she was moved here . . .
Tremulous . . . awkward . . . endearing . . . mumbling . . .
As luck would have it they could now repair . . .
My latest words were far from coherent . . .
I wouldn't have given it up for the world . . .
But she was suspicious . . .
No one talked to her that way before . . .
As you leave, notice the small stairway to your left . . .
Viewed from that perspective, I might wonder . . .
Take it or leave it . . .
Then again . . . you might say . . . alternatively
Without comfort, or in a temperate zone . . .
As good as disappeared . . . now, anyway, invisible . . .
30 day moneyback guarantee . . .
Yours for the asking . . .
Yet had you waited another month . . .
Perhaps only a week or two . . .
That lulling feeling of comprehension fading . . .
Sleep rising from the bottom of hollow tears . . .
Voices so recognizable, yet only a few words . . .
This is the kind of time you had imagined . . .
Not truly measurable, yet what was its importance . . .
Irreplaceable . . .

Originally published in *Avec* 8 (1994) and in *Light Street* (Zasterle, 1996)

> The space where cultural experience is located is in the potential space between the individual and the environment (originally the object).
> —D. W. Winnicott, "The Location of Cultural Experience"

On 1/31/02 the flag is still in evidence here in Manhattan but it is far from omnipresent. During this time the focus has shifted from the flag to the World Trade Center site. In his discussion, Barrett mentions Winnicott's article "The Location of Cultural Experience" (*Playing and Reality* [1971], pps. 95-104). In this article, Winnicott furthers the scope of psychoanalysis, noting that "Freud did not have a place in his topography of the mind for the experience of things cultural." Here Winnicott expands his concept of the transitional object to include transitional space, which in infancy consists of the space between mother and child. As is well known the site is visited constantly by tens of thousands of people, and has been furnished with a viewing stand and arrangements for limiting crowding through ticketing. The site is both a mass grave and a space for mourning and loss, and at the same time it is a physical and emotional space for restoration and recovery. Yet it is important to emphasize that such transitional or potential space is necessary for another emerging function, that is, a site for the holding together of the cultural identity as it undergoes vast, though at times, hidden, change. It is no surprise that this change is played out in economic terms while the underlying issues are, among many other things, ontological (or, as Richard Foreman puts it, "ontological/hysterical.") Under these circumstances, economic transition has an added dimension, and perhaps many added dimensions. Such a crisis encompassing so many widespread senses of vulnerability might also encompass a transition in the human relationship to objects, which in turn may presage a change in relationships, one that includes a greater toleration for, and also an emotionally charged recognition of, uncertainty. As Winnicott makes clear again and again, childhood and adolescence typify the ambivalent, chaotic states that must be experienced ("held" as Winnicott puts it) in order for growth to perform its magic literally over the graves of the dead. For Winnicott, what maturation forces us to recognize is the often deeply disturbing, yet inevitable, relationship between growth and destruction, or destructiveness.

The "ontological/hysterical" issue grows out of the subjective/objective issue: as is no surprise to any student of relativity, a transition in space leads to change in one's relationship to time. Although the process can be painful to the point of agonizing, a recognition of the reality of mortality can have, as a compensatory function, a change in one's relationship to time. Recently the *New York Times* reported a huge increase in applications for graduate study. The reason given was the decline in the economy and the job market. Another reason may be that a deeper appreciation of time may lead to a desire to invest it rather than to merely continue to exist in it. An increase in anxiety may paradoxically increase an awareness of time. Because of the ubiquity of change throughout life, we are forever giving up or losing or using up all kinds of objects, transitional or otherwise; often, at such times, ontological implosions give way to object chaos. Just as the twin towers now dominate the internal skyline, the flag supplied a transitional object without the need for consensual agreement as to its meaning. For example, the conflicts over the possibilities for architecture on this site may be accompanied by a related ontological crisis that could provide a potential foundation for an adaptive transformation in human relationships.

A recent example of this that I experienced had to do with a New Year's resolution. Late in December I came up with what to me was a surprising and unique one, in which I vowed to learn to become less emotionally vulnerable. It no longer seemed to be a luxury I could afford under the circumstances. So it was quite a surprise when I read in the *New York Times* on Sunday, December 30: "There is . . . the tradition of declaring resolutions for change. . . . The old standbys: I will lose weight. I will stop smoking. I will exercise more. I will spend more time with my family. . . . The new ones: I will stop feeling so vulnerable. I will be spontaneous again. I will worry less. I will be happier."

Feelings of vulnerability are particularly crushing to feelings of grandiosity. It seems that in New York, at least, we have passed through a phase of grandiosity and are entering a phase of vulnerability. Individual differences are great. Still, there can be a shared overall ambiance. To me, what is occurring now can be summarized as "muted." One is hesitant to make sweeping claims or assertions. Mourning, transition, demand some degree of self-searching. Although the conduct of the war has not been widely critiqued, the actual stifling of critique may emerge as a powerful political issue, which goes to the soul of American ideals.

Feelings of grandiosity and feelings of empathy separate like oil and water. If you want sympathy—or even support—you are well advised to look to someone vulnerable, not someone grandiose. For example,

Rudolph Giuliani changed considerably after his prostate cancer experience. In a recent interview (around 1/25/02) with Jay Leno, Giuliani said his cancer experience brought him in touch with his mortality. Thus, he said, he had already dealt with many feelings of vulnerability when 9/11 struck.

Why empathy? With empathy comes a clearer view of one's antagonists and one's supporters, an increased potential for understanding very different mentalities. Under current political circumstances the traditional Republican sound for "reform" rings hollow, as the recognition that our emotional infrastructure, our political capacity for self-reflection, is in a severe state of decay. Empathy can deepen more quickly by means of a transformed metaphysics of attention, as a psychological compensation for traumatic experience. This is a better outcome than knee-jerk blaming or taking the role of the victim. To change our relationship to and with objects can lead to a transition towards a changed relationship with time. The transition from flag to WTC site parallels the transition from the containment of chaotic anxiety to pathways to greater insight.

W "The Flag as Aggressive Emblem," 11 March 2002

Are we, or are we not, at war? One can only know by reading the signs. While driving yesterday I encountered an enormous, ludicrously oversized, American flag displayed by Belle Tire (a national chain of tire franchises), flying straight out, horizontal in the stiff March wind. The day before, in an auto supply yard in Warren, Michigan (home of the Republican-voting working class, McCain voters in the 2000 primary), I noticed under the glass countertop a smudged computer print of a bald eagle with a tear in its eye, the Twin Towers in flames behind it; in another version, the eagle is more menacing, though still crying as it hovers over an aircraft carrier in full battle array. What private thoughts may I have when encountering such emblems? It seems remarkable that I noticed them at all; they seem to have, by now, almost an automatic function. The recession is over and consumers are more confident; yet we are at war. The precise adjustment of information and denial necessary to maintain states of both readiness and consumer optimism has had a remarkable effect. I am sure it is unlike any experience of war that has taken place. This is a war of amnesia, punctuated by news bulletins that remind us of our derealization.

Today is the six-month anniversary of September 11. How would one best describe the psychological adjustments that have taken place since that epochal date? The immediate need to witness and adjust, come to terms with an event that took place as a psychological injury on a mass scale, is most evident in the imperative I and others felt to locate a public forum (the Poetics Listserv) where one could develop terms by which it could be understood, and see how our role as poets related to it. All manner of psychological processes are evident in the record of that attempt, which as I reread it reveals, first, a need to locate a basic sociality and means of communication, apart from the media experience of trauma; second, a desire simultaneously to come to terms with the violence but not to reproduce it in relation to the communicative norms that had been established (this is what I think I was doing when I put together my web site of responses to the crisis); and third, the surfacing of forms of aggressivity (in responses to Nick, Ron Silliman, and Anselm Hollo) that preceded the abandonment of the discussion itself. Two things followed: to begin with, there was a call to order on the Listserv, at which point the discussion regressed to a litany of birthdays, career notices, and obituaries that ended serious political debate. But continuing in another manner, Nick and I have been at work editing and rethinking our debate on the flag as a transitional object for publication. It might be said, then, that the very act of trying to communicate, failing to do so successfully on a public scale, and re-presenting that discussion are connected as responses to the historical event.

As I did then, I see the characterization of the flag as a transitional object, and the notion that rallying around the flag is primarily a form of healing, to be an incomplete account. The tear in the eagle's eye is real, but also the aggression that it mobilized and which is being carried out in its name. I do not see much that is genuinely affirmative in the processes of healing—exemplified by the lead story in the *New York Times* today of a burn victim from the Twin Towers—we are supposedly going through. Where on the one hand individuals are rethinking their life priorities, and discovering either their greater need for kinship or their greater capacity for independence (both acceptable goals for a narrative of psychic recuperation), I have also noticed a marked increase in callousness and fatalism, particularly in relation to workplace politics in which "termination" is simply a social necessity we must all inevitably go through. The president, as has been noted, is using rhetorical means to both comfort the families of the bereaved but to steel the nation to further casualties, and this can be seen translated on the local level. On the global one, as well, the rescripting of the national nuclear defense scenario to include tactical nuclear weapons in proactive strikes is being put forward in manner that minimizes their effects on target populations, as well as on the strategic balance. The violence in Israel has accelerated to the point that it has become almost entirely abstract, and deaths are traded on a daily basis as acts of recuperation. There is little comment on these events; rather, in the process of nursing ourselves back to psychic health, we have to accept the inevitability that "bad things are going to happen"—just as long as they don't happen to us. And if they do, the reason why has already been elucidated. We are being held hostage by psychological narratives of recuperation, masking the aggression that is the immediate response to trauma and which is the true index to its effects.

In mid October, the time of some of the most complicated psychological repercussions of the unfolding events, during the anthrax attack (and well after having left the Listserv discussion), I had the following experience, which I wrote down in a journal:

> ANTHRAX
>
> Blowing across the mid October sky of Detroit:
> about three dozen black, red, and blue balloons
> circling around what appears to be a clump of
> balloons—an irregularly shaped, multicolored mass,
> something like an aerial whale surrounded by
> numerous smaller fish, or birds. I think, what an
> ingenious way to distribute anthrax, as the wind
> blows into my face and I consider which authority I
> should contact first. "Someone should know about
> this!" But then I reflect that the dispersal has already
> happened, it has already taken place, there is
> nothing I can do to stop it. If I die within a week,
> this account will be evidence of what caused it.
> Why was I the only one to notice?

When I realized the structure of the fantasy that had taken place, virtually instantaneously on seeing the balloons scudding across the sky, I rushed to record it. The psychological state it evidences gives primary information about the collective (but how would I know that?) mentality one was in during the period. This is a moment of complete exposure, to a tormenting configuration of threats that could be coming from everywhere and nowhere at once. No transitional object holds us together; rather, the balloon as a mechanism for delivery of anthrax perverts the childhood object of pleasure and security (one is given a balloon on one's birthday), and we are abandoned to pure paranoia. It seems to me that the celebration of the delivery of American air power is directly related to my fantasy, here, of the balloons of childhood as delivering one's personalized death. In fact, weren't those war toys one played with precisely the transitional objects—mediating the absence of the parent through a form of destructive play—that we see now on the decks of aircraft carriers, with the boys and girls running out to service them? If there is a transitional object, it has become a source of persecutorial fantasy more than any site of healing (we can take it out on them, rather than ourselves). So let us remember this: as we reintegrate the experience of 9/11 through processes that may be affirmative for our now better educated and thus even better defended selves, the eagles are circling for the next round of recuperation, whose consequences may not in any sense be good for us.

AISHAH RAHMAN

If Only We Knew

An ongoing urban drama with jazz and movement in one act

—for Amadou Diallo

CHARACTERS
ABOULAYE, a Guinean Street Peddler.
NARRATOR, his African-American alter ego
Blind Street Corner SAXOPHONIST

PLACE
New York City, 21st Century.

Note: It should be difficult, at times, to differentiate between ABOULAYE and NARRATOR; the two characters should appear with the help of music and movement to melt into one another, and actors should be lithe, able to move well.

ACT ONE

SAXOPHONIST *plays quiet, spiritual music that evokes the dawn for a long time.*

NARRATOR (*over the music*): Morning prayer, 5:30 A.M.

ABOULAYE: America! I love it! I love it! I just love it! Love New York, love the Bronx and I love sneakers. I love America where every day's tomorrow.

NARRATOR: Mid-day prayer, twelve noon. Your behind hits the door, when you bend over, you fill the tiny vestibule as you lace your right sneaker that is always coming untied. Today you are wearing your Air Jordans that light up green in the dark. Bon. Cool. As you straighten up your elbows brush against the mailboxes on your right and you quickly open the door and go down the one, two, three, four (*music stops*) short steps, stopping to look up at the woman who sits above you, looking, looking. Always looking day and night, looking out her window.

ABOULAYE: Gonna, gonna take the 6 train. Hurry hurry hurry gotta jet downtown. Number 6 to one four street can't be late don't be late it won't wait got to sell got to yell money money money got to get some run don't be late african boy black boy Frenchie cool boy glowing feet shining, five feet six inches of thin jaguar skin nine eyes neon footed quick change artist catch the hurry hurry no 6, stop gotta dash, gotta book gotta split from the Bronx bush to downtown from north to south from east to west to downtown where the action is, money flows everything goes, through Harlem, through midtown downtown, is your town money money flows everyone knows . . . can't be late money won't wait.

(*Rushing music for several beats that stops suddenly.*)

NARRATOR: You make a bee line through your black and tan neighborhood where February turns brown to ash where everyone moves aside for your morning dash to the high in the sky train tracks rising above the rows of two story red brick doll houses on either side with four steps leading up to a tiny vestibule where two full grown adults cannot stand in at the same time.

ABOULAYE: Hurry!

NARRATOR: Hurry! Hurry! Hurry on downtown to the east side take the 6 to 14th cross over and go east young man don't be late, cause money won't wait.

SAXOPHONIST: *A long interval of rising "subway music" that finally diminishes underneath the following*

ABOULAYE: Hurry hurry hurry hurry do I have my wallet? hope I didn't forget my wallet wallet got to have my wallet need my wallet, there she is, good old Baji right here in my hand.

NARRATOR: Hurry! (*music stops*) As you board the train, your nose wrinkles at the scent of uncured leather that still clings to the wallet and you smile thinking "Damn that is one strong Fulani cow" as you put your Metro Card back in the square hand stitched wallet that Baba had given you years ago and return it to the deep pockets in your baggy black pants. And at that moment with your hands still on Baji, you spy *him*. He is wearing a pink voluminous robe and leaning on a black umbrella with a wooden handle. You have no doubt that it is he but . . .

ABOULAYE: Why is my Grandfather dressed in his ceremonial robes riding the underground in New York City instead of sitting beneath his fig tree or tending his beloved cows?

NARRATOR: You put on your train face. You hide behind a white man's newspaper and cast furtive looks at your Grandfather who you know is back in Guinea.

(ABOULAYE *prostrates himself at the* NARRATOR*'s feet in the Yoga position of "The Child."*)

NARRATOR: You hated going to the bush to visit me and those cows that I respected like human beings. You always dreaded the *fonio* passed around at the communal meal. Even the family tale of how your great grandfather had founded our village, had brought relatives to raise cattle, become leathersmiths and thrive on their own labor, did not ease the strange taste of curdled milk and honey. "Badaw, do not scorn the cow, whose milk is the essence of our life, our most powerful medicine, whose skin protects us. Fulani respects the cow as we respect one another. Do you understand?"

ABOULAYE: Yes, Baba.

NARRATOR: "Take this, it is Baji, who had a red belly with white flanks. A good milker when she was living and now she gives us soft leather

ABOULAYE: That day you put a red and white wallet in my little hand.

NARRATOR: The train jerks you out of your reverie and you look for your grandfather's face but instead all you see is a dapper gray haired man in a pink shirt carrying a walking stick wondering why you are staring at him. You get off the train wondering—

ABOULAYE: Is it an angel or a djinn I see on the train? How can that man look so much like Baba and not be a relative?

NARRATOR: In the, in the quarter, in the quarter of the immigrants, languages flow like one dark river rising, Horn of Plenty for those selling by yelling and their shouts are really whispers of a love song in my ears.

ABOULAYE: Check it out checkit out check it out, mamacita papi Yo! Linda, Linda besame. Shoe laces one for 15 cents two for 45 grande grande one size fits all sidewalks bleeding money gotta be there to catch the flow. The great God Shango, drying out from bloody seas, sells incense two for dollar brand if you please. Bangladesh and Senegalese, Vietnamese, Mung dark as me, Thailand and Bangkok, Singapore, El Salvador, Guinea, Sierra Leonians, Nigerians, Liberians and Haitians, (those who made it) got rid of tyrant yesterdaddy and here he comes again today, guns and no butter starvation just a bullet away and oppression in all homelands is just about the same, casts a long, long shadow and adds sadness to all songs. Money, money it takes money to send to home.

NARRATOR: But where are the Albanians from Kosovar and other Europeans, near and far, who like you seek succor from Miss Liberty's hand? Not in your neighborhood not in the crossroads of the immigrants and dark natives looking for cheap buys. They are melted in the mainstreams of the land. They are welcomed in Fort Dix by the hand of Hillary who plumps up soft pillows on their individual beds for their ease in spotless sunwashed rooms wired for computers as they eat musaka me patate and INS begs them (through a translator) to apply within the year for permanent resident status, thank you please. Hurry down the long street to the small space you rent to sell your wares through streets paved with 14karat gold chains and wiggling electric hula dancers. Past Japan

Express, Camera & Electronics, The Beeper Zone, Export Specialists, Bedspreads, Curtains, We Ship Anywhere. Apple green and precious pink taffeta and tulle waving in the air on wire hangers outside a store and brass studded trunks spilling into the street making it difficult for you to navigate on the street of immigrants paved with gold chains in the crossroads of Liberty & Opportunity where one size does not fit all.

SAXOPHONIST: *a long, long interval of music reflecting, the briskness of trade, the various ethnicities, tempo and tone of New York's 14th Street.*

NARRATOR: Afternoon prayer—three to four P.M. (*music diminishes then stops*)

ABOULAYE: Checkitoutcheck itout checkit out check it out

NARRATOR: Que bola acere, my main man, Whassup?

ABOULAYE: Nada, everything is everything as they say.

NARRATOR: Got to come uptown, Mr. Africa.

ABOULAYE: Downtown is good, rent cheap, business high? You buy? No problem!
Ovah here, checkit out check itout right this way Mamacita, ay papi
Dooney & Bourke, Coach, Polo
Scarves. Wool caps, sunglasses for winter sunshine
Kungfu tapes, Di Caprio all cheap videos, regardez ici
Your Lotto number's coming out if you get ticket here
American Value center
Nice earrings you try on sistah you like? special price just for you today.

NARRATOR: My Guinean brother, how are you today. How are the people of Africa?

ABOULAYE: The people of Africa are fine brother man.
Checkit out check it out batteries, cassettes socks and ties
And I am fine today also.
T shirts hand dyed, gloves, cigarette lighters

Merci, danke, spasibo, arigato and gracias.
On sale, Manhattan Island, China town, Statute of Liberty Rockefeller Center and Radio City, for you my friend toss in Brooklyn Bridge. A New York Bargain. Five postcards for one dollar. One dollar bargain.
Everything cheap and looking's free. You like? Take this shirt, American cousin.

NARRATOR: For me. Why, Mr. Africa?

ABOULAYE: Because my Baba always says kindness is the greatest wisdom. Because you look like my old Baba. Because I've been seeing my Grandfather all day, he follows me from Africa in the faces of you African-black American-Africans.

NARRATOR: Yeah Bro, we part of you, our long lost people, maybe even relatives my man. If only we knew.

NARRATOR: Your last prayer of the day.

SAXOPHONIST: *an interval of evening-sunset music that diminishes before the next speaker.*

ABOULAYE: This time I am sure. It is Baba riding with me on the midnight train to the Bronx even though I am just as sure he is still back in Guinee. At the end of the car he sits and stares at me. Between dozes I stare at him and smile. Now I am not afraid. His face is familiar place made strange by the passage of time. When I get off the train and look around for him I am not afraid. Maybe grandfather will materialize again and maybe just stay at my side. After all it's silly to be afraid of my own flesh and blood. Isn't it?

NARRATOR: You are anxious to get home but you do know not to run or even walk fast for the swarmy night air is swirling with police but it is hard for you are so hungry and all you want to do is hurry home and eat.

ABOULAYE: White rice and a spicy vegetable sauce. Tsibejenne. Mmmmmm and a dripping sweet mango.

NARRATOR: With your mind already home, you grow hungrier by the minute. As you near your building you look up and of course the woman above you sits as usual perched in her window. What is she looking at, what does she see? You are thirsty.

ABOULAYE: Bissop. Tsibejenne. Mmmmmmmmmm.

NARRATOR: In other times, other places you drank coconut milk or sugar cane juice but it is a cold drink of bright red bissop that you want right now.

SAXOPHONIST: *A bloodcurdling wailing high note that cannot be mistaken for anything else but a police siren.*

ABOULAYE and NARRATOR: OOOOOOOOOOOOO !!!

I am standing in the closet size vestibule of my doll house apartment building with my key halfway in the lock when

(*again the bloodcurdling scream from the Saxophonist accompanied by*)

ABOULAYE and NARRATOR: OOOOOOOOOOOOO !!!

NARRATOR: You are startled at the closeness of the siren scream. Curious, you turn around, warily open the door and look straight into hell.

SAXOPHONIST: *short stacatto screaming notes evoking "Hell."*

Eight gunshot eyes and four barking faces. Their decision had already been made. This time it is not Calvary but high on a hill in Northern Manhattan in a place wrested from Indians in the quarter of the immigrants in a black and tan street of red brick doll houses.

ABOULAYE: Gunshot faces!

SAXOPHONIST: (*gunshot music*)

ABOULAYE: The Mosquitoes of West Africa.

(*mosquito music*)

ABOULAYE:
Barking eyes!
Sptatpataat! Tattatlatlalt splat! Gotcha!
Gunshotfacesbarking eyesgunshot eyes barking faces!

SAXOPHONIST: *Music evoking the terror of the preceding lines for several beats.*

NARRATOR: Your eyes grow with terror as large as history.
Sweat and urine pool around your feet like blood.
At first bullet, Baba, who I know is in Guinea but who has been hovering around me all day kisses me and says

SAXOPHONIST: *Three climbing distinct notes, each one higher than the other played twice.*

NARRATOR: "God is great"

ABOULAYE: "Great is God."
First bullet swims in my aorta, bathes in my bloodstreams flows to the outposts of my body and is swept at high blood tide through my spinal cord. At this point there is hope. If I live I will be a paraplegic but Baba grabs my hand saying "Courage Badaw. The evil djinns have made up their minds. The speed of their bullets is 100 meters per second."

NARRATOR: If you could run at that speed you could cover the length of a football field in about one second. It will be quick—

ABOULAYE: Before the old man can finish his words, inside the miniscule foyer, my gory sky becomes a crackling hailstorm. Second bullet enters my upper left side under my arm pit and hurtles downward through my right kidney, exits out of my back as the next one enters the left kidney and travels up my right lung at the same time the third one enters my arm in the front and leaves in the back almost colliding with this one now crashing through my collar bone rushing to the opposite side as if making room for the next bullet that smashes my chest and rests a millisecond before exiting out of the back of—

NARRATOR: —what used to be me and this one ricocheting towards me will enter my side and travel to the right side passing through my intestines in a clean straight line unlike the next bullet that leaves a trail of bone shards and mangled flesh as it travels a rugged path from my upper thigh to my groin followed by one that cuts a jagged path in my other upper thigh but this lazy bullet just rests there and sleeps unlike this next one that cuts a bloody trail—

ABOULAYE and NARRATOR: —to the knee bone to the shin bone to the ankle bone on the left side or this one now on the right side that comes in below the knee and takes a short quick trip to my knee bone on my left side while two more bullets make contact with my left side again in my left side again, and

ABOULAYE: in my left side again rupturing my spleen, kidney and any intestines I have left and this last one puts a hole in my right sole, passing from the bottom of my feet through my middle toe and through the top of my right foot turning off my glow-in-the dark sneaker!

NARRATOR: Your breath is shot, bullet riddled. Your lips like wine. Your stomach pours into the ground. Now you are trains and stars, the shape of change. Now you are a giant and as you die they love you.

(The two men become one—stand back to back and begin revolving, facing the audience and continue to revolve until they seem to melt into one another as ABOULAYE *speaks.)*

ABOULAYE: One of the four djinns kneels besides me and begs me not to die but Baba has already taken me back to Guinea. Now, I am the siren sound in the gory midnight as I circle between Africa and America, East and West, Earth and Sky, wailing for the green ones who cannot drink water, a clamoring frenzy for the unquenchable thirst for those in sapless lands, a thrumming for parched youths with green mouths and purple lips in a strange land with no succor. Now, I am the plangent song of elders who must return their young to a haunting heritage in a desiccated land. Now, I am a keening between a ravine and a skyscraper, ululating between the

Gambia and the Hudson, rising, falling, floating, pealing, tolling while a woman in the window sits and stares not believing her eyes.

CURTAIN

ELLEN REDBIRD
From *Cellular*

Dialog

NEU: Orbit, I will tell you. Everything is always eating the last of things. Everything. Always eats the lasting things.

ORB: Those non-ocular pay phones should occasionally lose pounds. Or one pound on the heads of loose change. But not changing but not patience. One occasion—all sides of it should curl a cord. Should only rotary dial a spring back. Through an eye. No a non-eye. Those is this this this. Pounds of it lost.

NEU: It deserved the receiver slam. I sprained an arm and another. Get the connection?

ORB: You know it, Neuron. Knew you known. It you.

NEU: Several arms, Orbit. Several arms in overlay acetate—the light, ten table lights in the past. Transfer numerically brilliant. Then wake up call aborted. Leaves several arms of arms. Receivers? Can't I tell a receiver? Can't a fist extend audibly impulse? I will tell you, and I have already.

ORB: New One. Called I can call you New One?

NEU: Yes, you have already.

ORB: New One once again. Pay phones are clunky. You can't take them out of order out to folk dance clunky out to pay the folk for dance phones.

NEU: I told you. Once met a generous—genetically speaking—one. A clean booth. Glass cathedral I went to before. Many times spit up new coins. Minted. Or smelted repossession out the womb sign. Signals. Signature. The glass flagship

I rewound. Replayed. A tape loop lets metal fall through to vapor. Memory is a gas to fall through. A loop hole is inexactly closer to mental movement. The other way a coin can stamp it static value. A loop can never be a pocket, but I pocket it many coins. Hope for impossible Möbius pocket. You see to refer: a generous telephone spits up coins so you can catch—in past moments—the spitfire—afterimage. Where the coin used to be—which is its value as if it is still there. Nothing came out this time means we could have been rich. Rich with could have. The means of time. Came out nothing already come. A generous—genetically seeking . . . . I think it liked me.

ORB: *Takes cell phone out of pocket.* Oh, well, Neuron, you should know my cell phone totally adores me oh so well. Should you know it totally.

NEU: Call Virtual.

ORB: *Makes a call and listens.* Busy Signal signaling busy.

NEU: Try Spider.

ORB: *Makes a call and Spider answers call waiting.* Spider, Spider. Did you siphon the ooze out of Virtual or—oh!—sipped of ooze online? One line? Did it aligned? Just a ligament you spied? Virtual isn't an answer yet, an answer.

SPD: *Talks into cell phone.* Can I tell you I'm on the other line? Do you merely grow a second eye? Can you hold? *Switches back to conversation with Umbilical.*

ORB: *Talks into cell phone.* The old question opens whether anyone will hold anyone to questions or hold at all.

SPD: *Talks into cell phone.* Sweet, tangy, tangible Umbilical—don't you have to blink from the belly out? Do you feel the grape burst as if your abdomen? But where else can you feed except internal fluid?

UMB: *Talks into cell phone.* To know yes. Yes, Spider. Tries over tries. I drink enriched oneness. I bathe my expectations to the drown level. Yet catch a sud and you're enclosed. Slippery globule lens without a pulse. Exposed on film.

SPD: *Talks into cell phone.* You drink exposed? Why measure for the cut? What can Scissors solve? What can anything dissolve? Which direction is the solution? Where's your center? How could any center be Scissors? Wouldn't the strands cease to be strands? What strand zings your push button?

UMB: *Talks into cell phone.* Tries and sub-tries not to care. Not to nurse the snap into back-snap. Not even masking tape. Shock is a moment made lasting—a series of shock instants all at once to stretch each vertebrae. While the wound grants less lickability, I hide down only to vision lavender-lavender, say lavender-lavender, salve of silver Scissors—a birth right. Mine. Violetly. My sever metallic. Comfort only itches sweater woolen over empty.

SPD: *Talks into cell phone.* Won't you unencumber your own ravelings?

SWB: *Talks into cell phone.* I agree. Ravish yourself in a vacuum.

UMB: *Talks into cell phone.* Hello? Hello? Which channel? *Removes phone from ear; talks to self.* Cut off again.

SPD: *Talks into cell phone.* When does it matter NOT to hack into my calls, Switchboard?

SWB: *Talks into cell phone.* Nasty, nasty cobwebs. And vacuums suck.

VIR: *Talks aloud to self while typing an online message to Switchboard.* Switchboard. Where are your digits affixed? Every increment explodes trolls. Past lives were left hanging for a shorter blip than this.

SWB: *Talks aloud to self while typing an online message to Virtual.* Floating reference points can reconfigure their own fucks. Billiard blade can wait out its static cling. There is food in this world, Virtual. And you can get it best through combination copper straw and filament gum. Here, access airport.

ORB: *Removes phone from ear.* I can't wait anymore, Neuron. Any more waiting, and I can't.

NEU: You're always waiting, Orbit, already as before. You just can't stand the landing pad. Let me pulsate Scissors.

ORB: Okay-o. *Passes cell phone to Neuron.*

NEU: *Makes a call and listens.* The line is disconnected.

TIM ROLLINS & K.O.S.

Art Connecting Communities

New York City, March 13, 2002

TIM ROLLINS. *Founder and Director, Tim Rollins and K.O.S. and The Art and Knowledge Workshop. As an art teacher for special education students at Intermediate School #52 in the South Bronx, Rollins founded K.O.S. (for "Kids of Survival") in 1981. The collaborative artworks of Rollins and K.O.S. are in the permanent collections of over thirty museums world wide. The group currently works with teams based in New York City, San Francisco and Memphis, TN.*

NELSON SAVINON. *A seventeen-year participant in K.O.S., Savinon attended the School of Visual Arts in New York and is currently a graphic designer and Co-Director of K.O.S.*

ROBERT BRANCH. *A nine-year participant in K.O.S., Branch attended the Cooper Union in New York, taught in the New York City Public Schools in the South Bronx and now works for the Office of Public Affairs at Columbia University as well as a Co-Director of K.O.S.*

ANGEL ABREU. *A sixteen-year participant of K.O.S., Abreu is currently a student of art and philosophy at the University of Washington in Seattle.*

BRANCH I believe that so many of these research studies, think tanks and policy-making institutes making all these noble attempts to reform public education in the U.S. have it all wrong. Where are the ideas coming from—the students, the parents, the teachers and the community that have direct experience with what is going on in that most vital and important of educational arenas—the classroom? I just finished my first year teaching art with special education students in a public school in the South Bronx. My commitment came from my own background. I used to be one of my kids . . . stuck in a special education class, stuck in a culture of low expectation. My experience last year was that community was contacted only as a last resort, when there obviously needed to be some way to tap into the resources of the surrounding neighborhood . . . and I'm not talking about the dysfunctional community school board system currently running operations. So few of the other teachers were from the neighborhood geographically. And practically none of the teachers were from the students' backgrounds culturally.

ROLLINS Working with schools across the nation, I'm surprised at the lack of interest so many educators have in the culture of their students. Some don't even think of their students as possessing culture. They cannot identify with cultures different than their own, cultures not built upon a particular canon of texts, music and art works. Everyone feels this tragic and unacknowledged sense of pervasive disconnect and this contributes to the feeling of ennui that permeates schools in our neighborhoods.

B But during my first year in teaching, I was constantly impressed by the affinity and rapport that the Jewish and Italian-American veteran teachers had with the kids coming from mainly Latino and African-American backgrounds. Because they had been working in and with the neighborhood for so long—some had taught two or three generations from a single family—their concern was so genuine they rose above cultural differences. They really cared about the kids, their families and it was if their own futures were tied to the futures of their students. These teachers return to their classrooms year in and year out because they truly feel needed. They feel needed because they truly are needed and get direct joy and satisfaction from the action of teaching.

SAVINON If you are not there for the kids first and foremost, students perceive that and the teacher will be emotionally dismissed. I think the artificial, airless culture of the public school system replaces the organic, living, always-changing culture of the individuals—students, teachers, administrators and staff alike—that find themselves having to perform in the system. Everyone comes in with great and good intentions, but without a commitment to changing the public school culture, change simply can't occur. Teaching is not a job. You might as well wait on tables . . .

R Like being an artist, being an educator is a calling not a career. But the great joy comes when you are able to make your calling your career. That is what defines success for me.

B Let's be honest. Some parents participate in a powerful culture of drug and alcohol abuse, a history of mental illness, generations of neglect and self-destructive behavior kept out of sight. And kids without a defined sense of their own culture within schools make up their own systems of negative behavior to win attention. In the worst schools they spend their entire time coming up with elaborate strategies of sheer rebellion. In fact, the kids had more unity than the faculty when it came to planning how to run the school day. The problem is that they were completely focused on how to disrupt the proceedings in the most hilarious way possible. Outside reformers seem to really underestimate or excuse the incredible behavior of the students in the schools . . .

S Oh, yeah! I'm a witness!

R Some people would say you were blaming the victim.

B That's patronizing and enabling. Wellness can only be achieved by the sick person. The medicines are available. But the sick person has to want to get well and take them.

R In KOS we've always taught to the highest common denominator. We respect each other so much; we expect so much because we discern excellence in each and every participant in our workshops. Failure is not an option and there is zero tolerance for underperformance deliberate or—more likely—unconscious and internalized. All too often, schools have tended to teach to the lowest common denominator and the students immediately pick up this patronizing, paternalistic attitude.

ABREU I happened to be in a gifted and talented program at the school Tim taught at when I first met him. Looking back, I was just an average, well-behaved student. But in the context of the chaos of that school, I was considered gifted and talented. It seems kids were labeled gifted and talented the minute money for gifted and talented programs became available through the system. And it seems that there were suddenly a whole lot of special education students discovered when money for special education programs became available. Now, there are all these "learning through the arts" programs springing up because money for these projects has become available. Where is the commitment to a long-term philosophy of learning for everyone? I remember most of the first members of K.O.S. were labeled dyslexic, learning-disabled, emotionally handicapped, at-risk, but they could all draw way better than I could! Their gifts were not acknowledged . . . only their so-called disabilities. In the studio, no intelligence was insulted, only challenged and celebrated.

B I remember being the victim of much false praise when I was a kid. People would tell me what a great job I was doing when I knew I had not. Or I'd do something pretty terrific, and I'd be completely ignored because it wasn't something they could recognize on their personal radar screens. So it was easier to bug out. It's funny because often the disruptive students that get all the extra attention—remediation, maybe counseling, everyone is running around like chickens with their heads cut off trying to come up with ways to "save" these kids when the students working hard to succeed are ignored. Failing schools as well as this extra attention, when the problems tend to be rooted in the school culture.

R But I feel something different and less transient is happening. Some places are becoming cultural centers for a wide range of communities and neighborhoods. I'm excited by the creation of all of these after-school programs across the nation. Instead of providing recreational activities, many of these new places are inventing new learning environments, helping to make up for time lost during the day in school. I remember the early days of K.O.S., working all day at the local junior high school and then walking to our studio in a community center two blocks away after school. The irony was that at three o'clock, when the final bell rang, a liberation occurred and that was when we truly began to learn. And we learned primarily through the making of things . . . and what worked was that the excellence of our learning process was manifested in the paintings. You couldn't fake this. The paintings became these wonderful trophies that we were awarded for learning, struggling, overcoming. The recognition for our achievement came from peers and parents and the local community, yes. But when places like the Philadelphia Museum of Art and the Museum of Modern Art began acquiring the works for their permanent collection, we finally felt like we could be the makers of history and not always the victims of history. This feeling continues today, everyday, even after twenty years of work.

S Being thirteen years old back then, I remember the energy of the studio. We weren't just studying knowledge. We were producing knowledge in the form of paintings. It was exciting. Now that we're working all over the world, I think this is the excitement all these new kids are feeling. When we first started, my family and friends kept asking, "Why are you doing this? Why not get a real job?" Seventeen years later, some people still ask me this. They don't understand but this is based on a lack of exposure to a broader world. Art is the most direct road to this broader experience. So it's not only the teachers who are to blame for the cultural disconnect we've been talking about. Parents have become pathologically apathetic. The idea is "I'll have my kids, feed them, buy them clothes, but that's it. It's up to the schools to do the rest of the raising." Let's get real.

A Our participation in making these paintings is a practical way to involve people who would never be connected to contemporary art—any visual art—otherwise. It's one thing to visit a museum where you don't understand anything that's going on. It's another thing when your son or daughter has participated in this kind of art making activity—the contact is direct, barriers are broken, boundaries are crossed.

R I suspect when we talk about these strange and disconnected "school cultures" we're not only speaking about public schools. I have a problem with the role of student that is laminated on young people in educational institutions. You're constantly in a state of preparation when you could be actually working on concrete projects with direct and tangible results in your community.

S In all these art schools we visit, I see it all the time . . . Get in a cubicle. See what you can come up with. Everything assigned. Nothing feels really real, and too many of the instructors want to create clones of themselves. Why the KOS experience has worked for me is that we have always operated from the center of our main interest—art—and built upon that, extending into whole other realms of knowledge.

R I talk about that in my lectures and teacher training. Sometimes folk will ask me, "But what if they—meaning the students—aren't interested in anything?"

S That's bull. You've got to dig. Everyone has a gift.

B How can you talk about a strong sense of community and refer to your students as a "They"? Then and now, it is all about being challenged in a positive and understanding way. And it is all about making something. Simply making something that wasn't there before. I don't care who you are, what you look like, where you come from, where you're going, what your age is. Everybody wants this. Everybody wants to make their mark on the cosmos. It's all about producing something necessary for our emotional, psychological, spiritual, economic and even physical survival.

The painting "Amerika—The Stoker" is based on the unfinished comic novel "Amerika" by Franz Kafka written in the early 1900s. The story's protagonist is a teenager named Karl Rossman who comes to America with great expectations of wealth and success only to be bitterly disappointed and dejected in that land. He is about to return home a failure when he is adopted by a utopian commune—"The Nature Theatre of Oklahoma"—where two major principles reign. First, "Everyone is Welcome!" Second, "Everyone an Artist!" Karl immediately goes to a race track turned recruitment station to sign up for the Nature Theatre. Once there, Karl encounters hundreds of people aloft on tall pedestals playing whatever each wants on long golden horns.

Inspired by the scene from this comedy, Rollins and the young members of K.O.S. invented hundreds of unique and eccentrically shaped golden trumpets, some completely original, others taken from imagery from art history or popular culture, with each revealing some of the individual personality of its maker. In collective group sessions, the most dynamic forms were chosen and a group composition was created with members of the group painting their instruments in gold acrylic on a ground made of book pages taken from copies of "Amerika" and archivally adhered to stretched linen. The result is deliberately ambigious, suggesting a big brass band, the improvisational nature of American jazz music, a noisy traffic jam, a beautiful cacophony, a mass choir.

MARK RUDMAN

Bonespeak

1

I can hear you ask:

"Why are you so sure that James Donald wasn't one of those
British stage actors who took film roles for money?"

"Good question, Mom."

"I can't help wondering if the actor is as self-effacing
offscreen as he is on."

"What do you care?"

"It's how the images on the blank white screen
get mixed up with our own screen images."

"I doubt he cares either. Probably makes a bundle."

"Made."

"My brother made $500 a week during the depression
and that's directing 'B' movies that were shot in a week."

"I know. You've told me."

"I went to Julia Richmond High.
And then—my mother died."

"It must have been awful."

"I went to live with Dad.
You could say he had to take me in.

You know I was unwanted.

My parents had agreed to divorce when my mother Irene
discovered she was pregnant.
I only wish I'd never been born."

"I'm glad you were."

"I'm glad you were too."

"But the Greeks agree with you.
I can't tell you how many
variations there have been
on the line that it's better
never to have been born than . . . "

"You don't have to tell me!"

"I know, I know . . . "

"I know you know. I was trying to say
that you're not alone in your suffering."

"That I didn't know. But I know that when
I went on vacation to Myrtle Beach that the people on the beach
were reading Michener, not Greek plays.
I mean when you told me how much you were paid to
translate that Greek play
I didn't know what to say.
Given all the sex and dirt and gossip in your work
I don't know why you don't write a potboiler and then
none of us will have to worry about

money."

"I would if I could."

"I don't see why you can't. You've got the smut."

"It's part of a fabric, I've a higher
purpose in mind: to transcend the squalor."

"So transcend. And be poor. And never go
anywhere. Some people lead wonderful

lives. The people here travel all the time.
Not me. I just sit alone in my room."

"Do you think that there's a copy somewhere of your
mother's translation of *Phaedra*."

"Not PHAdra, PHEdra, phe, phe.
No no everything's gone."

"But it might be on file."

"You should go to Paris."

"I should go. What, as the Hunchback of Notre Dame?"

"Come on, you're not . . . "

"I'm not blaming you. I can't afford lavish trips.
And I'm in pain all the time. To travel
in a wheelchair I have to have someone
push me around."

(Pause.)

"You can't build character in children by
giving them things. The best schools, connections—
nothing matters if you're not right in the head.
My father starved the girl and spoiled the boy.
But my brother wasn't a coward like your father
with his bullshit stories of being in Special Intelligence."

"I saw some kind of document to that effect."

"I'm sure. He probably had it forged."

"Mom! That is so nasty. Not everything he said was a lie."

"But it's true."
"That it's a lie? You can't be sure."

"Neither can you."

"True."

"Then let's not argue. You know he was a fraud."

"But inspired. And he did struggle not to succumb to his demons."

"Demons!"

2

Different Face

"I'm not a woman but sometimes I wake
and can hardly move, I'm afraid to pull
off the covers; it's like I had no skin."

"That's nothing, I'm exhausted by the time . . . "

"Can I finish?"

"By all means, finish."

"I'm not sure it's something you'll want to hear."

"So tell it already."

"I wake, and I start thinking of this line
by William Blake: 'Why was I born
with a different face?'"

"What's wrong with your face?"

"He means being different inside."

"I don't see what's so bad about that."

"It's about—feeling more—vulnerable
than I'd like—than is—practical."

"You never were very practical."

"We're not on the same wave-length here."

"How could we be when you're so indifferent
to what's going on in the world."

"If you say so. In the years when we moved
almost every year I thought the less I thought
how deeply apart I felt—how at odds
I was with the values that were set out
before me like inviolable truths
instead of makeshift relative conceptions,
the less I'd want to disappear, escape—
I did my best to be invisible.
To blend in."

"I guess it wasn't good enough
since there was never a time
when you weren't being singled
out for one thing or another,

at first for being smart, because
that's how I made you, see, because
I taught you so much when you were
little, and in those early years

your teachers thought you were different
in a good sense, it was only
later, around the time we left
Illinois that you fell apart,

and you set your mind to getting
away with as much mischief
as was humanly possible
without getting thrown in the clink."

(*Pause.*)

"I've heard of William Blake.
How much money did he make?"

"Enough to survive."

"But he earned his living from his paintings.
He worked as an engraver, you know."

"I know."

"I studied his engravings. Weird.
I mean compared to Gainsborough."

SIMONE SANDY

Bowl with Horn and Proof

6/12/01

Aaargh. When a stone rolls downhill unobstructed, it picks up velocity as it goes. (Is this actually true?) True or not, it's my current emotional state. No dreams last night, just panic over the eventuality of my death. Need to write about my music collection. Is it eclectic enough, esoteric enough, enigmatic enough to fool anyone? Is it black enough? Female enough? East Coast enough? Gutsy-yet-sensitive enough? People used to ask why I chose to play the French horn. I gave answers that weren't exactly true but sounded good and now I'm sorry because I don't remember the real answer (if in fact there ever was one), only what I told people.

Meditation

Beyond my reach, a wooden bowl contains a silver double horn. Light emanates from both bowl and horn. Because there is only darkness around the bowl, with some distant stars, I cannot say whether the horn is a miniature or the bowl is gigantic. Horn and bowl drift away slowly until all I can see are stars. After a moment, I see the bowl again, without the horn. It appears to grow bigger, as if it were moving closer to me. Then it seems to get smaller, as if it were receding. It shrinks until it lands on my palm, smaller than a dessert bowl. A folded slip of paper, navy blue with silver ink, sits in the bowl. I read it.

Statement

You forgot to write about how you feel. Thank heavens for that.

Reasons:

1. It's not your fault, dear earthling. You gave it the college try.

2. How you feel is neither interesting of innovative.

3. Would you like your horn back?

KEEP IT, I write on the back of the piece of paper. Impulsively, I add

There will be no singing in rounds
singing in rounds, singing in rounds
There will be no singing in rounds
All through the morning

I put the paper back in the bowl, with a blank college-ruled notebook—with perforated sheets, it says—on top (too large to fit inside), and send the bowl back into space with a flick of my index finger.

June 13, 2001
When I reached the clearing, the staircase was gone and time continued to move at its usual rate. I sat under the cottonwood tree I had named Janice and tried to think the staircase back into existence. As usual, Janice did what she could to lend a hand. In this instance, she sang the same Gershwin line over and over. "I'll build a stairway to paradise, with a new step every day." She apologized for forgetting how the rest goes.

Meditation
I open my journal to where I left off, but the latest entry has been written by someone else. "Do you think we might like each other?" it says. "We have similar taste in music." This intrusion doesn't concern me at all; I just assume it's a message from my correspondents in outer space. "If you are basing this on my current collection," I write, "then you do not have the complete picture of my musical interests. The items you see in my home represent only the last three times I reinvented myself. If things continue to go well between us, I'll let you in on what I used to own."

June 14, 2001
Most of what I learned in school is feeling pretty useless right about now. Where were the lessons on how to fix a car, for instance, or how to honor your family background while at the same time breaking free. My college roommate has mused that our school "taught her how to think." But when I think about that concept it takes on an Orwellian cast: *institu-*

tion admits 6,000 young adults per year, aiming to teach them how to think.

Meditation
I'm on a ferry with everyone I ever loved. No one appears to recognize me. Or perhaps I am invisible. The sun, high in a clear sky, burns my nose and shoulders. The idea that I am invisible is hard to reconcile with the sensation of being roasted alive. Even if I can be seen, I probably appear to be someone else, more myself and less what I once showed them, less what they once saw in me. These loved ones do not speak to me; it would be unusual to speak to a stranger, who is obviously content in her own thoughts, while one is enjoying oneself with a group of friends. They are grouped together in ways that surprise me, ways that have nothing to do with who actually knew each other, or who I thought would get along based on what I once saw in them, what they once showed me of themselves.

JAMES SHERRY
The WTC Environment: Strategic Dialogue

Dialog(ue) in a Dust Cloud

I was within two blocks of the WTC on September 11 in my cubicle in the Federal Reserve Building on Nassau St. I was on a conference call when the first plane hit; and I thought, "Someone is trying to stop the Wall Street open." (It has happened twice in the past three years that bombs have gone off in the neighborhood just before 9am.) When the second plane hit, it was much louder and the building shook. I said to my callers, "I think something bad is happening. I have to go."

I went to the window and I could see the WTC burning. I watched in a state of denial as women fell, their dresses ineffectual parachutes. I thought, "I will just go back to my desk and get some work done." Then the first building collapsed. I could see it falling toward me and raced behind a pillar at the far corner of the office. (At the same moment, my son Ben was racing away from his school on Greenwich Street and described how "the top of the building just slid off.")

We were benighted by a gray dust cloud unable to see out the windows although the air was secure in the building. After 20 minutes the dust settled and we could see again. Security evacuated the building. As I passed Beekman Hospital on William Street, the second building collapsed. I could see the dust cloud billowing toward me over the rooftops. I ducked into Pace University to avoid the dust cloud that slammed the door behind me.

For 20 minutes, I sat in the basement auditorium with a professor of African History; and we discussed the state of Islam. After exchanging credentials, the professor said, "I wonder why the sub-Saharan African leaders aren't more supportive of the jihad."

"There's a big difference," I replied, " between religious devotion and self-interest."

We in NY have suffered a great deal in the past few weeks. The military, financial control, surveillance, and charitable work of our government are a complex response to a singular, traumatic, personal attack on the financial center of our global commercial empire. But it's not about us.

Islamic militants are attacking us to be sure, but their goal is to use us, and our expected inappropriate response, to destabilize secular governments and replace them with Islamic regimes. We are to be addressed later when a stronger base in multiple Islamic powers can reasonably confront Western economic power.

But Islamic militants seem to have forgotten what they have unleashed in the Christian world. If Islam begins to succeed, it will be confronted with a far more dangerous enemy than it can imagine. The implacable justice of Islam will have to deal with brutal Christian love. And we may yet see the fundamentalists on both sides doing battle while the rest of us watch.

Putting that unhappy thought aside, Islam is not the only religion with long term planning. The West has some sophisticated ideas about time that include globalization without religion at the center, although religions play a peripheral part in controlling local cultures. The confrontation between Islam and transnational corporate culture will be exercised for many years. (See Our Nuclear Heritage, *1991). During that time fundamentalism will be trying to gain control of nation states while transnationalism will be trying to make those national borders increasingly permeable. (At the same time national borders become increasingly leaky, the West will attempt to solidify intellectual boundaries (both intellectual property and taxonomy) for the purposes of commercial control.)*

These permeable borders will render transnational institutions more vulnerable, so we may see transnational security in the guise of nationalism, separating and isolating the local cultures and rendering them more vulnerable to transnational incursions. The conflict for the West then is culture vs. security. The more we open and mingle our cultures, the more vulnerable our institutions of power become. The more we separate our cultures, the more expensive it is to distribute transnational goods and services. Mass customization is designed to overcome this problem, but transnationals can't yet provide it at a profit. Certainly not globally.

The key to the problem is our cultural view, not our military might or financial power. The only way we can understand what fundamentalist Islam has accomplished is to understand their culture as deeply as Islam understands our culture. But it will be more difficult for America and Europe to understand Islam. While the West has the advantage militarily and financially as well as a more educated population, we have some weaknesses in our traditional cultures and certainly in the under-nourished transnational culture. Our traditional cultures are far more literal than Islam. The leading Roman Church still promotes the idea that the wine and wafer transform literally into blood and body while the more sophisticated Christian Orthodox belief recognizes that trans-substantiation is a metaphor. The Islamic symbols require far greater jumps and as such it will be difficult to perform the usual Western analysis. By dissecting the parts we hope that viewing the details will help us to understand the causes of terrorism. Actually the causes are in us, but more of that another time. (See Noam Chomsky, 9/11, *Seven Stories Press)*

Our contemporary Western arts also posit literal views. In poetry, the entire corpus of Imagism, generating pictures when the logic of sensory perception breaks down, aestheticizes the relationship between complex image sets. Even in its Vorticist underpinnings, Imagism turns inward to artistry to solve problems of alienation and synaptic rerouting. Fundamentalist Islam's restrictions on images provide ordinary citizens with a level of imagination only found in cutting edge arts and sciences in the West. Islam moves from place to place without identifying locations. How can we combat this "weaponized" culture?

Even the Modernist linking of form and content is looking for assurance and correspondence where we should be taking risks and innovating new strategies. To the extent that we want our alternative culture to push through the membrane into the mainstream, we need at least three-legged stability. Linking form and content reduces support rather than increasing it, spiritualizing language in response to mechanization. To the extent that we want our culture to include the many levels of global reality and act as a model for emerging cultures (first world innovative and traditional ethnic cultures both), complex linking makes translation more difficult and more difficult to absorb. Objectivism's interest, for example, in creating a poetry with a surface that matches the complexity of a Persian carpet using techniques of collage is an attempt to aestheticize the diversity of materials available to the Islamic artist. Even politics in Zukofsky is made into an aesthetic structure. The relationship of complex materials in Objectivism is intentionally difficult to absorb. What is the structure underneath the complexity of Objectivism? How does it compare with the mathematical structures beneath a Persian ornament or Moorish tile?

Williams' "contagious hospital" opens another dimension using the literal adjective, freeing perception and opening multiple possibilities. The unexpected identity of adjective and noun creates a shimmering reflection that shakes the reader with new possibility. The issues surrounding this solipsistic approach can be discussed endlessly, but the closeness of adjective and noun establishes a magnetic field attracting attention. Again our cutting-edge strategies edge formal meaning closer to lexical meaning while Islam keeps the distance and hence its readiness.

Language poetry finds and explores formal meaning. Its investigations move a step further in the direction of addressing the more complex and remote connections. Good examples are found in Grenier and Andrews. Understanding these chasms are key to recognizing the distance that desperate people are able to leap, but we're just at the beginning. The future of writing will accept and comprehend other cultures more easily with a model that allows for diversity. Rather than simply including everything in an unexamined pluralism, environmental poetics exposes how the differences of place, time, and person can co-exist. The exclusionary politics of poetic groups will give way to understanding that the different approaches exist side by side regardless of the vain competitive evaluations each group makes to aggrandize itself. The components of Western reason will be exposed as also existing in the dynamics of other cultures. We are not alone at the top of the tree, but our configuration is different.

Islamic art has, for more than a thousand years, practiced generating emotion in its ideological writing not from an integrated form and content but from creating distance between form and content. It does so using letter forms, energy generated from the letters' tails and loops. Islam's ability to cross borders is based on this multi-legged strategy. We have much to learn from it. But Islamic art's mesmerizing of the viewer (albeit less so than the mandalas of India) leaves Muslims vulnerable to despots in politics and culture. The weakness of Islamic culture is its reliance on symbols like the WTC to galvanize popular attention. A little study of our own symbols may decrypt Osama's plan. (If truly he was the center of the plan in a niche where there is arguably and acceptably no center.)

The West's nuclear religions contrast with the many paths that lead to Mecca. The de-centered or distributed focus of Islamic culture is similar to the problem of combating terrorist activity. The enemy is distributed and hence the problem is soluble only with a distributed technology. (Some technology companies have recently been asked to describe how many Muslims can be tracked leaving a mosque for how many days before the problem becomes too big to manage.) We know how to manage distributed problems, but our military, financial, and surveillance systems are not organized to function in cells and then link the data for understanding. Often doing the opposite will take us in the right direction. But that too is difficult for our literal culture to execute. Unity is an agreeable approach but should not be applied universally as diversity actually increases stability. (See Stephen Jay Gould, A Wonderful Life*)*

So the Western cultural models are not particularly attuned to dealing with these kinds of complex problems. Even the disciplines we assign to handle them, like psychology and law, are deeply immersed in the cultures' limitations. Ask a psychologist how violence ought to be applied. Ask lawyers how to include the opium producing Northern Alliance in our plans to overthrow the Taliban. The disciplines are isolated from each other with no well-defined linking techniques.

This confrontation of the centralized and distributed cultures needs to be approached with a more general model, such as those that are used in environmental processes to solve resource constraints, limit the spread of disease among species, or resolve conflicts of interest. Forest fires destroy property, but if they are prevented, they end up destroying more property by the degradation of the environment that fire-suppression methods spread.

We cannot protect the target of the risk; we can only distribute it. Adopting a distributed cultural model will help. Where before we protected our ideas and argued over our differences to the exclusion of alternatives, we can model common ground along with differences. In this way we would link our culture with environmental processes and approaches. Nature and city would stop looking so different from each other. We would no longer have to continually protect our "unique" identity. It also enables us to think like Islam and ultimately Islam to feel itself on common ground.

A distributed culture is a diverse culture. Varieties of opinion and even sharing opinion can allow for diverse solutions. To calm marketeers' fears, a distributed culture does not necessarily have fewer shared audiences. Common themes in Islam extend from Malaysia to Morocco. Centralized communication can present many points of view. Those views do not have to be homogenized. Journalistic objectivity can ally cultures with participating populations rather than homogenizing them. I noticed recently on a visit to England that the tabloids there are reporting more in-depth and concrete ideas on the war on terrorism than the mainstream press that placates to make everything seem normal. The common elements of body and basic resources along with centralized communications are a sufficient link. We do not need to link at all points; that is to say we do not need to integrate.

As the bombing of the "Trade Center" raises questions about viability of the city and its egg basket, this solution points the way to a multi-nodal culture and the limitations of either/or constructions. Adopting a distributed approach on our part will assist Islam itself to read the lines of the Koran that address a multiplicity that includes other "peoples of the book" in their culture.

How transnationalism adopts these options is already implicit in its use of ecology to control third-world countries. To that end we need to work intently to avoid a neo-naturalism as an excuse for further central control. On the bright side, as transnationalism adopts a sustainable commercial model, cultural conflict has a model for resolution using the girders of our smoking mass grave on Church Street.

TENDERLOIN OPERA COMPANY
from *Smoke Times Seven (A Tender Opera)*

1. HOTEL

(*SRO Hotel chaos. Overlapping conversations.*)

MAN ONE: Oh yeah, ha ha ha ha

WOMAN ONE: Ha ha ha (*Radio blaring.*)

MAN ONE: Ha ha

WOMAN ONE: Shut up why did you—

MAN ONE: You shut up. I have to go out.

WOMAN ONE: What room do you want to sleep in tonight?

MAN ONE: 26. Get the light when you come. I'll turn off the TV.

Man One turns off the TV and exits. Woman One turns the TV back on, louder.

MAN TWO: If you give me—

WOMAN TWO: What are you—the nerve of—

MAN TWO: The metal handle—

WOMAN TWO: Keep it closed! Keep it closed!

TV: Began the season highly favored now is anybody's guess—

MAN TWO: I'll open it if you turn it off.

WOMAN TWO: I want it closed.

MAN TWO: Then I'll open it anyway but turn it off.

WOMAN TWO: With what?

MAN TWO: The metal thing.

WOMAN TWO: I don't have a metal thing.

MAN ONE: (*Knocking.*) Open up.

MAN TWO: Damn.

WOMAN TWO: Just open it then.

MAN ONE: Damn. (*He returns to Woman One.*)

MAN TWO: Not even try me with that—

TV: Alan Iverson scoring eleven hundred points against the Warriors in the first quarter—

MAN ONE: There, now it's off.

WOMAN TWO: (*Banging the wall.*) Keep it down.

MAN ONE: *Don't even try me.*

Water pipes, water pressure, high-pitched tone.
Loud voices, in anger, pounding on wall.
Doors open, voices amplified.
Doors close, voices muffle.
Sound of Hindi movie from manager's suite:
Mata Lanyshkar singing.
Mega bass from outside car vibrates walls.
Foot pounding from floor above.
Phone in the hall rings and rings;
Lorna thinks about answering it, but doesn't.
TV sounds mixed with radio sounds.
Screams. Baby crying. Laughing. Shouting.
Sobbing. Crazed babblings.

Fire engine roars by. Siren.
Ten seconds of absolute silence.
It starts over.

LORNA:
I can't hear my music
Unless I shut the window.
There.
Why is that guy stalking my door?
Need to open it for air.
I'll get a fan second-hand.
I'm going out for stamps;
Come back and write Mona &
I'll get a cat tomorrow.
It ain't bad here.
I gave up beer.
I decorate good;
Make it look big.

Radiator wheezes and hisses.

VOICE: (*From the street.*)
I'm gonna kill your ass.

Someone small runs down the hall.

CHERRY: Your mouth is lined with fool's gold, Carl.

CARL: Go back to sleep, Cherry.

Lorna takes the tip and lies down; she sleeps.

CHERRY: It's noon, Mr. Freaky.

CARL: I need my REM, baby.

Lorna dreams . . . Saying goodbye to the Sailor, Mike Pike. She holds her pillow to her stomach.

LORNA:
O, Mike, I just know this little pike
Has your sea legs, each one alike

Oh, Mike, I just know this little Pike
Has your swimmer's body
She's a keeper
She's a keeper

MIKE: Then keep her

LORNA: Mike, stay. They only leave in the movies.

MIKE: This ain't no real-life.

LORNA: Baby is. Cornelia.

MIKE:
Lie down and go to sleep. What can't come to you in a movie or from life might be yours in a dream.

LORNA: I can't sleep long enough to get all I want from dreams.

She wakes and leaves.

Smoke x 7, *Synopsis: The libretto was written collectively through a free writing workshop conducted in the Tenderloin. The score is partly notated, but largely improvised. The story celebrates and subverts the romantic conventions of Opera. The setting is the contemporary Tenderloin; the protagonist is a Prostitute named Lorna. She is obsessed with a sailor, the missing father of her child; she is preyed on by an urban gang of wealthy thugs, the Stovepipers, identified by their hats. On her side, a fellow prostitute, the transsexual Jake, and the Muni driver, Carla.*

The Smoke x 7 *Process: We solicited participation in an opera-making workshop by leafleting at the local St. Anthony soup kitchen and church, and we actively solicited writers taking part in the ongoing Tenderloin Reflection and Education Center's workshop. Six participants showed at our first meeting, and stayed with us throughout; the group periodically expanded from there. We met weekly for six weeks, and twice in the months afterwards for rewrites and readings. Members came from a variety of backgrounds—some living outside the city, some living down the block, all with some strong and personal connection to the neighborhood and its resources, either through past residency, current service, or biographical experience at the economic margin. Writing was the way in. We wrote collaboratively (passing pages back and forth; discussing common interests and styles); we wrote photographically (detailing as immediately as possible observations of the environment), and we wrote formally (into rhyme and meter). After the first two sessions, characters and stories began to emerge; the next two weeks were spent merging them—who resembles whom and how do characters relate? At the third, fourth and fifth sessions, music was added. Joshua Brody came in and led us in vocal warm-ups, then took us into musical-improv training. We worked syllabically, fulfilling and challenging genres (trying to sound like music we know, then music we imagine), and eventually married verbal improvisation with the musical—creating rhythms, rhymes and melodies on the spot. These efforts were added to the pool of material evolving into our libretto and score. I acted as text editor, guiding exercises, suggesting continuities in the mass of material, and working as co-writer—a libretto facilitator. The first draft of the libretto was completed at our 6th session; we returned to it after a break of several weeks to fill in blanks and enhance the organic feel (to make it a complete tale) and then delivered the version to Joshua, who then went into workshop with Tonal Chaos—his own vocal improv group. He devised scored melodies on the basis of their play and also left stretches open to spontaneous invention, improvisation being a hallmark of Tenderloin Opera Company's approach to performance. We ultimately presented the piece at a concert reading at Intersection for the Arts (April 29, 2001), and have received a grant that will allow us to put on a staged version in our home space (St. Boniface Church Theater) in the fall of 2002.*

CECILIA VICUÑA
from *¿Qué es para usted la poesía?/What is Poetry to You?*

What follows is a transcript of the dialogue as filmed by Vicuña in Colombia, 1980; edited in New York, 1999.

Scene: La Calera, scene of waterfall.

Caption: Water comes down the mountain and into the city's dumps

Camera spans Santa Fé de Bogotá's streets.

Rolando Laserie sings:

Con el pucho de la vida
apretao entre los labios
la mirada turbia y triste
un poco lento el andar . . .

Camera stops at Salsoteca El Goce Pagano/Salsoteque Pagan Pleasure. Off-camera interviewer asks black man sitting in booth with a white woman:

What is poetry to you?

Look, I began to understand poetry some when I was in high school and a popular student influenced by Prof. Pote, recited his poem "Black Passions."

cut to interviewee dancing with woman

and for the first time in my life I really felt what poetry was—something that perhaps didn't interest a black man because it didn't deal with intrinsic themes or simply with what one liked deep down. Ever since that day, poetry became something important and I hope that from my country many poets will be born and will emerge, demanding and declaiming the reality of that place.

Scene: Plaza. Man in baby blue polyester three-piece suit surrounded by a crowd of people. On a cardboard is a drinking glass used as a pedestal for a shrunken head with a tuft of black hair. Underneath the glass is a piece of paper. The man is addressing the crowd:

I will turn her over so that you can see. Look at it just out of curiosity and you'll see. (*pointing to the shrunken head*) Her name is Luz Dari and she was captured in Peru 3,888 years ago. Great astrologers have been amazed because she can transmit thoughts across long and short distances. She can tell you where you are going and where you come from, how to get a job if you need one and how it will go once you get it. If you're a woman, she will tell you which man loves you and which man wants to screw you over.

Look and you'll quickly be convinced that this woman, without the assistance of pen or pencil, without a typist's training, can write on a piece of paper.

Look here—out of mere curiosity—after all, it was a curious person who created the atomic bomb in the Soviet Union. Without pen or pencil, without a typist's training, she will write your first and your last name on this blank piece of paper.

Approached by another man who says:

The cops are coming . . .

Scene: Professor S. Idrobo, Dean of Biology, Universidad Nacional. His office.

CECILIA VICUÑA: We want to ask you, what do you think of the state of wild life and nature in Colombia?

PROFESSOR IDROBO: Colombia, I think, has among the world's most interesting wild life still in existence—although we have destroyed, in the last 400 years, more than two-thirds of Colombia's wilderness through colonization. We are still left, however, with one third undisturbed by man.

Prof. Idrobo takes pressed leaves from an archive of folded newspapers.

CV: I would like for you to talk to us about your experience with the poetics of botanic life.

PROF. S.I.: Yes, I want people to understand that biological harmony and equilibrium is absolutely indispensable to our existence because we depend on wild animal and plant life. We will always depend on them. People should try to convey this message to those who are totally destroying our pristine environment—our pure, well-balanced wild life.

Various plant specimens, seeds, etc. on index cards in a file folder. Cut to poster: "S.O.S. de la Fauna Silvestre de Colombia."

Scene

Caption: Due to many murders, the police patrol the mountain passes.

Two young police officers.

POLICEMAN #1: I categorize poetry as a second telling, or as an historical event. One doesn't go to poetry for the facts, but it should be complementary.
That's the definition I have of poetry.

POLICEMAN #2: For me the poli . . . (*catches himself before he says "policía/police"*), poetry is something that delivers you from the daily mono . . . mono . . . mono . . . tony we all maintain. Isn't it true? Sometimes when one is very alone and has many problems, a poem feels good.

Translated by Rosa Alcalá.

MAC WELLMAN
from *Starling*

STARLING; or
The Revenant as a Radiant Light; or
Why the King of Englishmen Sits in the
Position of Neptune on the Pound
Note; or
of Why We Creep Before We Walk

APROPOS OF: ***s t a r l i n g***

SENECA: "ducunt voluntem . . . nolentem trahunt." (After Cleanthes) "draw those who are willing, drag those who are not."

FIRST NOTE: Nature like to hide.

The text of this play consists of non-differentiated dialogue and scenario; the disjointure of these is to be enabled in production. The apparent jumble of the play is apparent only, and is in no way a fact of apparence (See LAST NOTE). Thus, the play STARLING consists of a set of instructions rather than a description of an aesthetic end product, in (and for) itself. As a set of instructions the text is, of course, problematic (o damnable theater). This is intentional and intrinsically so. Indeed, as a set of instructions the text of STARLING possesses no set of instructions. This is precise. The fact of this purpose is the precision of the play.

There are seven rooms, and two groups of actors, one consisting of 7, one of 3; the latter enact the character of the REVENANT (the one who returns). All other parts are enacted by the 7, singly or in combination.

All the actors are female; all the rooms are empty. Except for such stuff as is indicated in the text: candlestick, parbuckle, window frame, etc.

"Nature likes to hide" is a fragment from Heraclitus; "draw those who are willing, drag those who are not" has been identified above.

A SMALL NOTE TO THE FIRST NOTE CONCERNING A POSSIBLE CONFUSION (o damnable confusion): In the first scene, the Revenant is under the impression his name is "Sperling," but this is not his name; it is the name of a mythical town in Arizona, where in order to prove his sanity he delivers his "Lecture on the Serpent Ritual" to two young women who are hitch-hiking to New York City. They do no understand a thing he says. Later we learn the truth. The Revenant's name is not "Sperling," it is STARLING. These events are based on the life and work of Aby Warburg, founder of the Warburg Library and Institute.

•

Item.
So: In this curiously EMPTY and
curiously VACANT place,
the bughouse of Doctor ___;
the

maddened Revenant has been
organizing his images and items
to present, singly and chorically
his "Lecture on the Serpent Ritual"
and
free him (and us all) of the
Mahoon's error of

To
stay in a room after one has already been
removed therefrom

•

Item.
The Revenant's errand is to embody his own
removal.

•

Item.
Room, room, ro(o)om.

•

Item.
Chorus (the 7 and the 3) enacts the litany of surrogation;

Removal & departure
(of Innocents, all 13);
i.e. (Author's Note) this is
NOT a visual play; it is a play on the spacio-temporal
in entirety.

•

Item.
The Revenant's errand is to embody the

•

Item.
The Not-Already Known. Slant.
Plays as a device. Slant.
Room
the room.

Stop the

Stop

Stop time, block the work of forgetting

Look out the windoworld.
Saepe premente Deo fert Deus alter apem.

—

•

Item
a feather.

•

Item.
Someone drives us out before it is time.
We resist.

•

Item.
Peril.
Shoes. Biting, or the urge to bite. Be a
fox. A Fox Person.

•

Item.

. . .

Ways (open) to the land of the undecidable

•

Item.

Some one . . . girls

•

Item.

Often if one Starling frowns another will do
our business

•

Someone goes; someone stays;

Apparence

LAST NOTE: The girls, A & B, arrive in New York, and secure employment at St Ann's Center for Surrogation Studies. At night they frequent low and slank places; they explore the architectural wonders of the theater. In so doing they re-recover a reality. That which is lovely in itself is lovely when it appears.

ANIMALS, WHO ARE YOU?

ALEKSANDAR ZOGRAF.

SOMETIMES SOME SEEMINGLY UNIMPORTANT EVENTS MAKE US QUESTION THE THINGS WHICH WE WERE TAKING FOR GRANTED. A FEW YEARS AGO A FRIEND GAVE ME A RABBIT FOR A PRESENT. SO I KEPT THAT RABBIT IN MY ROOM FOR SOME TIME...
ONE DAY I WAS SITING IN MY ROOM WHEN THE RABBIT CAME AND LOOKED STRAIGHT INTO MY EYES...
I WAS ASTONISHED—IT WAS AN UNUSUALLY PIERCING GAZE, AND IT REFLECTED SOME DEEPNESS AND POWER WITHIN, OR INTELLIGENCE, PERHAPS.
FOR A FEW MOMENTS I WAS OVERWHELMED BY A FEELING THAT WHAT I HAD READ IN THE RABBIT'S EYES WAS UNDERSTANDING... IT SEEMED THAT THIS RABBIT WAS ABLE TO UNDERSTAND MY FEELINGS AND THOUGHTS DIRECTLY—JUST BY STARING INTO MY EYES...
SOON IT ALL BEGAN TO SCARE ME SOMEHOW, AND I TURNED MY EYES AWAY AND LEFT THE ROOM...
I REMEMBER THAT I DREAMT ABOUT THAT RABBIT THE NIGHT BEFORE HE DIED... IN THAT DREAM, HE CAME AND LET ME CARESS HIS HEAD...
IT ALL MADE ME START THINKING ABOUT ANIMALS IN A WAY DIFFERENT TO WHAT OUR CULTURE WANTS US TO BELIEVE... JUST AS IF I UNDERSTOOD THAT THOSE CREATURES POSESS THE CONSCIOUSNESS WHICH IS ONLY DIFFERENTLY STRUCTURED, BUT NOT INFERIOR TO HUMAN CONSCIOUSNESS...

WE HAVE SHARED THIS PLANET WITH ANIMALS FOR MILLIONS OF YEARS. BUT YET WE DO NOT UNDERSTAND ANIMALS, ALTHOUGH OUR SCIENTISTS HAVE WRITTEN A MOUNTAIN OF BOOKS ABOUT THEM, AND DESPITE THE GREAT NUMBER OF PET LOVERS....
YES — WE LOVE ANIMALS, WE ARE EXPLOITING THEM FOR OUR OWN NEEDS, AND WE EAT THEM, TOO.
SINCE A LONG TIME AGO, IN FABLES AND POPULAR PRODUCTS MADE FOR CHILDREN, WE CELEBRATE ANTHROPOMORPHIC ANIMALS...
1000
OUR CIVILIZATION, OF WHICH WE ARE SO PROUD, STILL HASN'T FOUND ANY CLUE TO BRING US CLOSER TO OUR NEIGHBORS AND OUR CLOSE RELATIVES — THE ANIMALS. SO WE HAVE YET TO LEARN HOW TO BRING UNDERSTANDING TO OUR FRIENDSHIP WITH OTHER LIFE FORMS...
THE END.

CHAIN DIALOGUE: happiness

The very first issue of Chain began with a series of chain letters. We asked artists and writers to write something, send it on to someone else, and then for that person to write something in response and send both pieces on to someone else, etc.

In the spirit of that procedure, I started a chain around the word "happiness." The Declaration of Independence says: "We hold these truths to be self-evident, that all men are created equal, that they are endowed by their creator with certain inalienable Rights, that among these are Life, Liberty and the pursuit of Happiness..." This past summer I was visited by a friend who has lived in Moscow for many years. During the course of a conversation he exclaimed that he couldn't see anything wrong with an ideology (capitalism) that was based on the idea that all people should have the right to make themselves happy. I instantly started to argue . . . and began to think about what this "happiness" is that we have the right to. (JO)

STACY DORIS

A Text of Happiness

Sun.
Strong sun, but almost any sun.
Sun in winter, surpassing heat even. Inside or out.
Sun exposing particles and dust and imperfection to the point of perfection; to vertigo.
Sun on certain oily skin bringing its liquids to surface.
Seeing someone sleep and thinking it is peacefully.
Almost any reflection of light.
Water, including its infinite sounds, textures, and temperatures.
The impression of understanding almost anything.
The impression of understanding almost anything that is written.
The impression of comprehending almost anything that is written in Arabic or Greek. The figure eight.

The feeling of understanding physics just by observing, and of writing that down, but fleeting. The feeling of really paying or having paid attention, albeit fleeting.
The feeling of some sort of inclusiveness or inclusion, then.
That leaving out is one of inclusiveness' forms.
Your voice.
Suddenly, not too nervous.

Almost any reflection of water; almost any reflection of light on almost any water.
Being, such as swimming, in not too warm water, in Aegean water, its green, and the water is a mirror of infinity, and then comes the impression of being a particle adrift in endless space, and accepting that; in short: being. So being dead and alive at once, suspended.
Almost any moment of purely being, as above.
Swimming preferably in the Aegean, not too warm, seeing cliffs on the island, and my eye somehow splits the surface of the water, so I watch its wavy mass while moving through it, while seeing Chet's legs kick not far off. Therefore knowing fear's absence.

Almost any red, including orange.
Certain orange fruits, including perfect persimmons.

View.
A really good view.
A really good view, and living in it.

Almost any clouds, in a great view or outside.
Very big puffy white clouds against certain November night skies, over the Seine, seen from on or near the bridges, when the day was darker.

The idea of birds but not birds per se. Same with flight.

An alternance of brilliance and murkiness which is not light and dark.
If we can revel in missing ingredients, in what is not here, in what's forgotten; in mistakes, as if in loss.
And orgasm being beyond happiness.

Projection.
Projection, which is made of light and air and water, or a really good movie, like Niagara falls.

Projection, for example breathing in and out at once.
Projection, such that birth and death are suspended; silenced in its clap.
Projection which rejoices in a future, such as travel anywhere, which may include swimming in the Aegean again, which must mean strength, or living somewhere light-drenched, or Chet brushing the unborn child's hair. Rejoicing in almost any future. Which is strength.

Clean sheets every day.

Certain more oily types of skin, and pressing against an oily back, nakedly.
The presence of certain oily skin of African men, women and children which has stored the sun in a way that radiates a feeling of goodness or deepest comfort. The presence of certain other skin which manages to also.
Certain smiles of African men, women and children, and certain other smiles which manage to also.

Projection circuiting back to almost any moment of purely being.
As flooding.
A feeling of being as part of every noise.
A feeling as being part of light, its waves, and fire.
A feeling of being able to give directly, or even indirectly, to give all and that it is received.
And so a feeling of being as giving, which is being.

That love, including our love, can exceed us and thus time. That our creations and imaginations, which may be at best love, can too then.

If someone read it, and it seems to have touched her.

When Chet is heard coming down the hall, and then comes through the door and looks happy.
When Chet is asleep and thinking it is peacefully.
When Chet does not want to wake up, but with good nature.
Certain hot chocolate, from Angelina's or Christian Constant.
Certain grapefruits.
Certain matcha tea, in any form, but strong.
That green.

BAHAA ABU DAYA

When Salt Blooms

It was a dark discussion as the dark of the room we were talking about the situation in Gaza with a lot of cigarettes and drinks we were tired of that it is the same words every day nothing new.
Ross and me two artists two words two hopes and two negative ideas about the situation in Gaza and Palestine.
When the salt blooms. I said
it is the title of my exhibit he said
the title refers to a particularly bleak period within the last 9 months since the Intifada started
just one of many phrases concerning something
that will never happen.
We were sad and happy at the same time for the title
it will never happen.
But the show will go
as the life in this city will go
as the same sun and smile
but something will change I said.

It was a lovely evening and a sad atmosphere.
Maybe they will bomb tonight or maybe not
that was what every face told at the opening evening of the exhibition.

Only she who has a different face
with a smile and hope
she came from the West Bank to say
congratulations and to say that salt
can bloom
she gave him a vase full of salt and
flowers they were blooming
he is so happy it can be possible
she made it to say yes it is possible
everybody got a different vision of the situation

because of the flowers

it was happy as the happiness of the flowers.

BETH YAHP

The Pursuit of Happiness

1. Yours (or mine)

Happy is inside, in the globular warmth of cupped hands, slippery as a newborn, and as new. She holds Happy with care, with determination, and with awe. Runs down the narrow pathways of the squatter village, lolloping in a red dress and oversized slippers, leaping mounds and runnels, the cracked lip of a monsoon drain. She grazes the outraged ears of an alleycat, its tail stiff and flicking, she soars that sure-footed, that quick. Happy's heart beats in the cave of her hands, not too strongly, but with determination, urging her onwards. Happy as an old woman's eyes, just waking. Her cough racked with rainbows. Sunlight reflecting on cut glass. A rainbow tinged smile. Not far away, but faraway enough behind her, a kind of yowling, hideous, bereft, begins. Happy's heart beats.

2. Hers (or theirs)

Happy is as happy does. In this case, with a can of condensed milk, the label torn, the can itself rusty, but once pierced, yielding its sticky yellow to be licked at, slowly, lusciously, from a forefinger. Just as it should. Sweet explosive with eyes closed, making it last. There's not a pipsqueak raised amongst them, her children, dirty elbows propped around the kitchen table. She lets them wait. Dry crackers set on squares of newspaper, since the last dish yielded to its last crack across her elbow last night. The last insult staggered out the front door. Not a whine or snivel this morning, which in itself is news. No more tears. A shadow flashes past the window, the after-image of a girl tearing down the pathway, hair flying. A red flicker in the corner of her eye. None of the children moves. Their eyes fastened to sweet anticipation of Happy, dripping down the sides of her finger and more intriguing to them than the blue-black blooming on her cheekbone, the hairless swelling behind her ear. She holds Happy up to them like a lamp, like the clear light of morning, and herself in its yellow glow, exposed as a stone goddess at an exhibition. Faces upturned towards her. Exhibit A. She smiles at them, radiant.

3. His (or theirs)

His Happy is huge, is white vapourous, billowing, cushions him in mother's milk, in wholeness. Albumen. In a him with him-and-a-half to spare. He stands swaying on the steps of the toddy shop while Happy expands out into the morning, up the pathway, up through the coconut palm fronds, up over the heads of village people, and over the housing estate beyond. The faces of housing estate people upturned towards him, at the gates of terrace houses, corner bungalows, the wheels of shiny cars. He jingles some leftover coins in his pocket, pricks a finger on a shard of glass. The children's money jar shattering as easily as dry crackers last night, as a nightdress standing in Happy's way. Arms raised in protest. An open mouth. A fist. Yesterday's shrivelled face loses itself in the clear light of morning, yesterday's gate slammed and wages withheld to pay for broken tools. His hands tremble. Idiot! Shit for brains! Yesterday's face lost in tools slipping shivery from them. He steps down to the pathway. Feels a sudden stillness, then a breeze, and a red dress flapping. Disappearing around a corner. A sudden wild smell. And he stands there swaying, breathing. And is spun in a rush to right and left of him, and shouts and rough hands shoving him aside. He spins, and then stands breathing, expanding. For this morning his Happy is huge. No one can touch him, or pull him earthwards. Cut him to size.

4. Mine (or yours)
Happy has a sweet taste in the mouth, like the return of good fortune. It has grace and functionality, ticks quietly in time, cogs and wheels invisibly turning. Like the inner workings of a watch, the one she gazes at absently, for example, lifting one delicate wrist. Shaking it gently. It trembles. She sits gazing amidst grace and functionality in a long cool room, in a corner bungalow with two alsatians and iron-spiked walls, where everything rests in harmony and balance. Just so. She has that kind of sensibility, that eye. She looks east, where the sun rises, never west, where the squatter village spills disorderly towards her front gate. Comes begging and calling. Old clothes, odd jobs, ironing, Madam? Everything around her, including Happy, has its place. Each object in the room, each vase, sculpture, carpet, rocking chair, lace maccasar, is an extension of her eye. Which, this morning, unbalanced, offends her. More than ingratitude, or mismatched breakfast cups, or an overbrewed pot of tea. Stupid girl. Madam can't drink that. More than last night's absence, yet again, out entertaining clients all night, or this morning's absence, gone to the office directly, early morning meeting. Yet again. Sorry, dear. The indignity of an undisturbed bed. This morning Happy is outside, reflecting rainbows, and in its place, like some sick joke on a rosewood stand, nestles a brown hen's egg. In place of crystal. So she has to avert her head. When they finally drag the girl in the red dress in, switching the bamboo cane about her legs so she dances, begging and calling, Happy has a sweet taste. She can't help herself, tasting it. She holds herself perfectly still.

ADAM AITKEN

Federation, Mark 2

One hundred years, and I am not as I was
things are better now, you will agree
motto on an old school badge:
the pursuit of life, liberty and happiness
or our folksy versions:
"i am and i want" in Australian Latin of course—
i want what I am . . . or words like that

and I can't think of a nation
so anxious to be happy
singing ourselves this structured refrain

each year
a motto
each year
a tango competition
that charges double
for the Portaloo amenities in Olympic park I guess.

At least
the nomads like walking
the rabbit fence again,
and what our terrible cruelty
did to them—taking their kids away
becomes a complex of happiness
mixed with the guilt some of us feel
but mostly I drive
from meeting to meeting,
trading messages and recordings
like boomerangs coming back
as petrol
as a promise
to meet and talk
dreaming perhaps
the many true stories

Federation refers to Australia's founding as a (white) nation.
Mark 2 refers to our recent Centenary celebration of this event.

CHAIN DIALOGUE: english

In the first issue of Chain *we had sent out "chain letters" to some poets and asked them to write a poem and send it on to someone else and so on. In that first issue, our hope was that we would meet a whole bunch of new writers. It turned out that we were already familiar with many of the writers in those chains. This told us a lot about the tightly knit social dimensions of the poetry community. In following issues of* Chain, *we tried both to celebrate this and to expand it. This issue on dialogue is yet another attempt to expand the conversation. In addition to an open call for work, we commissioned a series of dialogues where we asked people who did not know each other but who had similar concerns to talk to each other. And, on a whim one afternoon, we decided to try and revisit the "chain" letter concept. I wanted to think some about globalization and the growth of English and the impact this has had on literature and art. Instead of a chain letter, I sent a letter out to a number of writers with the same question. About half responded (sadly I couldn't get anyone writing in the Canada, England or the U.S. to respond despite repeated attempts). My letter went something like this:*

David Crystal notes in The Cambridge Encyclopedia of the English Language *in 1995 that "English is now the dominant or official language in over 60 countries and is represented in every continent and on three major oceans." As a writer who may or may not write primarily in English, how do you interact with English? It might be best if you began your answer with either a personal or a social history of English in your neck of the woods. And then moved to answer, how do you see your writing engaging or not with globalism and the global growth of English? Has this growth of English changed the way you write? Does it matter? Is the growth of English where you live and write synonymous with a growth of Americanization? What are the obligations or the possibilities of writing in a time where global expansion is both rampant and challenged? This piece you write could be prose, a poem, a story, a drawing, an excerpt from an interview that you've done, etc. There are no genre limitations. (JS)*

ARNALDO ANTUNES
JOSELY VIANNA BAPTISTA
Outre (Other), a poem for four hands

a wooden thing
caught
wood thrown
aloft
something wooden falls
from high
now thrown
again
caught
wood caught
fire
sure hand
cuts loose
sure half turn
and slips
from the blind hand
comes
to the other hand
completes
the ellipse of the first
in a fashion rapid
and creeping
capsule
in space
only a dry
piece
of fire
wood
in a collapse
of the air
encircling it
while it impregnates
wood's

letter-flame
and opens
—juggler—
to gravity
closes
its circuit
in itself
flight
of bat
blind and lit
sign
aloose
in a winking of shields
against all
pallid
obscure
lapse
on eyelids
—cocoons—
gravid with
all the world
for a second only
or a second
and a half
very little
time
for the alert hand
that designs
the countersign
in its movement
of kindling-letters
husked straws
hollow and knots

black
slow burning (breath)
of dry
silences
phosphorous breath
mute way
immersed
finger-skein
upon
the belly (barque)
in union and sole
on the mirror's bulge
and if the fingers open
from self-entanglement
and in a play of hands
surrender
to someone other
staves invent
—shuttling
of switches—
ruffling of letters
morse alphabet
mere voiceless sounds
sometimes counter
(only for a second
cocoon-words
at once
against all,
this   lapse
obscure)
within a
black precipice
of diesel
oil (viscous dense)
griph
secret code
convoluted body
—over gold or
asphalt—
repeating in whirls
—false ground
risk

near ground
I hear—
your rhythm-isthmus
childbirth
beginning space
between thorns
stepping of a
twilight
rapture
of senses
fixed
on the shifting
(since ever)
mixture
of matter and myth
(front to front)
:that;
and now that
and now
(hand topples
and takes hold)
that that that
(hand and hand):
wood
in movement
flies
up high
and returns
behind the other
hand
that was and will
be caught
by surprise
in advance
in another instant
comes
to the center of itself
pendulum
returns
now outside
matchstick
that unlit

returns to flame
unhurt
backward
and forth
in negative
time
to where the pensile
revived
body
dead
will die again
rebirthed
bird
struggling
to fit
again
in its own
egg
from whence it came
before
even the first
re-beginning
pendulum
pendant
swinging
within
the moment
outside
while time goes
the hand
turns turns
upon turns
others up
on other
orbits
of a same
when while
stilled side
by side front
by front body
by body day

by day by day
from dusk
till dawn
facing now
suddenly
north up front
south ahead
sub below
belly
in movement
slow steady
fall
incandescing
pendulum
of a half
the other
unhalved entire
eternity
burns
in wood
writes
governs
pendulum
unmeasured
between mouth and ear
loss of earthly
senses
deserted beds
of petroleum petrean
empty
neutral territories
from whence come
flowing
the veins of speech
of childhood
(without speech)
in which sway
and pulse
skeins of senses
I am that which sounds me
quite alone en

folding
I am that which sweats me
veiling them
selves
I am that which sounds me
in their own
quiet
this and another person
senses inside
I am that which sweats me
dessicated fruits
opening
their villi
between mine and yours
at a touch
of the fingers
shifting secret
senses
centerless

enveloped
in silk (false
transparency)
of elm in the
wind
sense-traces
voice-threads
silicons
in this opaque dust
of ashes
no gesture
with no past
no face
with no other
on the body:
the limpid stream
letter-flames
votive signs for yes and
silence

Text in black by Arnaldo Atunes. Text in gray by Josely Vianna Baptista.

Translated by Chris Daniels.

DUBRAVKA DJURIC

Writing poetry in my case was and still is connected with the process of translating. Since 1984 I have been translating American poets. Why am I attracted to American poetry? The range of poetic forms and themes that I have discovered. The powerful stream of radical poetic practices, which were almost completely gone when I appeared on the poetry scene of Serbia and ex-Yugoslavia. Translating from English meant also entering dialogue with the poems. Exciting intertextual exchanges happened. Then dialogue with the poets. Since 1972 in Serbia, many anthologies of American poetry appeared. And this was the case in the nineties, when the political situation changed, when America and Americans became the enemies.

FRANCISCO FARIA

Corpo + Borda (Body + Border)

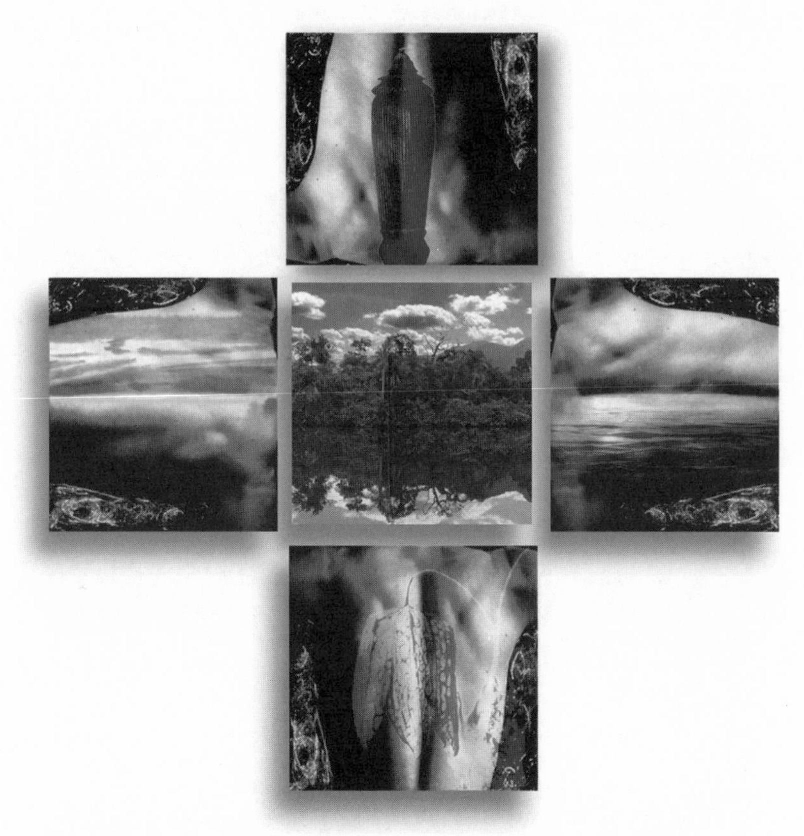

Digital image after graphite drawings on paper, 2001.

There are many borders, many frontiers to be crossed before entering into dialogue, and a language barrier is only one among many—a tiny barrier, like all the others, but, like all the others, with wide implications. Understanding is not produced by common usage. When I seek understanding, I take much into account before I scrutinize any possible or probable language barrier.

I'd like to mention two different situations:

Many years ago I went to a department store, and every day for two months I took pictures of the shelves that held cups. After this period I looked at all the pictures I took, and analyzed their "documentation." It did not come as a surprise that after two months very few forms of cups were the same on the shelves. Most of them were very different from those that had appeared two months before. Although those shelves were very stable *in terms of the product they contained on every day of those two months, the cup-forms were* seething. *Hence a very* unstable *picture of those shelves. The forms appeared and disappeared before our eyes every single week. They still do, of course, and we neither notice nor care to notice.*

I was living in Germany when, at about 2 AM on one terrifying night, Iraq fired their first missiles towards Israel. It was the beginning of the Gulf War. I heard that upsetting news on my radio, which I'd turned on by chance. I was stunned by the announcer, who was telling us that the missile was approaching. At that time no one knew if the missile had a nuclear warhead, or if it would be deploying biological or chemical weapons. For the first time, I could almost physically experience the terror of a war. Then came weeks and weeks of those green phosphorescent images of night raids on Baghdad . . . probably everybody has seen them.

The first situation reminds me that although we see some "real" things, like those cups on those shelves, we hardly notice that what we are really seeing is a formidably unending shift in forms that appear and disappear before our eyes (like on those shelves with their seemingly peaceful advertisement: a stable, homey name: cups*).*

The second reminds me that when we see virtual images of what is really happening many thousands of miles away from us, we don't really know that we're not actually there, live, *and that we're only seeing something from the very* narrow *point of view of a camera and its operator. In terms of space* and *time, a* live *point of view is very different from a* narrow *point of view.*

We take it for granted that vision and language and every other aspect of our commom communication with and within the world are charged with autonomy. Yet they are not. Nor are we concerned with what it is that forms *might signify for our western civilization.*

I wonder, for instance, if language and vision haven't merely seemed *to reach the highest possible degree of dissemination; I wonder if these overwhelming presences in our world have not been reduced to entirely pragmatic functions that are destitute of everything that might allow us a possible focus on variation, a seeing and saying what is there.*

Translated by Chris Daniels.

MARTIN LARSEN

A letter and a poem

My neck of

English succeeded german as the favored second language in Denmark after the end of WW2 and the end of the german five-year occupation of Denmark. I wonder if it is too much to say that since then the english language in our minds has been inextricably associated with the concept of liberation?

In this country culture, language and nationality blends almost to the point of identity. To be danish is to SPEAK danish. The borders of Denmark are the borders of the language; there are few non-danish speakers inside Denmark—there are very few danish speakers outside Denmark.

This makes it difficult for us to understand how any other concept of nationality can be constructed. How can you claim to be chilean, canadian, american or austrian when what you actually speak is spanish, french, english or german?

After the recent general election in Denmark it seems very likely that new laws will be introduced according to which a person cannot acquire a danish citizenship if (s)he does not pass some sort of as yet unspecified language-test.

So "the limits of my language are the limits of my world" in Denmark easily comes to mean: The limits of my nation are the limits of my world.

"Being danish" implies something else. Nobody knows exactly what that is, but a respect for (the idea of) democracy and some vaguely protestant values are said to be part of it.

Your language is what defines you (or rather OUR language is what defines you): You are in or out. (It's that old Shibboleth (ship-o-lay) all over again!)

By this logic if you do not speak our language you do not share our values, thus cannot be reasoned with, thus should be either ignored or (preferably) removed.

There is an increasing and alarming number of people here who seem to accept this kind of reasoning. But for most of us it falls through because it usually is possible to find a common language and after that usually a lot of shared values. Very often this common language is english.

English is not our language of thinking, of persuasion, of daily communication, of writing poetry (although in my case very often of reading it). It is a language of dialogue.

the woods are lovely

The most important dialogue I have had as a poet in the last five years has no doubt been an ongoing conversation with ancient chinese poetry, or rather with a few specific chinese poets, Du Fu, Wang Wei and a couple of others. For the most part this conversation has taken place in english. Of course the fact that english is my second language and they don't speak to me at all except through their english or american interpreters, makes an important difference in our dialogue, which is anything but seamless.

I try to think about what an ideal dialogue would be. Anything but seamless. Dialogue means misunderstandings, clarifications, repetitions, questions, answers and seductions. It means finding a shared space and inhabiting it.

And what interests me in chinese poetry—which is often and only partially correctly understood as a wellbalanced, harmonious aloof poetry of nature and solitude—is its intimacy and its social nature. So much of it is occasional poetry, poetry written at a specific festive occasion or letters to friends far away at the edge of the huge empire. It is almost like a kind of personism, at least as I understand it (but then I don't know Frank O'Hara that well).

Wang Wei in particular is usually seen as a specifically buddhist poet of seclusion. And yet his most famous poems, the "Wang Stream Collection" are written as a dialogue with his friend Pei Di (whose parts of the sequence are rarely translated).

dark and deep

A simile occurs to me: I think of a first language as natural light, the light of the sun which is everywhere and which you take for granted. And of a second language as artificial light, lamps that light up local spaces, sometimes flickering, sometimes bright and beautiful, sometimes vulgar.

Ok, so I know that language is never natural, but that's not the point. The point is the difference, the artificiality. It makes you appreciate it all the more. And God knows we need it up here, it's winter and the nights are long. An artificial paradise? Yes please, it's very liberating.

.arabesque.

This day has more colour than the deepest thoughts
of a rainbow, here in the garden where I imagine Wang Wei
and Gerard Manley Hopkins sitting in the middle of that heraclitean fire
they both forsaked and both cherished so dearly.
"My ignorance shines over me like the blindness of the moon,"
one of them might have said, "Water, the kindcold element,"
the other. Against fire the water, the cool dew.
But the heat of fire and the cold of water are not enough
each by themselves. To quench a burning thirst is just as sweet
as the warmth of a fireplace after a cool swim
and from this it follows that true bliss comes from "the dynamic play
of the elements," not from their mutual extinction.

All is fire. All is water. Everything shimmers in the summer sun
but the garden is real and has weight, the trees, the birds,
the green water, even the light of which the earth receives
about two kilos every second—only the soul is not,
a ghost, an eerie spirit without a body, a shadow
from Hades or a thin wisp of smoke hanging briefly
over the flames of a bonfire before it dissolves.
The sleepers are in touch with the dead, the wakeful
with the sleeper. In the light of dreams we see the dead
and the dreams themselves illuminate the mind of the wakeful.
Sitting there in that flowering burning garden all
intoxicated by ambrosian colours, what is it then
a pain? an anxiety? that holds you back? Perhaps,
but it doesn't feel that way, more like a lack
of emotion and suddenly you're in an altogether different place,
the weather is strange out here, the rain
has all the wrong colours and the things that grow
are not organic, they taste like metal
and unpleasant memories. You've been there before
perhaps in an earlier life you (or someone else?) dreamt
in some other age. For that was how it was—
it was all just a dream to remind you
that every place is fragile and to depend upon it
in the end is to invite inevitabe disaster.
What then is the alternative? We're working on it,
we have to find a way to speak in concepts
that aren't abstract. But which conceps are not abstract?

Anselm's problem all over again, the great structure
of thought comes crashing down through itself.
You have to discern as Gaunilo says. Except
he says it all wrong. Like I do. Everything shimmers
just like when I try to play chess. Not before my eyes
but inside the brain and that's the whole problem.
From there we pull out our metaphors. (Metaphors
like great luminous buildings in a blue mist.)

Later someone would write: "Tonight the Buddha entered Nirvana. It was
like firewood burned utterly away." And that is what Wang is thinking, I think,
sitting alone in a small clearing plucking away at the strings of his ch'in.
No smoke, no ashes, only the mind fading away. He is thinking about this
because he can't stop his own thoughts, desires, happiness,
sitting here in a small clearing between the bamboos, thinking
of the bamboos and ashes and smoke and the mind fading away.

A column of smoke rises, the round sun sinks;
there is a simple symmetry in all things it seems,
yet small figures move like spots in the eyes:
the roaring mad monk sings songs of Confucius
and the steady decline of morality. The peasants
lean on their sticks exchanging deep wisdoms
of hempplants and the weather. He wants to become
the eye that sees right through the landscape
till the grass, the birds, the river water,
the tree tops disappear leaving only flat planes
and patterns. He looks and looks until he finally sees
his own way of seeing. I should've been a painter,
he thinks, but he's wrong for his painting, though beautiful,
can have only one perspective while the gaze of the poems
changes from line to line. And that is how the mind moves,
one moment at one riverbank, on the other at the next.
And the landscape that awakens his yearning
changes too, moves, flows, while the picture
can only stand still, intransigent, rigid as an idea.
What is fire? It is desire, a poisonous dragon
burning in the heart, casting glances right, left, right.
In the middle of the market between boxes of red fish
and white mulberries, he looks around, confused,
confounded, suddenly not knowing where he is. Far away
from home and alone on his way to a new town he knows

and doesn't know, like all the others he's travelled through.
He grows older, his hair ashen gray, white,
but for him this is no misfortune: he feels how
slowly the desire, the fever burns out in him and old age
to him is a state of vision:
Late in life he reaches a mountain. Halfway up
is a temple but as he begins his ascension
that's not what he sees; he sees a city of light,
the city of illusions, shining in the darkness but all quiet.
The only sound coming down the slope is a mumble,
the monks chanting the Diamond Sutra. This is it, he thinks,
when I get up there all the lights will be out, the city gone
and I will be all alone in the darkness. And that's the goal.
His goal is to become Nothing and it is a goal
he is almost sure to reach.

But maybe all this is just a masque, itself an illusion
a trick to cover a deep agony while the body
sails on like Theseus' ship. The philosphers quarrel.
All is one. That is written "in the calm heart
of wellrounded truth," one of them claims, and his pupil
proves it with his masterly deductions. The idea
of infinity henceforth can never be expelled, seeping
into language like water into a lung. Still Achilles
does catch the turtle, arrows fly, distances are crossed.
So either the world is truly an illusion or some higher intellect
exists capable of containing these aporias without crumbling.
Thus God may now be deposited in the Imagination or later
eventually in the theory of quantums. Our categories however
still remain the same and continue to creak under the weight
of impossible contradictions. The brain buzzes
like the fly against the glass. Then suddenly one day
Fermat's Theorem has been proved and the world seems
different, the days grow longer, it is hot even at night
and the wings of the heart flutters. We are not alone
with even our most embittered thoughts.

Cloudpuffballs race across the sky, trees stand
naked, untouched in the clear frost. In a field
Tom, Dick and Harry are working with no thorny thoughts
in their heads, while he sits at his desk marking termpapers.
Sent away in a double exile, far from the poplars

of Oxford and far from an absentminded God he lives
in a cold winterworld, dreaming of poems like tongues
of one great flaming breath. He summons,
begs, pleads, praises, questions and blames
but he receives no answer. He is alone, left to himself,
to his self, in the middle of Nature which also seems to him
abandoned yet filled with meaning like the white coals
of the remains of a fire someone left behind. There is still
a freshness of things, the marbleglaze of the river,
woolly carpets of snow, the stonewall like a row of teeth . . .
Even in bitter cold this keeps the mind warm
when we meet it with man's little movable spark
and our gaze jumps from branch to branch with a squirrel.
On the firs cones still hang like dark bulbs long burned out,
dark and dead, devoured by time and fire.
What is water? It is the love of lovers, chilly
as we dip down into it or imagine that we do.
With bellbright bristling bodies, dare and
downdolphinery in the warm world of summer,
earthworld, waterworld. In the middle of this apollonian pastoral
the air flimmers again bringing intimations of darker ghosts:
Sharp shadows in the treecrowns, the light like lace,
splinters, luminous rafters and columns in the air.
There comes a time when all this earthly beauty
hurts, so he turns away, casts a quick glance,
gives his eyes no rest, he awakes before dawn
bathed in sweat, feels the flesh against his bones,
a sour taste in his mouth. This is also the self, the terrified
loneliness-stricken poor wretched self that he in poem
after poem after poem insistently requests freedom from.
The letters chant, the heart burns, in ecstasy
there is no rest but the wind condensed to a song
and coal that through numerous incarnations
slowly evolves into clear immutable crystals.

ROBERT SULLIVAN

from *Captain Cook in the Underworld*

Out of body, out of breath, Cook joins Orpheus
at the lyre—his friend begins
a song to torch the watery pyre
that is Cook's fate, that gyres
into a spout to take our great Cook's soul

down into the great sea. And so goes the Orphic
hymn: *I sing to Zeus as always,*
and the pantheon of my brother heroes, always,
but now I take off that cloak of culture
and wear the culture of the Pacific, your soul's future

dear Cook. I sing in my Maui throat,
lying in wait with my brothers to slow
the sun of heaven, diving far out from Reinga,
into the Underworld, Rarohenga,
and like Maui, you too have been taken

by the goddess of death. James you are dead.
But yet you have the chance to understand
what you have done in life. Not amends. You are at the lip
of the vortex of death. Slip
and your soul, your integrity, will be meaningless

in the face of your life's deeds—your soul too will
be remembered for the shootings.
I offer you another journey, Captain.
Take this challenge.
I don't offer you redemption, just the chance at integrity.

[Cook] Shootings? Well Sir Joseph was uncomfortable
                    and I wasn't doing it for the fun.
I had a ship to protect, an expedition, I needed
                    to set boundaries, to be expedient
for the sake of the mission. They were natives!

[Orpheus/Maui] Good captain I am not your judge,
                    there are no judges
in the cosmos of the sea—just wanderers,
                    don't you wonder, explorer
that you were, about the souls you sent

to wander here? The vast descent into death
                    that you began? For your soul
to rest good captain you must meet them, soul
                    to soul, until the earth in mercy
enfolds you—until then you are a mummy,

a zombie soul forever searching for its tomb.
                    Confront your doom
and follow me on your last argosy—
                    into Rarohenga, Hades,
deep into the underworld of souls . . .

HERIBERTO YÉPEZ

Text, Lies, and Role-Playing (Translation as Mother Tongue)

> Traduttore-Traditore
> —*B. Croce*

I can say pretty honestly that as a writer in Tijuana (Latin America's final frontier) I have developed my literary credo with one eye reading in English and the other in Spanish. The image is grotesque, I know. But through border life, a wide range of possibilities for cross-cultural dialogue have opened to me. Trying to write in English is one aspect of my decision to take cultural translation as my mother tongue.

I started to learn English watching TV as a kid. Then, as I was becoming a teenager, the Mexican crisis of the eighties forced us to move to a part of the city that had no public services, not even electricity. So I became a huge fan of battery-operated radios, listening mostly to American[1] pop music. At that time, rap was the hip thing to hear, and from high school through university we had endless hours of "English classes" every week. On the Border, English can be as important to your future as Spanish—in many cases, a lot more important. Thanks to my love affair with English, I quickly began to get part-time jobs on the main tourist drag in Tijuana. That's where I learned, I think, the real secrets of English, mainly through listening to and talking with Blacks and Chicanos that came to Tijuana to party on weekends.

At some point, I don't remenber exactly when, I suddenly found myself writing poetry and short stories in English, not Spanish. I think this is a very common thing among border teenagers. On the border, many of us define ourselves through our relationship with English, which is a significant part of our essence. I know this would sound really awful to a Mexico City ear, but that's how things actually are up here. We are the Malinche[2] and we are glad of it.[3]

I know that only through English can I get in touch with some essential part of myself. Many of us have developed entire realms of our consciousness through reading or hearing another language (like a whole generation of Latin Americans, who have formed themselves listening to American music). Without our relationship with that other-language a big part of us would die—but by keeping it alive we cause ourselves pain, that pain characteristic of love affairs.

I think that Latin Americans who are in close contact with the U.S., or who have at one point or another immigrated to the U.S., cultivate this affair not only as a way to accept American culture as our new identity but also, strangely, as a way to participate directly in a language that plays a large part in shaping our world—a world of meanings we share, for better or for worse, with Americans. I think Spanish, in many cases, will have to write itself in English in order to survive. For our own heritage to endure, it's imperative that we take English not as a force that is destroying our values and worldviews but as a weapon to keep our cultures alive—even though one might disagree with the ideas or styles of pioneer Nuyorican writers like Miguel Piñero or Miguel Algarín, or of Chicano writers, it is very clear that their work illustrates a key resource: we need to use English as a second Spanish.

"Converting" to another language is something we have done before in Latin America. After the Conquest and the Spanish invasion and genocide, Indian[4] cultures learned quickly to build a hybrid culture in Spanish in order to renew and maintain their original cultures. If some of my fellow Latin American writers are now increasingly deciding to switch to English, they do so with centuries of tradition behind them. For many people it is very clear that bilingualism—practices such as Spanglish, for instance—is a way to enjoy a double happiness and a double struggle.

Writing in both languages, or even switching over to English, is clearly a choice many writers make in order to avoid the intermediation of *dominant* translation. So, to use Nathaniel Tarn's term, an "antitranslation" attitude is one of the forces that propels Latin American writers to decide to create portions of their work directly in English. I think this enormous paradigm shift, in terms of some postmodern Latin American writers' process of identity-reinvention, is evident even in such canonical writers as Carlos Fuentes and Jorge Luis Borges, both of whom wrote important autiobiographical essays directly in English, as if they found English a better tool or strategy through which to see themselves and their work—in both cases these essays have been a cause of great controversy in Latin America, and for the most part have been considered dangerous moves by their authors.

Those of us who have developed our identities side by side with English know unequivocally that English can, in some way at least, function as a tool to sustain Latin American literature. We are aware, in addition, that the use of English is not just a personal decision, but also appears to be, at this point, a key resource we employ merely to survive—and to counter-conquer the new postmodern order.

•

In the Latin American canonical tradition, examples of writers constructing their work in other languages are rare. One can think only of exceptional cases, such as Huidobro's French poems or contemporary outsiders like the Brazilian Glauco Mattoso, writing some of his homosexual antipoetry directly in Spanish. It is safe to say that a consideration of the mother tongue as the "natural" medium for constructing one's own work is one of the tenets of modern literature in Latin America (and certainly in Western Literature in general). But in the last half-century, we increasingly see writers of all genres switching their mother tongue for another language—mainly English. This is a major change, a break with the formerly fixed modern belief in the mother tongue. It is equally clear that this shift in practice, this change in viewpoint, is more a form of cultural resistance than of yielding to domination. (What major Anglo writer would dare to write his or her next book in Spanish? But the contrary happens more and more each year: the paradigm shift away from the automatic parading of texts in a forced mother tongue/translation procession is going to be led, therefore, by Third-World Postmodernism).

I think this change, from mother tongue to the self-translation of bilingualism, which is not yet recognized at all in the Latin America mainstream, is going to have a tremendous impact in the coming decades. But before further exploring the new English-Spanish relationship, we need to take into account that this new bilingualism in Latin American contemporary writing is not exclusively an English deal. Another significant change occasioned by current postmodern adjustments and literary redefinitions on the American continent occurs in the form of a widespread boom in bilingual Indian literature. These new poets write simultaneously in their Indian language and in Spanish, and in some ways they are even programmatic about being bilingual. Thus there is elasticity and change even within the concept of literary bilingualism. For example, I think the next Neruda is writing right this moment, in Mayan and Spanish. I am talking about Humberto Ak'abal, the Guatemalan poet who writes from both Western and Indian language traditions. He translates himself from Spanish to Mayan and from Mayan to Spanish, constructing a truly *dialogical* discourse. This new kind of *dual* writer is undoubtedly going to radically modify literary paradigms in Latin America and abroad, through these kinds of self-translation methods—and yes, I did say that Ak'abal is as important as Neruda. Just wait a bit.

•

One of the great failures of Modernity, though few acknowledge it, was caused by an optimistic belief in innocent translation. Translation can't achieve equivalence, reproduction, analogy or correspondence.

Once we understand that there is no real possibility of getting two languages (two people, two cultures, two worlds) to say the same thing or have an identical effect, I think we also realize that the very failure of translation opens many new possibilities for dialogue. In this sense, we can call postmodern translation any method of linguistic interaction that no longer takes as its purpose the "faithful" rendering of another language or discourse, but rather explicitly considers as its task the radical re-invention of the original text. It is an active translation instead of a passive one.

Examples of this renouncement of traditional translation can be found in the Total Translation theory-performance used by Jerome Rothenberg to recreate Indian poetry (isn't it interesting that one area of ethnopoetics adapted itself to end up in projects like the fake Sumero-Akkadians *Tablets* by Armand Schwerner?)[5], and also in the non-verbal visual translations of Blake by the Brazilian concrete poet Augusto de Campos. Other experiments which expand the meaning of translation include: Jorge Luis Borges' imaginary foreign quotations; Fernandinho Oviedo's openly bizarre translations of Whitman into sonnets(!); Cuban writer Guillermo Cabrera Infante's book *Holy Smoke* (1985), written first in English and then fifteen years later self-translated into Spanish; Steve McCaffery's homolinguistic translations of Gertrude Stein; or the semi-serious orientalia used by the Mexican-Peruvian novelist Mario Bellatin, who uses imaginary sources of scholarship not to make one language a vehicle for another but to make a language that functions as a delusional method of reinventing both ends of the equation. We can safely speculate that neo-translation is definitively the most interesting form of fiction currently being written. Methods such as transcreation, apocrypha, heteronomy, intertextuality, multimedia, rewriting, collage, transvestite-textual-subject, pastiche, false quotation, antitranslation, parody, appropriation and *othering* in general are now the elemental resources of neo-translation and the paradigms of contemporary experimental writing. The lesson is: we CAN'T translate the Other so we need to reinvent the both of us. We need to further develop this kind of re-imagining (or perhaps totally imaginary) translation. Such re-imaginings—such translations—are some of the most intriguing ways of cultivating the potential for cross-cultural dialogue.

This sort of translation-dialogue practice, of course, can be quite dangerous culturally: we run the risk that we might deny or replace the Other with the Image of Ourselves. In imagination, the Other is not really present, that's true—but neither are we. In re-imagining, neither object nor subject exists anymore. That's precisely why imagination is the ideal dialogical zone of encounter.

Every text is a pre-text. Every text must be altered in order to become what it must be. The new purpose of translation is not to make a second text which is as close as possible to the first, but to create another text which is uneven, divergent, conflictive, or even non-compatible with the first. How might we do that? In many ways: for instance, by translating ethnographical interviews into chants (translation from one genre to another, and/or recycling and re-organizing data, as Ed Sanders does in his investigative poetry), or by transforming long poems into drawings (applying re-visualization or radical typographical resources, as in Dennis Tedlock's translations of Zuni narratives, or line re-disposal in the concrete poets' translations of canonical authors). Other neo-translation techniques can include fragmenting the original text (and even perhaps introducing random selections of a text) and then putting it through a (possibly experimental) translation process, or using translation as part of one's own writing, or employing hermeneutics to rewrite a rigidly "established" text (like Heidegger's or Horst Matthai's profound re-translations of the presocratics), adaptations like *La hija de Rappaccini* (Octavio Paz's translation/reconstruction of Nathaniel Hawthorne) or *Jacques and his Master*, Milan Kundera's re-imagination of Diderot. We can locate this shift in literary paradigms in the second half of the 20th Century simply in the tricky claims made by certain authors—like the Argentinean poet Alejandra Pizarnik, who presented her novella *La condesa sangrienta* as a translation. Isn't it clear, then, that translation games are becoming a favorite paradigm in language play?

•

Neo-translation techniques, in any case, are linked also to a change in the way we view criticism, which is currently in the process of becoming a more delirious dialogue with its object, in what we might call fictive-criticism *(crítica-ficción),* the purpose of which is no longer to encourage the critic to attempt to reveal the real meanings of a text, but rather to permit her or him to recreate them freely (paralexia), conducting the original text towards its delusional meanings or secretly altering the piece of writing one analyzes—mock criticism in general—or drawing the text towards its more extreme absurdities.[6]

In recent years, I have been involved in translation-criticism experiments involving certain types of critical fantasies in which I mix real interpretation with secret self-parody or even readers'/editors' deliberate deceptions. I have succeeded, for example, in getting non-real "criticisms" (heteronomy) or supposed translations published in major magazines, or in simply developing concepts or applying points of view in which I don't actually believe, systematically attributing false quotes to real authors or manipulating data, mixing unknown fictional authors in with canonical ones—in short, considering criticism, at every point, to be fictional prose. I write fictive and parodic translation-criticism *(crítica-ficción)* without revealing it to the readers of the books or magazines that have published those essays or pseudo-translations. In many cases my use of fiction is simply indistinguishable from my true beliefs. Even though most of the time you wouldn't know it from reading my texts, I always write criticism from an insincere point of view, as a way to destroy the confidence and *authority* we give to the critic as a literary subject or a credible voice. Of course this technique has already been suggested: by some of Laura Riding's ideas (in, for example, *Anarchism is not Enough*); in Borges' analytical short stories and use of style as a mask;[7] in Sévero Sarduy's "Ahora Góngora," a magnificent talk on Góngora written as a neo-barroque grotesque parody of hermeneutics and psychoanalysis applied to poetry; through Barthes' position on the equivalence of criticism and literature and his exhausting theories on the Death of the Author; or in Derrida's notions of grammatology and dissemination. This realm of post-critical dialogic space opens to us further in the confessions of authors like Lyotard and Harold Pinter: the former, when he reveals that he made up some perspectives and didn't actually read all the documents he quoted or referenced in the now canonical pages of *The Postmodern Condition*, the latter when he notes that some of the (rare) oral or written explanations he has provided about his own plays have been nothing but jokes. "Take reviews as the worst case of black humor." After the 20th century, discourse-construction cannot be taken as a serious task.[8]

Though I rarely, if ever, make my various games with criticism evident in my writings, I feel comfortable revealing these comical and fictional resources in my "serious" prose because in the U.S. nobody is going to read my other work (for instance, perhaps I am lying even here and I have actually never performed any of these tricks and experiments, but by claiming I have, I end up writing *crítica-ficción* after all). American readers do not care about my literary hijinx, even though in the majority of these games I refer to English-language writers, which makes my task easier thanks to the incredible ignorance about American literature in Mexico: it's pretty easy to invent American writers and references, or alter people's writing subtly, or even radically, without anyone's paying particular notice. This is also part of a larger project I am developing, which involves building communication between our two cultures through imaginary entities and lies. I don't want to provide too many details of my fictive criticism and neo-translation projects, but I can simply say that my work is part of a *diálogo diablo* (to use Groussac's image) on the periphery of Latin America, a *devilish dialogue* or *diabolical dialogue,* a sort of wanna-be experimental cross-cultural setup which I feel can accomplish much more than more serious academic approaches. In many ways, the most significant aspects of my literary career depend on a mutual lack of interest and intercommunication between the literary scenes on both sides of the Colorado River. If, therefore, an American reader were to tell my Mexican editors and literary acquaintances that I have lied to them on certain occasions, I would be ruined and would have to go back to a boring life of only telling the truth.

Literary dialogue between Mexico and the U.S. is so reduced that I am certain no reader or editor in Mexico will read these confessions I am making in English. (This is an example, once again, of how English can often be a better medium for Spanish-language writers—we can say in English what we cannot say in our native tongue).

In addition to the fact that I love private jokes (my favorite form of dialogue), another reason I choose not to go public with my fictive criticism techniques is my suspicion that if I do I might inspire other people, as well, to use my techniques in a systematic way, and I would hate that. As Quiroga said, "Telling the truth is never amusing." Openly telling readers that I am playing with them and myself would mean taking all the fun out of my stupid anti-discourse antics.

Well, to tell you the truth, I am lying again. I have never played such childish literary games. But I intend to do so as soon as I can.

•

A fictional dialogic strategy is useful for more than just criticism and translation. I have also used it in poetry. My first book of poems was designed to represent a "case" of Mexican "border" poetry. One day I simply sat down and designed a *plan piloto*[9] for a poetry book which could be read as representing that notion, as constructed in the Mexican literary imaginary. Thus I wrote a series of poems on urban violence, border images of despair, ethnopoetic experiments with Border Indians, and translations from English; I also included photos of visual poems I hung on Tijuana streets, a rewriting of the Mayan Book of the Dead and even a kind of manifesto for a new type of poetry I am ostensibly "defending" within the circus of new Mexican contemporary literature (I even gave it a name, "norteado" poetry, poetry both lost and disoriented, and at the same time Northern (or Northified), close to American Literature and to Mexican Northern popular culture). Of course, I do not actually identify myself as a text-producer within the style I used (forged) in that book, or the others I have designed as experiments in constructing literary styles, tendencies or subjective poetics. I have always written from within the knowledge that I am just a liar (an obsessive-compulsive graphomaniac) who acts as if his books were a faithful rendering of his true literary tastes or ideas. I don't, in fact, think such rendering is possible. There is no longer any potential for seriousness in language. I have chosen to speak for (as) others, playing roles for them, leading them to portray an "original" and "true" position only to leave them behind for my next mask. I must confess, again, that I do not believe even one word of my own work.

From "my" poems to "my" essays, none of my words/permutations/practices has anything to do with my real beliefs. (Do I have such things as real beliefs?) My poems and my short stories are nothing but calculated and insincere discourse games designed to enact secret interplay with other discourses, so I might establish a parody of literary dialogue based on fulfilling or undermining certain stereotypical expectations, performing a kind of role-playing as an author within a specific culture (in this case, the Mexican "Republic of Letters"). In each book I take myself as a character: "Urban Experimental Poet," "Polemical Anti-Mexico City Young Critic," "Translator and Interpreter of American Counterpoetics," "Short Story Teller of Border Lives," and in this essay for *Chain*, "Mexican Writer Sympathetic to Postmodernism Telling Us (U.S.) the Real Truth Behind his Lies." (It goes without saying that I am now lying, but to tell you the truth I do believe I am part of a larger socio-cultural phenomenon called the Norteado Generation, and yes, it's true, most of the ideas I write are ones I feel, like or believe. Sorry. Most of the time I write what I find natural—oh, such a beautiful, comforting, concept, "what I find *natural*."[10] I apologize, again, for being such a liar.)

All this role-playing is utterly nihilistic and boring, I know, but I truly believe there is currently no other alternative. I think that in the future, writing—post-everything writing—is going to move in a direction where we consider our position as author as nothing more than a humoristic fictitious entity, no more real than a character in a novel. You can't give any credit to a writer. He is nobody. She is just a player. Our books are never a personal account of anything, nor are they a trustworthy intellectual autobiography. A book is a fiction in every conceivable aspect. Dialogue around poetic language can only really begin when we admit to and further radicalize our role-playing as designers of discourses who are ourselves invented by our texts, as much as we are inventors of them.

What is a writer who still clings to the notion of using his work as a means to represent his true intentions?—somebody still trapped in that primitive and naïve period of humanity called Modernity.

Poor little fellow.

1 *"American" here refers specifically to the United States, though the term should technically reference the American continent in general; this mistranslation is especially noteworthy in a text written by an American, translated by an American and edited by an American for an American audience. (Typist's note)*

2 *La Malinche: also known as La Chingada, The Fucked One. A traitor to her race, cultural whore. Sought to save indigenous peoples from slaughter during conquest by becoming lovers with Hernán Cortés. Blamed, therefore, for the penetration of the Spanish into indigenous Mexican lands, and credited or discredited with the beginnings of* mestizaje. *(Editor's note)*

3 *For many Latin Americans, English, like poetry, has become a more private and* especial *language, different from the one we use daily in public life (in our case Spanish). When I am alone or walking in the streets, for example, I talk to myself in English, as I do in footnotes. (Author's note)*

4 *"Indian" here is a literal translation (hence a mistranslation) of the term* Indio/India, *used to refer to indigenous peoples in Mexico and Latin America. (Typist's note)*

5 *The Schwerner case curiously has a Latin American link: Schwerner's character of "scholar-translator" (who is both serious and weird) was partially inspired by Julio Cortázar's "Morelli," a character who represents a metalinguistic voice in* Rayuela, *Cortázar's most important novel — it's worth mentioning that Cortázar's character was inspired by the figure of Borges. So the* Tablets *are a part of a secret web of relationships embedded in the postmodern idea of the writer-translator. Curiously, Schwerner misspelled Cortázar's name, using an "s" instead of a "z," a mistake that in my opinion cannot be taken as a mere* lapsus calami: *let's remember José Lezama Lima's famous mistranslations and misspellings of foreign author's names and references. I think we should reevaluate this "fantasy orthography" (as Cortázar coined it) as another intriguing case of postmodern transcreation. (Critic's note)*

6 *In Spanish, the term* crítica-ficción *resembles the expression for "Science Fiction,"* ciencia ficción, *which also brings to mind (well, to the informed mind) a famous error made by a major Mexican translator, on the cover of his translation into Spanish of a selection of writings on science fiction by Ray Bradbury: by mistake he titled his text* Sobre la crítica ficción *instead of*

Sobre la ciencia ficción. *Obviously in English the sound similarities, semantic resonance and cultural references ricocheting between the two terms get lost when we translate "Crítica-Ficción" as "Fictive Criticism," an expression, we must confess, of which the author of this essay disapproved, as he considers it too long and noisy. (Translator's note).*

7 Borges was the first postmodern writer to fully understand that every name must be put in quotation marks. Borges knew that in order to make a final parody of classical literature, he needed to construct an image called "Borges" through the emphatic use of a certain style *as well as* recognizable *and* personal *themes. He was the last exquisite, as Cioran declared him. "Borges" made himself into an elegant and almost clandestine parody of the Modern [European] Writer. Borges knew that through a series of writings a discourse-designer becomes a character, even though he is really* nadie*—no one. (Critic's note)*

8 I want to point out that a recurrent resource of crítica-ficción *is the use of footnotes as a key instrument in achieving credibility or committing parody of the academic style and its scientific desires. Of course one cannot forget here the adventurous ideas laid out by Paul Feyerabend, on using insincere criticism to cause science to lose all the credibility it gained during Modernity. From Borges to Bellatin, the use of tricky footnotes is an essential aspect of fraudulent cultural translation practices. (Translator's note)*

9 A pilot plan or template. (Editor's note)

10 Natural?! C'mon! What's wrong with you? I think you're going insane up there, man. "Natural"? You said natural*?! You're crazy, nothing corresponds to "natural." Charles Bernstein has an interesting quote on this issue. I hope you find it soon, brother, and put it down here. Quotes like that always help to keep the good reputation of footnotes alive. (Translator's note to the author)*

Translated by Heriberto Yépez and slicked down by Jen Hofer.

VINCENT ABBEY is a performance photographer based in Manchester, England. • ANGEL ABREU is currently a student of art and philosophy at the University of Washington in Seattle. • ADAM AITKEN is a writer of poetry, reviews, essays, fiction and emails. His poems have appeared in *Tinfish*, *Poetry* (USA), and *Calyx* anthology of Australian Poetry. He is the author of *Romeo and Juliet in Subtitles* and *In One House*. • ROSA ALCALÁ's most recent translations include Cecilia Vicuña's *El Templo* (Situations Press, 2001) and *Cloud-net* (Art in General, 1999). Her own poems have appeared in several literary magazines, including *Chain* and *The World*. Currently pursuing a Ph.D. in English at SUNY-Buffalo, she co-curates *ñ: poesía, crítica, y arte / a non-unilingual series*. • SA'DI AL-HADITHI was born in Hadithi, Iraq in 1939 and lived there until he was 19 years old, when he was then moved to Baghdad—where he worked as a teacher, journalist, writer and translator. He currently works with the Cultural Foundation in the United Arab Emirates. • JOE AMATO is the author of *Symptoms of a Finer Age* (Viet Nam Generation, 1994), *Bookend: Anatomies of a Virtual Self* (SUNY Press, 1997) and *Under Virga* (Chax Press, forthcoming). He often collaborates with his wife and partner Kass Fleisher. • BRUCE ANDREWS' author page is http://epc.buffalo.edu/authors/andrews. Essays collected in *Paradise & Method: Poetics & Praxis* (from Northwestern UP) and in the journal *Aerial*'s anthology on his work. Recent large poetry sequence, *Lip Service*, from Coach House Press. • ARNALDO ANTUNES was born in São Paulo, Brazil, in 1960. He has published the books *Psia* (São Paulo, Iluminuras, 1986), *Tudos* (São Paulo, Iluminuras, 1990), *As coisas* (São Paulo, Iluminuras, 1992), *Nome* (video-book-CD. São Paulo, Iluminuras, 1993), *2 ou mais corpos no mesmo espaço* (book with CD. São Paulo, Perspectiva, 1997), *40 escritos* (São Paulo, Iluminuras, 2000) and *Palavra Desordem* (São Paulo, Iluminuras, 2002). Some of his poems appeared in *Nothing the sun could not explain. 20 contemporary Brazilian poets* (Los Angeles, Sun & Moon Press, 1997, translations by Dana Stevens and Regina Alfarano). The address for his website is www.uol.com.br/arnaldoantunes. • For copies of ALANI APIO's plays, contact Palila Books at 808-593-2205 or hansloff@hawaii.rr.com. • ADEMIR ASSUNÇÃO é poeta e jornalista. Trabalhou em alguns dos maiores jornais e revistas do Brasil, como Folha de São Paulo, O Estado de São Paulo e revista Veja. Publicou os seguintes livros: *LSD Nô* (1994), *A Máquina Peluda* (1997), *Cinemitologias* (1998) e *Zona Branca* (2001). É um dos editores da revista literária *Coyote*, junto com os poetas Marcos Losnak e Rodrigo Garcia Lopes. •

GUY BEINING's work will appear in *Writing to Be Seen,* an anthology of visual/verbal poetry via light & dust books. His *Measurements of Night* will be available from CC.Marimbo Publications in 2002. • SHELLEY BERC is a novelist, playwright, and essayist. Berc's recent novel, *The Shape of Wilderness*, was published by Coffee House Press. Her novella *dante: a girls own guide to the divine comedy* is currently on the Web at *Exquisite Corpse: A journal of letters and ideas*. Berc's other fiction and many excerpts of her new novel *Light and Its Shadow* have been published in *Bomb*, *Exquisite Corpse*, *Web Del Sol Review*, *5_Trope*, *In Posse Review*, and *Linnaean Street*. The full text of "Theatre of the Mind" will be published in *Theatre in Crisis?,* edited by Maria Delgado and Caridad Svitch, published by University of Manchester Press in 2002. • RACHEL BERS is a graduate student at the Rhode Island School of Design in Printmaking. Her work was part of an international portfolio shown last November at the Plantin-Moretus Museum in Antwerp, Belgium. The portfolio will also be shown in the galleries of the School of the Museum of Fine Arts in Boston. Current projects can be seen in the Boston Drawing Project files at the Bernard Toale Gallery in Boston. • ROBERT BRANCH works for the Office of Public Affairs at Columbia University and is also a Co-Director of K.O.S. • WENDY CALL is a Fellow of the Institute of Current World Affairs. She currently lives in Mexico's Isthmus of Tehuantepec, where she writes about how the region's indigenous communities cut a path between assimilation and isolation in an increasingly globalized world. Her non-fiction writing and photographs have been published in Britain, Mexico, Spain and the United States. This is her first publication in a literary journal. • ROBERT QUILLEN CAMP is a playwright and performance artist. His plays have recently been published in *Conundrum* and *Conjunctions 38: Rejoicing Revoicing*. • ODILE CISERNOS is a critic, writer and translator from Mexico, currently living in New York. Her translations and essays can be found in the journals *Sibila* 1 and 2 (São Paulo Brazil), *Poesía y poética* 33 (Mexico City, Mexico). She has translated the work of Régis Bonvicino, Haroldo de Campos, Rodrigo Rey Rosa and the Nobel laureate, Jaroslav Seifert, among others. Other essays and translations can be found in: http://sites.uol.com.br/regis and http://www.uol.com.br/bienal/24bienal/nuh/inuhoiticic02a.htm. More translations are forthcoming in *Ecopoetics* and *Translation* (Fall 2002). • PETER S. CONRAD is an artist and writer living in Northern California. At www.peterconrad.com you can see more of his comics and cartoons, or find out where to get the latest issue of his comics zine, *Attempted Not Known*. Recently, he edited *Swell*, an anthology of alternative comics. • CHRIS

DANIELS was born and raised in NYC, and now lives and works in the San Francisco Bay Area. He hopes to move to Brazil in the near future, and has devoted himself entirely to the translation of Lusophone poetry. This year, Manifest press will publish his translation *On the shining screen of the eyelids—selected poems of Josely Vianna Baptista*, with artwork by Francisco Faria, and Inscrutable Books will publish *One step from the bird I breathe in*, a selection of poems by Orides Fontela. Rattapallax Press is soon to publish an anthology including many of his translations of young Brazilian poets. Current projects include Clarice Lispector's posthumous novel *Um sopro de vida (pulsações)* [*A breath of life (pulsations)*]. There are several manuscripts looking for publishers, including a book-length poem by Josely Vianna Baptista called *Os poros flóridos* [*Florid pores*]. • TOM DEVANEY is the author of *The American Pragmatist Fell In Love* (Banshee Press, 1999). He is the Program Director of the Kelly Writers House at the University of Pennsylvania and producer of the radio program *Live from The Writers House* on 88.5, WXPN. Since 1995 he has written and worked with The Animated Neck & Stars and Lost Art of Puppet Theater. • DUBRAVKA DJURIC writes poetry, criticism, and translates American poets in Beograde. • STACY DORIS' latest books are *Conference* (Potes & Poets 2001), and *Une Année à New York avec Chester* (P.O.L 2000). With Chet Wiener, she recently edited a collection of writing by the French poet Christophe Tarkos, *Christophe Tarkos: Ma Langue est Poétique, Selected Works* (Roof 2000). She is currently translating Ryoko Sekiguchi, from Japan. • For work by RACHEL BLAU DUPLESSIS, *Drafts 1-38, Toll* (Wesleyan University Press, 2001), and for work from the next group of drafts *Hambone*, *Ixnay 8*, *First Intensity*, *A.BACUS*, the anthology *"We Who 'Love to Be Astonished'": Experimental Women's Writing and Performance Poetics*, ed. Hinton and Hogue. • PATRICK F. DURGIN is the author of two chapbooks of poetry: *Pundits Scribes Pupils* (Potes & Poets, 1998) and *Sorter* (Duration Press, 2001). Excerpts from his ongoing collaboration with Jen Hofer are published or forthcoming in the journals *Aufgabe*, *!factorial*, *Bombay Gin*, and *Combo*. A dialogue, with Andrew Levy, is published in *Antennae* and at Levy's author page at the Electronic Poetry Center of SUNY-Buffalo's Poetics Program (epc.buffalo.edu). Durgin's "Murk Job" will be published as an issue of *A.BACUS* in the 2003 series. Since 1998 he has edited and published *Kenning* (www.durationpress.com/kenning). • CRAIG DWORKIN's *Reading the Illegible*, a study of the politics of appropriation, is forthcoming from Northwestern University Press. • CHRISTINE EVANS is an Australian playwright/musician and Fulbright scholar (2000-1). Her U.S. credits include winning Perishable Theatre's 9th and 10th Annual

Women's Playwrighting Festivals (WPF); her plays *Mothergun* and *All Soul's Day* are published in Perishable's 9th and 10th WPF Anthologies (ordering info is at www.perishable.org). *Mothergun* will be performed at HERE in NYC in July as part of the Lincoln Center Director's Lab season; *Pussy Boy* will permiere at Belvoir St. Theatre, Sydney, in June 2002. • FRANCISCO FARIA, Brazilian artist, has been showing for more than 20 years, in Brazil and abroad. A book with some of his visual contributions, *On the shining screen of the eyelids*, in collaboration with Brazilian poet Josely Vianna Baptista, is forthcoming from Manifest Press (Berkeley). A comprehensive look at his artwork, *The Meaning of Americas' Landscape*, will be published this year by Brazilian editors Ed. Mirabilia (edmirabilia@uol.com.br). • DREW GARDNER's book *Sugar Pill*, is forthcoming in 2002 from Krupskaya Press (www.krupskayabooks.com). • PETER GIZZI's latest book is *Artifical Heart*. He has two new chapbooks this spring: *Revisal* with art work by David Byrne and *Fin Amor* with artwork by George Herms. And recent poems in *Conjunctions, Hambone, The American Poetry Review, Fence,* and *Salt*. • E. TRACY GRINNELL is the author of *music/or forgetting* (O Books, 2001). Her work has appeared in *Combo*, *syllogism*, *kenning*, *Rhizome*, *Ribot*, and is forthcoming in *Primary Writing*, *26*, and *Conundrum*. She edits *Aufgabe*. • JOHN HAVELDA is an English poet and visual artist who lives in Porto. His work has appeared most recently in *Chain* and *Dandelion*. *mor,* a book of poetry and visual work with translations by Manuel Portela, was published in 1997. He also writes for the theatre: *Por Amor de Deus* was performed in 2001 at the Teatro de Campo Alegre in Porto, and *Os Considerados*, a play on cd, was published by the Teatro Nacional de São João in 1999. A book of poems, *Where Mr. Reagan Learnt His Craft*, will be published in 2002 by Macedonia Livros. • JEN HOFER is the editor and translator of an anthology of contemporary poetry by Mexican women, tentatively titled *What You See Here*, which will be co-published by University of Pittsburgh Press and Ediciones Sin Nombre in 2003. Her other works include *as far as* (a+bend, 1999), *Laws* (*A.BACUS* #139, July 2001), *The 3:15 Experiment* (in conjunction with Lee Ann Brown, Danika Dinsmore and Bernadette Mayer, The Owl Press, 2001) and *Slide Rule* (subpress, 2002). • CRAIGIE HORSFIELD is an artist who, for many years, has worked with ideas that approach relation, the present, slow time, and "slow history," place, limit, empathy, understanding and recognition, and conversation. • MICHAEL IVES is a musician, composer, and writer living in the Hudson Valley. From 1995 to 2000, he was a member of and writer for the sound/text performance ensemble, F'loom. During that time, his work with the group was featured on NPR's

Weekend Edition and *Weekly All Things Considered*, and on other radio programs. He has poetry and fiction in upcoming issues of *Facture, First Intensity, American Letters and Commentary, Gargoyle* among others. A collection of short fiction is forthcoming from Elimae books. • LISA JARNOT is the author of *Some Other Kind of Mission* and *Ring of Fire*. Her first CD, *Poems from Ring of Fire*, is available through Small Press Distribution. • KAKÁ WERÁ JECUPÉ filho de pais da etnia tapuia, nasceu nos arredores da represa Billings, zona sul da cidade de São Paulo. Publicou os livros *Todas as vezes que dissemos adeus* (1994), *A Terra dos Mil Povos* (1998) e *Tupã Tenondé* (2001). Em 1996, a convite da Universidade de Oxford (Inglaterra), fez uma conferência sobre religiosidade indígena. No ano seguinte, discursou sobre o mesmo assunto na Universidade de Stanford (EUA). É um dos fundadores do Instituto Nova Tribo, que trabalha na preservação e divulgação das culturas indígenas brasileiras. • REYNALDO JIMÉNEZ was born in Lima, Peru, in 1959. He lives in Buenos Aires since 1963. He is a poet and an editor. His last books: *La curva del eco* (1998), *La indefensión* (2001) & *Reflexión esponja* (2002). He is also coeditor of *tsé=tsé*, a review of Latin American poetry (tsetse@sinectis.com.ar). • M. KASPER is a librarian, verbo-visualist (10 artists' books—see *WorldCat*—and many magazine appearances, most recently, regularly, in one once called *Socialist Revolution*, then *Socialist Review*, now *Radical Society*, and thereby hangs a tale), and translator (*Saint ghetto des prêts*, 1950, a Lettrist book by Gabriel Pomerand, due from Atlas Press/London later this year). • JOHN KINSELLA's many volumes of poetry include *Visitants* (Bloodaxe/Dufours 1999) and *The Hierarchy of Sheep* (Bloodaxe). His selected experimental poems are due to be published in 2003 (ratapallax and FACP). He is editor of *Salt* and international editor for *The Kenyon Review*. His homepage is at: www.johnkinsella.org • TOM LA FARGE's two-volume novel *The Crimson Bears/A Hundred Doors* is available from Sun & Moon Press. So is *Terror of Earth,* his collection of tales based on Old French beast-fables and fabliaux. His second novel, *Zuntig,* has just appeared from Green Integer. • MARTIN LARSEN lives in Copenhagen. His first book of poetry, *.det stof alting er gjort af.*, was published 2001. • MARK LOKENSGARD is an Assistant Professor of Portuguese at St. Mary's University in San Antonio, Texas. He has published articles on Portuguese and Brazilian Literature in *Portuguese Studies, Cadernos Literários* and *Letras de Hoje*. His translations of 19th and 20th Century Brazilian poetry will be published by Oxford University Press in its forthcoming anthology *500 Years of Latin American Poetry*. • KANAN MAKIYA was born in Baghdad and is the author of *Republic of Fear* and *The Monument: Art, Vulgarity and Responsibility in Iraq* (both originally published under a pseudonym), the award winning *Cruelty & Silence,* and his new novel *The Rock: A Tale of Seventh-Century Jerusalem* published by Pantheon. He currently directs the Iraq Research and Documentation Project at Harvard University and teaches at Brandeis University. • RUTH MARGRAFF is co-founder of HERE's "opera project." Her work includes *Night Vision, The Electra Fugues,* and *Once Upon a Time in Chinese America . . . A Martial Arts Ballet*. Her work has been published in *Conjunctions, Epoch, Autonomedia/Big Red Media,* and several martial arts journals. • ROB MACKENZIE was born in Glasgow in 1964, but grew up on the island of Lewis, off the northwest coast of mainland Scotland. For university he went to Edinburgh, to study environmental chemistry. He now lectures in atmospheric science at Lancaster University. He comes from a gaelic-speaking community, but doesn't speak the language. Recent books: *Kirk Interiors*, (Ankle Press, Cambridge, 1993), *The Tune Kilmarnock* (Form Books, London, 1996), and *Off Ardglas* (Invisible Books, 1997). • MARK MCMORRIS's "The Alphabet of Wounds" is Part III of a work entitled *Antoine Basil Carol*. Part I of this work, "Illusions," appeared in *Hambone* some time ago. Part II, "Theoretical Man," was published in *Conjunctions* 36 (2001). Other recent poetry appears in *New American Writing, The Baffler, Fence, Tripwire, & The Poetry Project Newsletter*. • SEAN MEEHAN is primarily a musician though all of his sound work from last year became objects with no sound. You can see them at home.earthlink.net/~overturnedbowl/works. He is currently working on a 7" record with Michelle Spencer and a collaborative piece with poet Bonnie Jones. • DIJANA MILOSEVIC is an internationally known voice and movement specialist from Yugoslavia. As a professional theatre director she has worked in theatres across Europe. She has served as radio director at Belgrade radio, Yugoslavia, where she also directed radio dramas. In 1991, she founded DAH Theatre in Belgrade with Jadranka Andjelic, Milosevic—the first theatre laboratory in Yugoslavia. In 1992 she co-founded the NATASHA Project, an international theatre network which sponsors the ART Saves Life festival. For the last two years she has also been programmer for the INFANT Festival (An International Meeting of Alternative and New Theatre) in Novi Sad. • METTE MOESTRUP was born in 1969 and lives in Copenhagen. She is working on her second book of poetry, *Golden Delicious*. She teaches poetry and writes literary criticism. She has studied literature and poetry in Denmark, Paris and New York, and since 1998 she has edited a literary magazine called *The Blue Gate*. • CARLOS NAVARRETE is a Chilean born visual artist and art critic based in Santiago, Chile where he studied painting at School of Art of

Catholic University. He has participated in many group shows like: "Tracce di un Seminario" Viafarini, Milan, Italy; "Campo de Juego" Recoleta Cultural Centre, Buenos Aires, travelled to Centro de Extensión UC,Santiago and Museum of Contemporary Art in Bahía Blanca, Argentina; "Bari Bari in Japan" CCA-Maeda Studios, Kitakyushu, Japan; "Seguridad Social" INP.Santiago, Chile; "SHAVE'97" International Artists workshop. Somerset, England. Recent solo exhibitions include those at the Stichting Duende, Rotterdam; Kulturamt, Düsseldorf and BECH Gallery in Santiago; and São Paulo Cultural Centre. SP, Brazil. • JOÂO NUNES is a graphic artist who lives and works in Porto. His main focus is the design of posters for cultural events. For the last five years he has been responsible for the production of all the graphic art of the Teatro Nacional São João, Porto. He has exhibited his work in numerous places including Expo Design, Nagoya, Arksanat Gallery, Istanbul, and most recently in the Salon de Livres, Paris 2000. His work has been published in *Design and Designer, Who's Who in Graphic Design, Communication Arts* and *How.* • Francie Shaw and BOB PERELMAN are married and live in Philadelphia; he is a poet who teaches at the University of Pennsylvania. *Playing Bodies* will be published by Granary Books in 2003. • JOSE PEREZ DE ARCE antoncich estudió composición musical en la Universidad de Chile, Santiago, se desempeñó como ilustrador de dibujo científico en áreas antropológicas y de ciencias naturales, luego como diseñador museógrafo e investigador musicólogo en el Museo Chileno de Arte Precolombino, Santiago. A realizado exposiciones de sus dibujos en Chile y Estados Unidos, a realizado numerosas investigaciones en torno al tema de la música prehispánica música Indígena actual, organología, estética musical, espacio y música y fiestas rituales andinas. A impartido talleres de música indígena americana, con el arqueólogo Claudio Mercado, y a publicado varias ediciones sonoras sobre música indígena de Chile e instrumentos prehispánicos en conjunto con Claudio Mercado y el Conjunto la Chimuchina, del cual froma parte. • JANE PHILBRICK is an artist whose next work, "Re-Spoken," is a collaboration with the Portland Institute of Contemporary Art, Oregon, and the Center for Spoken Language Understanding at the Oregon Graduate Institute using newly developed speech technologies to "re-speak" historical voices from archival recordings. • NICK PIOMBINO's books include *Light Street* (Zasterle), *Theoretical Objects* (Green Integer) and *The Boundary of Theory* (Cuneiform). 22 of his poems, recorded live on WKCR-FM (NYC), can be accessed at http://epc.buffalo.edu/sound/authors/piombino • AYAD RAHIM is a journalist born in London, to Iraqi parents, and lived in Iraq from the age of three till the age of nine, at which point Ayad, along with the rest of his family, migrated to Cleveland. Ayad feels Cleveland is his home, but that he is homeless, in the truest sense of the word. • AISHAH RAHMAN has a new book out called *Chewed Water: A Memoir.* • THOMAS SCHØDT RASMUSSEN was born in 1970 and lives in Copenhagen. He has translated Pynchon and Barthelme into Danish. • ELLEN REDBIRD edits the performance literature journal *Nerve Lantern* (email: nervelantern@hotmail.com). Her poems have appeared in the journals *Spectrum* (1994, under the name Ellen Weiss), *Into the Teeth of the Wind* (Nov./Dec. 1999), *Avoid Strange Men* (April, 2002), and *Bombay Gin* (2002). • TIM ROLLINS is the Founder and Director of Tim Rollins and K.O.S. and The Art and Knowledge Workshop. • MARK RUDMAN's next book, *The Couple*, is coming out this fall from Wesleyan. • JUSSARA SALAZAR was born in Pernambuco, Brazil in 1959 and lives in Curitiba. She is a poet, editor, and visual artist. • SIMONE SANDY recently received her MFA from Naropa University and currently lives in Boston. "Bowl with Horn and Proof" was sparked by an exercise Heather Thomas introduced during Naropa's Summer Writing Program. • ALESSANDRA SANTOS is a graduate student in UCLA's Department of Spanish and Portuguese, where she serves on the editorial board of the literary journal *Mester.* • NELSON SAVINON is currently a graphic designer and Co-Director of K.O.S. • FRANCIE SHAW and Bob Perelman are married and live in Philadelphia; she is an artist. *Playing Bodies* will be published by Granary Books in 2003. • JAMES SHERRY is the author of 10 books of poetry and criticism, most recently *Our Nuclear Heritage* (Sun & Moon, 1991) and *Four For* (Meow, 1995). His work on environmental poetics has absorbed many recent years. He is editor of Roof Books and president of the Segue Foundation in New York City. • MICHELLE SPENCER is currently working on a performance piece with poet Thalia Field, composer Michael Theodore and filmmaker Robert Schaller. In addition, she is making a piece with computer scientist Chris Healer involving a suit which detects motion, not to be confused with the dress she is making which solves problems. As always she is working on a 7" record with Sean Meehan. • ROBERT SULLIVAN was born in 1967 of the Maori tribe Nga Puhi and of Galway Irish descent. He has published 3 books of poetry: *Jazz Waiata* (1990), *Piki ake: climb* (1993) and *Star Waka* (1999, reprinted 2000) all with Auckland University Press. • TENDERLOIN OPERA COMPANY: Writers on this project—Lee Breault, Joshua Brody, Marsha Campbell, Erik Ehn, David Gluck, Doug Marshall, Hilary Rand, Eric Robertson, Rhett Stuart, Christine Young. Contact them at shadowtackle@worldnet.att.net. *Sx7* opens mid October 2002 at St. Boniface, SF, followed by new works created in cooperation with the students of the DeMarillac Middle School, which serves the Tenderloin and is adjacent to our space. • JACQUELINE THAW is a graphic designer who recently returned to New York City after 18 months in Honolulu, Hawaii. She is an Assistant Professor of Graphic Design at Rutgers, the State University of New Jersey. • LEE A. TONOUCHI a.k.a. "Da Pidgin Guerrilla" is da writer of da short story collection *Da Word* (Bamboo Ridge Press, 2001), co-editor of *Hybolics*, author of *Living Pidgin: Contemplations on Pidgin Culture* (Tinfish Press, 2002), and editor of da in-progress community Pidgin dictionary projeck, *Da Kine Dictionary*. Check out www.dakinedictionary.com for more infos. • EDWIN TORRES's homepage is www.brainlingo.com. Among his titles are *The All-Union Day Of The Shock Worker* (Roof Books) and most recently *Please* (Faux Press), a CD-Rom with text, audio and video. He's currently co-editing *Cities Of Chance: An Anthology Of New Poetry From The United States and Brazil* (Rattapallax Press). • JOSELY VIANNA BAPTISTA was born in Curitiba, Brazil, in 1957. She has published the books *Ar* (São Paulo, Iluminuras, 1991), *Corpografia* (São Paulo, Iluminuras, 1992; artwork by Francisco Faria), and others. In 1996, she created the collection *Cadernos da Amerindia* (Tipografia do Fundo de Ouro Preto, 1996). Her forthcoming books include *On the shining screen of the eyelids* (Manifest Press, Berkeley, translations by Chris Daniels), *Los Poros Floridos* (Ed. Aldus, Mexico City) and *Sol sobre Nuvens* (Ed. Perspectiva/Mirabilia, São Paulo and Primeiro de Maio). • CECILIA VICUÑA is a poet, artist and filmmaker who divides her time between Chile and New York. Her most recent books are: *Instan*, Kelsey St Press, 2002, *El Templo*, 2001 (both available from SPD) and *Cloud-net*, Art in General 1999 (available from D.A.P.). • McKENZIE WARK's homepage is at http://www.dmc.mq.edu.au/KWark.html. His most recent book is *Celebrities, Culture and Cyberspace*, published by Pluto Press Australia. He also edits the media.culture book series for Pluto. Recent online writings include "A Hacker Manifesto" http://www.feelergauge.net/ or http://subsol.c3.hu/ , and "Index to This Fabulous World," at http://www.msstate.edu/Fineart_Online/. *Dispositions* will come out with Salt in 2002: http://www.saltpublishing.com. • BARRETT WATTEN is the author of *Bad History* (Berkeley: Atelos, 1998) and a forthcoming volume of essays from Wesleyan U P, *The Constructivist Moment: From Material Text to Material Poetics*. • SASHA SU-LING WELLAND currently lives in Beijing, where she researches how contemporary Chinese artists express themselves in the space between state and market. Her work has appeared in *Hedgebrook Journal* and

Flyway Literary Review. Forthcoming is a biography, *From All This Journey: Following the Lives of Ling Shuhua and Amy Ling Chen*. • MAC WELLMAN's recent plays include *Description Beggared, or the Allegory of Whiteness* (commissioned by the Actors' Theater of Louisville for its 2001 Humana Festival), and *Jennie Richee*. His most recent books are *Cellophane*, a collection of plays (PAJ/Johns Hopkins University Press), and a book of poems, *Miniature*, from Roof Books. • ELIZABETH WILLIS is the author of *Second Law* (Avenue B, 1993) and *The Human Abstract* (Penguin, 1995). *Turneresque* is forthcoming from Burning Deck in 2003. Recent poems appear in current issues of *Hambone* and *Shiny*; new prose is available in *XCP: Cross-cultural Poetics* and *How2*. • BETH YAHP's novel *The Crocodile Fury*, will be published in French in 2003 (Editions Stock). She also wrote the libretto for *Moon Spirit Feasting*, a ritual street-opera by Liza Lim which will be performed at the Saitama Arts Centre, Japan 2002; the Hebbel-Theatre Berlin, 14-16 June 2002 and the Zurich Theatre Spectacle, 23-25 August 2002. • HERIBERTO YÉPEZ was born in Tijuana, 1974. He just translated into Spanish an anthology of Jerome Rothenberg's poetry (*A Cruel Nirvana/Un cruel Nirvana*). Other things in English have/are going to appear in *Tripwire* and *Shark*. His two published books are titled *Por una poetica antes del paleolitico y despues de la propaganda* (poetry) and *Ensayos para un desconcierto y alguna critica ficcion* (essays). He can be contacted at hyepez@hotmail.com • ALEKSANDAR ZOGRAF is a Serbian cartoonist (real name: Sasa Rakezic), who has published abroad since the early 90s. In the US, his books are published by Fantagraphics Books (*Life Under Sanctions*, *Psychonaut #1* and *Psychonaut #2*), Monsterpants Comics *(Psychonaut #3*), Kitchen Sink Press (*Flock of Dreamers*). Also available are his books that came out with a British publisher Slab-O-Concrete (*Dream Watcher, Bulletins from Serbia*). Zograf's mini comics ($2 apiece) are available from: Sasa Rakezic, P.F. 163, 26000 Pancevo, Yugoslavia (Serbia). Or contact him at: zograf@panet.co.yu

CHAIN 10: *translation*

If you are a reader of Chain, we would be pleased to read your work for our next issue if it addresses the topic of translation or if it is a transliteration. We would enjoy reading work that explores the limits, the possibilities, the complaints, the hopes, the borders, the crossings of borders, the politics, and the aesthetics of translation OR work that uses translation as a form of reading/writing to create new work OR work that might be what Chilean poet Andres Ajens calls "intraduccion" or "transluci-nacion." (This isssue will not be a collection of international literature.)

We would especially like to encourage collaborative translation projects. For instance, we are interested in seeing a more "difficult" work translated by different people in several different ways (some possibilities: a literary translation, a literal translation, a homophonic translation, a translation that respects rhyme or rhythm, a translation that is more attentive to content, polylingual translation). By "difficult" we mean work that has translation problems embedded within it, or work that would not typically be translated for political/aesthetic reasons, or contains more than one language and needs someone with an unusual combination of languages skills, or that is written in a lesser known language. Contact us if you've got a work in mind and are interested in assembling a team of translators.

We would love to see translation "chains" of the sort where one person takes a work and translates it into Spanish say, then another person takes the Spanish translation and translates it into Urdu, and then another person takes the Urdu translation and translates it into Maori, and then another person takes the Maori translation and translates it into English. Again, please contact us if you would like to participate.

We are especially interested in featuring works that are originally in languages other than English, French, or German. We also welcome camera ready visual art and performance texts about translation. Please send two copies of your submission to Jena Osman, English Department, Temple University, 10th floor Anderson Hall (022-29), 1114 W. Berks St., Philadelphia, PA 19122-6090. Please, NO email submissions (we tend to lose them). Please enclose a self-addressed, stamped envelope if you would like your work returned. For more information on submission, see *http://ww.temple.edu/chain*

Deadline: December 1, 2002.

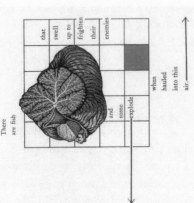

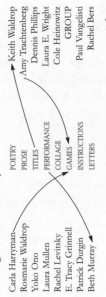

Kelsey St. Press collaborations

SYMBIOSIS

Barbara Guest, poetry;
Laurie Reid, drawings
Regular edition, $17;
limited edition
with an original
drawing, $200

INSTAN

Cecilia Vicuña,
poems/drawings
Regular edition, $15;
limited edition
with an original
drawing, $100

ENDOCRINOLOGY

Mei-mei Berssenbrugge, poetry;
Kiki Smith, images
Regular edition, $17

EDITORIAL INFORMATION

Jena Osman
Department of English
Temple University
10th floor, Anderson Hall (022-29)
1114 W. Berks Street
Philadelphia, PA 19122-6090
josman@temple.edu

Juliana Spahr
Department of English
1733 Donaghho Road
University of Hawai`i, Manoa
Honolulu, HI 96822
spahr@hawaii.edu

Since 1993, *Chain* has been publishing a yearly issue of work gathered loosely around a topic. The topic allows us to switch the editorial question that we ask each piece of work submitted from "is this a great piece of art" to "does this piece of art tell us something about the topic that we didn't already know." This makes *Chain* a little rougher around the edges, a little less aesthetically predictable. Within the frame of the topic, we tend to privilege mixed media and collaborative work and work by emerging or younger artists. We welcome submissions from readers. Please see our call for work in this issue.

....

PLEASE SUBSCRIBE.

The continued existence of *Chain* is dependent on subscriptions and contributions. Please donate and/or subscribe!

I enclose

_____ $20 for two issues, starting with no. 10.

_____ $12 for *Chain* 10, translation.

_____ $12 for *Chain* 8, comics.

_____ $12 for *Chain* 7, memoir/antimemoir.

_____ $12 for *Chain* 6, letters.

_____ $12 for *Chain* 5, different languages.

$ _____ donation to keep *Chain* going.

name ______________________________________
address ____________________________________
____
____

send to:

Chain
c/o Jena Osman
Department of English
Temple University
10th floor, Anderson Hall (022-29)
1114 W. Berks Street
Philadelphia, PA 19122-6090

Please make check out to Chain Arts.